A CHRISTMAS BOOK

AN ANTHOLOGY FOR MODERNS

But is old, old, good old *Christmas* gone? Nothing but the Hair of his good, gray, old Head and Beard left? Well, I will have that, seeing I cannot have more of him.

An Hue and Cry after Christmas, 1645.

Old Christmas is a-coming to the confusion of Puritans, Muggletonians, Anabaptists, Quakers, and that unwassailing Crew. He cometh not with his wonted gait; he is shrunk nine inches in his girth, but is yet a lusty fellow.

Charles Lamb to Bernard Barton.

Within the illustration:

Ad primam
Ens in adiutorium
meum intende

NATIVITY, WITH ST. JOSEPH AND A NURSE

*From a XVth Century Book of Hours
Diocese of Paris*

A CHRISTMAS BOOK
AN ANTHOLOGY FOR MODERNS

By D. B. WYNDHAM LEWIS
& G. C. HESELTINE

The music transcribed and
the decorations drawn by
A. C. Harradine

LONDON: J. M. DENT & SONS LTD.
NEW YORK: E. P. DUTTON & CO. INC.

PN
6071
.C6
L4
1951

PREFACE TO THE 1951 EDITION

"Sorry, no more Christmas cards left—only religious ones."
(A London shop-assistant, Christmas 1950.)

THUS artlessly, thus exquisitely, is summed up the remarkable though by no means unpredictable (or unpredicted) change in the status of the Christmas Festival in this country since this book was first published, twenty-three years ago. In 1928 the relation between the British Christmas and the stupendous Event this festival was established some sixteen centuries ago to commemorate was already vague and tenuous enough to a considerable majority; to-day that majority is so enormously swelled that it undoubtedly embraces some 75 per cent of the population, including at least one generation which has never heard of the said event. To discuss this very significant change, still not fully developed, and to discover the reasons for it are not the purpose of this preface. It is perhaps sufficient to note that the word Christmas, as commonly used in speech and print in this year 1951, has no connection whatsoever with either syllable composing it, and but for the warm-hearted enthusiasm of luxury tradesmen it would have no meaning at all. A Carol of the Twelve Christmas Joys of Bond Street seems long overdue.

That an anthology of the kind included between these covers should continue nevertheless to flourish sufficiently to warrant a new edition after nearly a quarter of a century's existence is therefore, to the compilers, a matter for gratification, not unmixed with mild surprise, seeing on what an unfashionable foundation it is based. As, on the other hand, the terror and ugliness of modern

*   v

civilisation increases, it is natural enough that any glimpse of beauty and happiness should become more and more precious; and there is a deal of both packed into these pages, whether inspired directly by the Mystery of the Incarnation or reflected from one of the myriad joyous facets of its assurances to humanity. For at this season there is twelve days' surcease from the pain of living, and hearts are light, and there is good reason to make merry. To make merry at Christmas for no reason at all is one of the more macabre diversions of the present age; for which reason the spectacle of a crowded smart restaurant on Christmas Eve is infinitely depressing and, to the sensitive mind, oddly reminiscent of those leaden hearts in the *Inferno*:

Tristi fummo
nell'aere dolce che dal sol s'allegra . . .

Hence, perhaps, a reasonable excuse for another edition of this book, with a number of new items and illustrations.

D. B. W. L.
G. C. H.

Christmas, 1951.

PREFACE TO FIRST EDITION

"God rest you merry, gentlemen. Let nothing you dismay."

THE Feast of Christmas proper extends from the Vigil to Twelfth Night. For the purposes of this Anthology we have occasionally in a rich and careless manner assumed the Feast to overlap a few days on either side of the Rubric.

The following essentials to any Christmas Anthology will be found nowhere in this Anthology: extracts from Dickens, Pepys (*with one exception*), and (*with one exception*) Washington Irving, and reference (*with one exception*) to Father Christmas; also fake-Gothic carols (including Good King Wenceslas), robins, property Yule-logs, synthetic snow, red-faced jovial Squires, wigs by Clarkson, Ye Olde Englysshe Yuletyde Cheere (18——), and all manifestations of the coloured Christmas Supplement. We have omitted Dickens—with a graceful gambade of reverence in the direction of the Master's shrine—because he is universal and instantly accessible, if the key to the bookcase in the morning-room can be found. Pepys, again, is to-day about as rare and secret as the Piccadilly Tube. Washington Irving is kind, but tedious. Father Christmas, Santa Claus, or Sankt Klaus, is the Victorian nursery substitute for the Christ-Child taken over from the Dutch Calvinists of New Amsterdam, fabulous, in this incarnation, as the griffin, and now indigenous during the season to Oxford Street. The simili-Gothic carol and the Drury Lane wassailings which stirred Thackeray's bile about the year 1860 are also Utilitarian, as is likewise that ensuing vague benevolence towards—as someone has said—those we rather like, which tired leader-writers writing leaders for dear life call *The Christmas Spirit*, and which is essentially gastric.

We have taken leave to consider the Medievals, rather

than Dickens and his successors, the Supreme Court of Christmas Appeal.

Nevertheless this is in no way a medieval anthology, but one freely ranging the ages from St. Hilary of Poitiers to Mr. Pooter,—nay, from the Saturnalia of Martial's Rome to the more ladylike revellings of post-war London— all mixed up jovially like a Christmas Pudding. Several passages in it are now printed for the first time. Our version of the Feast and Prose of the Ass is the famous one sung at Beauvais. There was also a Feast of the Ass at Rouen, but it was a solemn liturgical and scriptural drama, like the Resurrection dialogue enacted by the monks of Winchester at the Matins of Easter Day, and not a hilarious popular ceremony. We have chosen Beauvais, for various reasons. The swinging ballad of the murder of St. Thomas of Canterbury is from the Sloane MS., the account of the burglary of the College of Navarre from a document in the Archives Nationales; and so forth. The carol-music so charmingly reproduced for us by Mr. Harradine is the original, unharmed by those (as the monk of Gloucester admirably said in his Christmas sermon) covetous of unbuxomness; among whom he would undoubtedly have included the Dons and pedants, botchers, adapters, emendators, and arrangers, true spawn of the Enemy. Similarly for everything else, prose or verse, we have gone wherever necessary to primal sources.

It is impossible in a book of this kind to do more than skim the surface of the vast repository of Christmas devotion and merrymaking all over Christendom and throughout the centuries. A volume could be compiled on the traditional Christmas festivities of York alone, or Dalecarlia, or Hogsnorton-in-the-Marsh, or Andorra, or Besançon. There is, for example, a most pleasing type of carol, the Devotional-Satiric, combining the joy of the Manger with a few snacks (as ladies say at Bow Street) cast at one's neighbours. This type is especially native to France, for

irony is of the stuff of the French mind. We would have liked to give several examples, but we have been forced to confine ourselves to two. One is a celebrated brief Burgundian carol by Guy Barozai, in which the poet, contemplating the Ox and the Ass keeping their vigil, without thought of food or drink, observes sardonically, "How many oxen and asses I know in this Kingdom of France who wouldn't have done that much":

> *Que d'âne et de beu je sai*
> *Qui n'an airein pa tan fai!*

The other is an admirable Twelfth Night thing from Champagne, in which the anonymous poet, calling all the villages for miles round to the Crib, seizes the opportunity to take a swipe at the pretty girls of Florent, the muddy oafs of Passavant, the swearing unbelievers of Grange-aux-Bois, the bullies of Valmy, the miserly hounds of Chaud'-fontaines, and a dozen other of his neighbours. The artless gallop of verse is full of rustic savour. Alas! what splendid things have we not been compelled to abandon, which would inevitably have appeared in this book had it had expanding covers.

We have not held ourselves bound by any algebraic pedantry which would confine a Christmas Anthology to things about Christmas; but rather have we considered that many things have been done at Christmas lacking at first glance The Christmas Spirit, yet worthy of meditation at this holy time. On the eve of Twelfth Day, 1757, for example, a gentleman approached the King of France, not to wish him the old, old wish nor yet to sing him a carol, but for the purpose of driving a dagger between the Royal ribs. On the eve of Christmas 1456 the poet Villon and four companions burgled the College of Navarre in the University of Paris and stole 500 gold crowns. And again, on a Christmas Eve in the late eighteen-nineties the novelist Henry James was dining at a house in London; but do you think the ears of Henry James caught echoes of the angelic song, or that before the eyes of Henry James there shone in a golden mist the starry lights before the Crib? By no means, dear hearts. Consolamini. Henry James was too refined for that; as you may see.

We must add also that because the stomach has a right to a reasonable share of Christmas joy we have dropped into this book here and there such undated but festal things as the Discourse of the Drinkers from Gargantua, Dr. Middleton's dithyramb on Port, Brillat-Savarin on Turkey and Ambered Chocolate, and Mr. Belloc on Burgundy Wine. The recipes for the dishes our fathers ate at this blessed season are chiefly from the Arundel Collection. The recipe for Christmas Carol Punch has been composed specially for this book by a cocktail artist of international repute, Mr. "Harry" McElhone of Paris, whose gracious and instant response affected us much as Michael Angelo's sudden consent to design a hen-house would have affected an obscure Renaissance poultry-fancier of high principles but weak heart.

In conclusion we trust modestly (yet with manly cheerfulness) that although the riches of the medieval treasure-house are bewildering in their splendour and inexhaustibility, we have managed to amass a fitting number of jewels of the first water, that succeeding ages, even this present one, have yielded us something of delight, and that we have not fallen too hopelessly short of our devout desire to exclude the banal, the hackneyed, the false, and the sentimental.

. . . God rest you merry, gentlemen. Let nothing you dismay.

D. B. W. L.
G. C. H.

LONDON, 1928.

NOTE

The compilers' best thanks are due to many authors and publishers for their courtesy in permitting copyright poems and prose extracts to be included in this book. To

Robert Bridges, *The Times*, and Messrs. John Murray, Ltd., for "Christmas Eve."

Mr. Hilaire Belloc, for "Noël" and "On the Excellence of Burgundy Wine" from *Sonnets and Verse* (Messrs. Duckworth and Co.), and extracts from *On Saturnalia*, from *On Everything* (Messrs. Methuen and Co.), "The Sailor's Carol" from *The Four Men* (Messrs. Nelson and Sons), an extract from *Mrs. Markham on Christmas* (*G.K.'s Weekly*), and "A Remaining Christmas" from *A Conversation with an Angel*.

The Times and Messrs. Methuen and Co., for an extract from the late A. C. Clutton Brock's *Thoughts on the War*.

Professor E. Allison Peers, for his translation of a poem by St. John of the Cross (Messrs. Burns, Oates and Washbourne, Ltd.).

Mr. Ivor Brown, Mr. J. B. Priestley, and the Editor of *The Saturday Review*, for prose and verse.

Messrs. Ernest Benn, Ltd., for an extract from the *Norwegian Fairy Book*, by P. C. Asbjörnsen.

Messrs. G. Bell and Sons, for two extracts from *The Pepys Correspondence*.

G. K. Chesterton, for two extracts from *Poems* (Messrs. Burns, Oates and Washbourne, and Dodd, Mead and Co., New York), one extract from *The Queen of the Seven Swords* (Messrs. Sheed and Ward), and two extracts from *Charles Dickens* (Messrs. Methuen and Co.).

Messrs. Chatto and Windus, for two extracts from *Under the Greenwood Tree*, by Thomas Hardy.

Messrs. Constable and Co., for an extract from *The Egoist*, by George Meredith.

Mr. Peter Davies, for two extracts from his translation of *The Physiology of Taste*, by J. A. Brillat-Savarin, and an extract from *The Memoirs of Sergeant Bourgogne* (Peter Davies, Ltd.).

Mr. David Emrys, for his translation of the Welsh Carol on p. 277.

M. Eugène Fasquelle, of Paris, for the *Noël* of Théophile Gautier.

Miss Grace Guiney, for access to Louise Imogen Guiney's collection of Recusant Poems.

Mrs. Weedon Grossmith and George Grossmith, for an extract from *The Diary of a Nobody* (Messrs. Arrowsmith and Alfred Knopf, Inc., New York).

Miss H. E. Kennedy and Miss Sofia Uminska, for the translations and music of two Russian and Polish Carols.

M. Victor Kinon, for his poem on p. 321 (Larcier, Brussels).

M. Alphonse Lemerre, of Paris, for the *Epiphanie* of José-Maria de Heredia.

E. V. Lucas, for an extract from *Character and Comedy* (Messrs. Methuen and Co. and The Macmillan Co., New York).

Arthur Machen, for two extracts from *Dog and Duck* (Messrs. Jonathan Cape, Ltd., and Alfred A. Knopf, Inc.).

Messrs. Macmillan and Co., Ltd., J. B. Pinker and Son, and Houghton Mifflin Co. (New York), for the extract from *The Spoils of Poynton*, by Henry James.

Wilfred Meynell, for the extract from *The Death of Harlequin*, by Alice Meynell (*Essays*, Messrs. Burns, Oates and Washbourne).

Mr. A. A. Milne, for an extract from *If I May* (Messrs. Methuen and Co., and E. P. Dutton and Co., New York).

Mr. J. B. Morton, for a carol.

Cecil Palmer and Messrs. J. W. Luce and Co. (New York), for an extract from *Advent*, by August Strindberg.

MM. Plon-Nourrit, of Paris, for three extracts from the *Mémoires et Récits* of Frédéric Mistral.

Miss Louise Morgan Sill, the Yale University Press, and Messrs. Chatto and Windus, for an extract from *The Tidings Brought to Mary*, from the French of Paul Claudel.

M. Paul Claudel and the Nouvelle Revue Française for *L'Enfant Jésus de Prague* (English translation by D. B. Wyndham Lewis).

Miss Edith Sitwell, for the poem "Snow" from *Bucolic Comedies* (Messrs. Duckworth and Co.).

Mr. J. C. Squire, for an extract from the essay on Christmas Cards in *Life at the Mermaid* (Messrs. Heinemann and Co.).

Arthur Symons, for two extracts from *Cities, Sea Coasts and Islands* (Messrs. W. Collins, Sons and Co.).

Mr. Ogden Nash, for *Merry Christmas, Nearly Everybody* and "Aspiration," part of *Epstein, Spare that Yule Log* (copyright Messrs. J. M. Dent and Sons, Ltd., and Little, Brown and Co. New York).

The Sussex Archæological Society, for an extract from the *Transactions*.

CONTENTS

In Chronological Order

		PAGE
"I don't care where the water goes . . ."	Catullus	293
The Foreshadowing	*Vergil*, Bucolic IV. . .	2
The Festal Hearth	Horace, Carm. I. 9 (tr. C. S. Calverley)	121
The Poet is Gay	Martial	59
The Poet Explains	Martial	169
The Poet Complains	Martial	190
The Poet is Indifferent	Martial	228
The Poet is Judicious	Martial	245
A Present of Nuts	Martial	257
The Poet is Revengeful	Martial	292
The First Noël	St. Hilary of Poitiers . .	3
A Spanish Singer	Prudentius . . .	271
"Hail, Sweetest Flowers"	St. Augustine . . .	276
The Birth of France	St. Gregory of Tours . .	161
A Reproof for King Arthur	From *A History of York* .	62
The Passing of the Confessor	*The Anglo-Saxon Chronicle* .	296
A Gift for the Mint	*The Anglo-Saxon Chronicle* .	159
Anglo-Norman Drinking Song . . .	. . . . .	115
Fond Repetitions	From an ordinance of Epiphany by Eudes de Sully, Bishop of Paris .	196
The First Crib	From *The Life of St. Francis of Assisi*, by St. Bonaventure .	29
Christmas Song	By a Monk of Tours . .	76
Nativity	Jacopone da Todi (tr. Denis MacCarthy) . . .	313
Franciscan Song	Jacopone da Todi (tr. John Addington Symonds) . .	236
Vintage Note	*Le Ménagier de Paris* . .	319
The Death of Galahad	*La Queste del S. Graal* (tr. Sir T. Malory) . . .	134
The Search	Richard Rolle of Hampole .	34
Robin Hood's Epitaph	From gravestone at Kirklees .	240

xiii

My Lord's Expenses — From an Account of Expenses of Thomas, Earl of Lancaster — 198

In Dulci Jubilo — B. Henry Suso, O.P. — 8

The Happy English — *Ludus Corporis Xti*, XIVth Century — 70

Nowel! Nowel! — Geoffrey Chaucer, *The Frankeleyns Tale* — 17

Et Verbum Caro Factum Est — Geoffrey Chaucer: (i.) *The Prioresses Tale*; (ii.) *The Seconde Nonnes Tale* — 208

A Present for the Grand Turk — Sir John Froissart — 143

A High Company — Sir John Froissart — 194

A Twelfth-Day Prophecy — Sir John Froissart — 240

There is no Rose of swich Vertu — XVth Century MS., Trinity College, Cambridge — 28

A Lovable Fish — John Stow, *Annales* — 203

Neighbours — John Stow, *Annales* — 229

At the Sheepstealer's — Wakefield Second Nativity Play — 30

Shepherds' Salute — Wakefield Second Nativity Play — 126

For the Vigil — Cookery Recipes, Arundel MS. — 10

A Lordly Dish — Cookery Recipes, Arundel MS. — 63

A Chicken for a Lord — Cookery Recipes, Arundel MS. — 147

Sause for a Goose — Cookery Recipes, Arundel MS. — 242

Welcome-Song — Sloane MS. 2593, Brit. Mus. — 20

Three Little Carols — Sloane MS. 2593, and MS. at Trinity College, Cambridge — 27

Song of the Rose — Sloane MS. 2593 — 42

December the Twenty-Ninth — Sloane MS. 2593 — 53

As I up Rose — Sloane MS. 2593 — 85

This Enders Night — Sloane MS. 2593 — 210

Social and Personal — *Registers of the Chancellery of France* — 121

Carol of the Nuns of Chester — MS. *Processional* (St. Mary's, Chester) — 77

Out of your Sleep ... — *Bodleian (Selden) MS.* — 298

A Loving Wife — *The Paston Letters* — 123

A Parisian Miniature — François Villon — 97

A Night's Frolic — *Archives Nationales*, Documents of the College of Navarre — 13

		PAGE
THE COVENTRY CAROL	Coventry Nativity Play . .	235
CHECK BY THE KING	Letter of Charles VII. . .	190
THUNDER FROM THE THRONE	Pastoral Letter of Louis, Archbishop of Sens. Epiphany 1445 . . .	164
THE MARVEL OF THE SWORD	Sir T. Malory, *Morte d'Arthur*	63
THE GIFTS	*Le Grant Kalendrier des Bergiers,* 1480 . . .	112
THE SERVANT PROBLEM	*The Paston Letters* .	106
MEDITATION ON THE FEAST	*The Festiall* of John Mirkus .	78
ON THE NATIVITY	William Dunbar . . .	6
THE BOON	From *The Golden Legend* .	234
SERMON OF THE BOY-BISHOP, 1493	Wynkyn de Worde ed., B.M. .	225
JOLY WAT	Balliol MS.	4
THE WONDER	Balliol MS.	35
A SONG AGAINST BORES	Balliol MS.	110
CAROL OF THE FIVE JOYS OF MARY	Balliol MS. . . .	125
THE BOAR'S HEAD CAROL	(i.) Queen's College, Oxford .	166
	(ii.) Balliol MS. . . .	167
NOËL	Clément Marot of Cahors .	124
THE DISCOURSE OF THE DRINKERS	François Rabelais (tr. Urquhart) . . .	192
A CHRISTMAS BOX	Dame Agnes Merett .	106
THE LAWYERS' SATURNALIA	*Accompts* of the Inner Temple	264
TWO SPANISH PASTORALS	St. Teresa of Jesus (tr. Arthur Symons) . . .	84
A WELSH CAROL	Siankin Morgan (tr. D. Emrys)	277
THE BURNING BABE	Ven. Robert Southwell, S.J. .	142
"COME, LASSES AND LADS"	Vauquelin de Fresnaye .	150
TO MAKE A DISH OF SNOW	From *A Booke of Cookerie* .	89
HOW TO MAKE A TANSY	From *A Booke of Cookerie* .	239
THE WAIL OF GOD	St. John of the Cross (tr. E. Allison Peers) . . .	312
AN EPIPHANY GAMBOL	William Shakespeare, *Twelfth Night* . . .	71
FESTAL COCKCROW	William Shakespeare, *Hamlet* .	98
TWELFTH NIGHT, 1605	Ben Jonson	47
ON SNAPDRAGON	From the Play *Lingua* . .	268
FROM "THE MASQUE OF CHRISTMAS," 1616	Ben Jonson . . .	154
TWELFTH NIGHT IN CHAMPAGNE . . .	XVIIth Century . .	247

		PAGE
ON THE TURKEY	From a Cookery Book	110
TO MAKE BENICRZ	From a Cookery Book	111
TWO CHRISTMAS SWEETS	From a Cookery Book	260
A DESSERT:		
(i.) TO SCORCH CHESNUTTS		179
(ii.) TO MAKE HARTS HORN FLUMMERY		179
FROM "THE SHEPHERDS' HYMN"	Richard Crashaw	243
TO A COUNTRY AIR	French Carol with music	204
REVEL AT THE SHERIFF'S	Richard Evelyn for The Lord of Misrule	259
THE ARRAIGNMENT	Broadsheet, 1645	272
CRADLE SONG	German, Anon.	178
FROM THE PROVINCE OF QUEBEC	French-Canadian Carol	141
THE STING IN THE TAIL	*Women Will Have Their Will*	94
IN TERRA PAX	*England's Iliad*, 1645	107
IN OLD QUEBEC	Journal of Jérôme Lalemant, S.J.	211
THE TERRIBLE REMONSTRANCE	*Flying Eagle Gazette*	10
CAROL OF THE HURON NATION	Jean de Brébeuf, S.J.	267
CHRISTMAS EVE CEREMONY	Robert Herrick	11
THE STAR SONG	Robert Herrick	140
TWO FESTAL QUATRAINS	Robert Herrick	282
NEW YEAR'S GIFT	Robert Herrick	306, 311
THE END OF THE FEAST	Robert Herrick	322
TO MAKE SACK POSSET	Robert May	319
HYMN ON THE MORNING OF CHRIST'S NATIVITY	John Milton	99
CHRIST IN THE CRADLE	Hon. Patrick Carey	70
A LOVERS' QUARREL	Dorothy Osborne	297
THE CROMWELL MANNER	Evelyn's *Diary*	244
O SWEETEST NIGHT	Myles Pinkney	76
AT SEA, 1675	Diary of the Rev. Henry Teonge, Naval Chaplain	43
ON CHRIST'S NATIVITY	Henry Vaughan the Silurist	151
A DANCE AT WHITE HALL	Samuel Pepys	291
A CALL FROM MASSACHUSETTS	From a Tract of 1676	227
THE FEAST OF THE ASS	Du Cange, *Glossarium*, 1678	180
THE DUTCHMAN ARRIVES	The Pepys Correspondence	90

WITCH DANCE AT SALEM — Cotton Mather, *A Brand pluck'd out of the Burning* . 43

BURGUNDIAN CAROL — Guy Barozai . . . 224

OUR LADY'S LULLABY — Richard Verstegan (Rowlands) 137

INCIDENT IN SAXONY — Robert Burton . . . 196

A TARPAULIN MUSTER — *The London Spy* . . . 48

CHRISTMAS LEAVE — *The London Spy* . . . 184

A CUSTOM OF THE ENGLISH — The Pepys Correspondence . 242

FOOTNOTE TO HOGMANAY — Dean Ramsay, *Reminiscences of Scottish Life and Character* . 283

NEW YEAR DINNER — Sussex Archæological Society's *Transactions* . . . 197

NATIVITY, IN THE MODE OF SPAIN — Jean-Baptiste Labat, O.P. . 97

GREETINGS FROM THE DEAN — Dean Swift 24

THE FALL OF THE MIGHTY — Dean Swift 145

A NOTE ON ALE — Dean Swift 159

FROM A LETTER-BAG — Richard Steele, *The Spectator* . 239

HEIGH-HO! THE HOLLY! — Richard Steele, *The Spectator* . 20

A NEW YEAR MODE — Joseph Addison . . . 288

A CARGO OF PORT — Richard Estcourt to *The Spectator* 260

A DISMAL DEAN — Dean Swift 294

CHRISTMAS WITH SIR ROGER — Joseph Addison . . . 86

AND SO TO BED — Richard Steele . . . 197

THE RESCUE OF BRANDY NAN — John Gay 148

THE FAIR UNHAPPY — Hamilton, *Memoirs of Grammont* 283

SWEETS TO THE SWEET — *Journal de Police sous Louis XV*. 149

PLUS ÇA CHANGE . . . — Journal of the Avocat Barbier . 153

A HEBRIDEAN FROLIC — Dr. Samuel Johnson . . 295

A PRESENT FROM HORACE — Horace Walpole to Richard Bentley 149

NEWS FROM COURT — Horace Walpole to George Montagu 208

MORE OF THE TURKEY — Mrs. Glasse's Cookery Book . 187

FOOTNOTE TO THE ABOVE — J. A. Brillat-Savarin . . 187

THE MAN IN BLACK — Journal of the Avocat Barbier . 303

A NEW ENGLAND MISS — Diary of Anna Green Winslow 18

THIS AMERICAN BUSINESS — Horace Walpole to Hon. H. S. Conway 286

DECLINE OF AN ORATOR — Diary of Thos. Hutchinson . 69

NEWS FROM SALEM — Diary of Dr. William Bentley . 160

A CUP TO 1801 — Charles Lamb to T. Manning . 311

		PAGE
EHEU FUGACES!	Charles Lamb to T. Manning .	182
THE BELLS	Charles Lamb to S. T. Coleridge	55
PULVIS ET UMBRA	Charles Lamb . . .	273
CONCERNING A PIG	Charles Lamb . . .	113
CHRISTMAS WITH THE FANCY (1810)	Pierce Egan, *Boxiana* . .	299
THE END OF THE ROAD	*Memoirs of Sergeant Bourgogne*	205
AN AVENGING ANGEL	*The Gentleman's Magazine*, 1822	199
NIGHT-PIECE	John Howison, *Sketches of Upper Canada* . . .	215
CAME THE DAWN ...	J. A. Brillat-Savarin, *The Physiology of Taste* (tr. Peter Davies)	309
AT CHAINMAIL HALL	Thomas Love Peacock . .	144
THE INNS THAT ARE DEAD	Washington Irving . .	308
FROM MR. JORROCKS'S JOURNAL	R. S. Surtees . . .	262
ON THE LINCOLNSHIRE COAST	Alfred, Lord Tennyson . .	116
NOËL	Théophile Gautier . .	34
THE SPARKLING BOUGH	William Makepeace Thackeray	309
MORAL FANTASIA ON A DIARY	William Makepeace Thackeray	289
SNOWS OF YESTERYEAR	William Makepeace Thackeray	51
RURAL TIFF	Robert Browning . . .	281
THE HIGHER CRITICISM	Robert Browning . .	237
SIBERIA	Fedor Dostoievsky . .	268
THE SCHOLAR-GIPSY	Matthew Arnold . . .	90
VIE DE BOHÈME	Henry Murger . . .	44
THE PROVENÇAL LOG	Frédéric Mistral . . .	66
RETURN OF THE NATIVE	Frédéric Mistral . . .	279
THE THREE LOW MASSES	Alphonse Daudet . . .	170
A POET BESIEGED	A. Daudet to F. Mistral .	299
EPIPHANIE	José-Marie de Heredia . .	234
GLORIA IN EXCELSIS	Henry James, *The Spoils of Poynton*	138
THE RESPITE	August Strindberg, *Advent* .	229
THE FEAST OF THE DEAD	Charles Le Goffic . . .	258
FANTASIA ON PORT	George Meredith . . .	271
WHAT MIGHT HAVE BEEN	Rt. Hon. G. W. E. Russell .	74
NURSERY	Paul Claudel . . .	246
THE MIRACLE IN THE FOREST	Paul Claudel, *L'Annonce faite à Marie*	35
TROLL-FEAST	P. C. Asbjörnsen, *Norwegian Folk-Tale* . . .	117
THE MELLSTOCK ROUNDS	Thomas Hardy . . .	199

xviii

		PAGE
FUGUE FOR STRINGS	Thomas Hardy . . .	107
CHRISTMAS EVE	Robert Bridges . . .	7
A TALK FOR TWELFTH NIGHT	Arthur Machen . . .	152
A GIFT FROM THE LEGION	Arthur Machen . . .	292
MUSIC NOTE	Diary of J. K. Huysmans .	267
THE DEATH OF HARLEQUIN	Alice Meynell . . .	52
1914: A POINT OF VIEW . . .	A. Clutton-Brock . . .	23
. . . AND ANOTHER	Field-Marshal Lord French .	23
WITH THE POOTERS	George and Weedon Grossmith, *Diary of a Nobody* .	60
A LITTLE LITANY	G. K. Chesterton . . .	165
THE HAPPY HOWL	G. K. Chesterton . . .	202
SONNET	G. K. Chesterton . . .	273
THE FIGHT FOR CHRISTMAS	G. K. Chesterton . . .	276
A CHRISTMAS SONG FOR THREE GUILDS	G. K. Chesterton . . .	255
THE DECORATIONS	E. V. Lucas . . .	128
THE SAILOR'S CAROL	Hilaire Belloc . . .	12
MRS. MARKHAM ON CHRISTMAS	Hilaire Belloc . . .	56
A REMAINING CHRISTMAS	Hilaire Belloc . . .	216
DRINKING SONG	Hilaire Belloc . . .	93
NOËL	Hilaire Belloc . . .	133
ON SATURNALIA	Hilaire Belloc . . .	162
A HINT FOR NEXT CHRISTMAS	A. A. Milne . . .	168
SNOW	Edith Sitwell . . .	226
POLISH LULLABY	Tr. H. E. Kennedy and S. Uminska . . .	189
WHITE RUSSIAN CAROL	Tr. H. E. Kennedy and S. Uminska . . .	68
ON CHRISTMAS CARDS	J. C. Squire . . .	211
From "A MASQUE OF MISRULE," 1927	Ivor Brown . . .	156
CHRISTMAS WITH THE FORCE—1927 . .	A London Newspaper . .	191
A NOTE ON FATHER CHRISTMAS	J. B. Priestley . . .	252
ASPIRATION	Ogden Nash . . .	98
MERRY CHRISTMAS, NEARLY EVERYBODY	Ogden Nash . . .	317
THE STOCK EXCHANGE CAROL	J. B. Morton . . .	307
TWO FESTAL BREWS	H. McElhone and R. M. .	18
RECESSIONAL	Victor Kinon . . .	321

ILLUSTRATIONS

NATIVITY, WITH ST. JOSEPH AND A NURSE . *Frontispiece*

FACING PAGE

THE ADORATION OF THE MAGI 76

FRANCESCA: THE NATIVITY 140

GEERTGEN: THE NATIVITY 210

A
CHRISTMAS
BOOK

THE FORESHADOWING

Sicelides Musæ, paullo majora canamus.

Sicilian Muse, begin a loftier strain!
Though lowly shrubs, and trees that shade the Plain,
Delight not all; Sicilian Muse, prepare
To make the vocal Woods deserve a Consul's care.
The last great Age, foretold by sacred Rimes,
Renews its finish'd course: Saturnian times
Roll round again; and mighty years, begun
From their first Orb, in radiant circles run.
The base degenerate iron Offspring ends;
A golden Progeny from Heaven descends.
O chaste *Lucina*! speed the Mother's pains,
And hast the glorious Birth! thy own *Apollo* reigns!
The lovely Boy, with his auspicious face,
Shall *Pollio's* consulship and triumph grace.
Majestick months set out with him to their appointed Race.
The Father banish'd virtue shall restore,
And crimes shall threat the guilty World no more.
The Son shall lead the life of Gods, and be
By Gods and Heroes seen, and Gods and Heroes see.
The jarring Nations he in peace shall bind,
And with paternal Virtues rule Mankind.
Unbidden Earth shall wreathing Ivy bring
And fragrant Herbs (the promises of Spring)
As her first offerings to her infant King.

DRYDEN'S *Vergil*, Bucolic IV.

¶. *This hymn, probably the most ancient Latin carol.*

RÉMY DE GOURMONT.

JESUS re—ful-sit om-ni-um Pi—us redemptor gen—ti—um:
To—tum ge-nus fi-de-li-um— Laudes ce—le-bret dra-ma-tum.

JESUS refulsit omnium
Pius redemptor gentium;
Totum genus fidelium
Laudes celebret dramatum.

Quem stella natum fulgida
Monstrat micans per æthera,
Magosque duxit prævia
Ipsius ad cunabula.

Illi cadentes parvulum
Pannis adorant obsitum,
Verum fatentur ut Deum
Munus fruendo mysticum.

ST. HILARY OF POITIERS († 368).

Can I not sing Ut Hoy,
Whan the joly shepard made so much joy?

THE shepard upon a hill he sat;
   He had on him his tabard and his hat,
His tarbox, his pipe, and his flagat;
His name was called Joly Joly Wat,
    For he was a gud herdes boy,
         Ut hoy!
   For in his pipe he made so much joy.

The shepard upon a hill was laid;
His dog unto his girdele was taid;
He had not slept but a litill braid,
But "Gloria in excelsis" was to him said.
         Ut hoy!
   For in his pipe he made so much joy.

The shepard on a hill he stode;
Round about him his shepe they yode;
He put his hond under his hode,
He saw a star as rede as blode.
         Ut hoy!
   For in his pipe he made so much joy.

The shepard said anon right,
"I will go see yon ferly sight,
Whereas the angel singeth on hight,
And the star that shineth so bright!"
         Ut hoy!
   For in his pipe he made so much joy.

"Now farewell, Mall, and also Will!
For my love go ye all still
Unto I cum again you till,
And evermore, Will, ring well thy bell!"
         Ut hoy!
   For in his pipe he made so much joy.

"Now must I go there Crist was born;
Farewell! I cum again to morn.
Dog, kepe well my shepe fro the corn,
And warn well 'Warrocke' when I blow my horn!"
Ut hoy!
For in his pipe he made so much joy.

Whan Wat to Bedlem cumen was,
He swet, he had gone faster than a pace;
He found Jesu in a simple place,
Between an ox but and an asse.
Ut hoy!
For in his pipe he made so much joy.

"Jesu, I offer to thee, here my pipe
My skirt, my tarbox and my scrip;
Home to my felowes now will I skip,
And also look unto my shepe!"
Ut hoy!
For in his pipe he made so much joy.

"Now farewell, mine owne herdesman Wat!"—
"Yea, for God, lady even so I hat;
Lull well Jesu in they lap,
And farewell, Joseph, with they round cap!"
Ut hoy!
For in his pipe he made so much joy.

"Now may I well both hope and sing,
For I have been at Cristés bering;
Home to my felowes now will I fling.
Crist of heven to his bliss us bring!"
Ut hoy!
For in his pipe he made so much joy.

Balliol MS., XVth–XVIth Century.

RORATE *cœli desuper!*
　　Hevins, distil your balmy schouris!
For now is risen the bricht day-ster
　　Fro the rose Mary, flour of flouris:
　　The cleir Sone, quhom no cloud devouris,
Surmounting Phebus in the Est,
　　Is cumin of his hevinly touris:
　　　　Et nobis Puer natus est.

Archangellis, angellis, and dompnationis,
　　Tronis, potestatis, and marteiris seir,
And all ye hevinly operationis,
　　Ster, planeit, firmament, and spheir,
　　Fire, erd, air, and water cleir,
To Him gife loving, most and lest,
　　That come in to so meik maneir;
　　　　Et nobis Puer natus est.

Synnaris be glad, and penance do,
　　And thank your Maker hairtfully;
For He that ye micht nocht come to
　　To you is cumin full humbly
　　Your soulis with his blood to buy
And loose you of the fiendis arrest—
　　And only of his ain mercy;
　　　　Pro nobis Puer natus est.

All clergy do to him inclyne,
　　And bow unto that Bairn benyng,
And do your observance divyne
　　To him that is of kingis King:
　　Encense his altar, read and sing
In holy kirk, with mind degest,
　　Him honouring attour all thing
　　　　Qui nobis Puer natus est.

Celestial foulis in the air,
 Sing with your nottis upon hicht,
In firthis and in forrestis fair
 Be myrthful now at all your mycht;
 For passit is your dully night,
Aurora has the cloudis perst,
 The Sone is risen with glaidsum licht,
  Et nobis Puer natus est.

Now spring up flouris fra the rute,
 Revert you upward naturaly,
In honour of the blissit frute
 That raiss up fro the rose Mary;
 Lay out your levis lustily,
Fro deid take life now at the lest
 In wirschip of that Prince worthy
  Qui nobis Puer natus est.

Sing, hevin imperial, most of hicht!
 Regions of air mak armony!
All fish in flud and fowl of flicht
 Be mirthful and mak melody!
 All *Gloria in excelsis* cry!
Heaven, erd, se, man, bird, and best—
 He that is crownit abone the sky
  Pro nobis Puer natus est!

     WILLIAM DUNBAR (1465–?1520).

CHRISTMAS EVE

  ℞ *Pax hominibus bonæ voluntatis*

A FROSTY Christmas-eve ' when the stars were shining
Fared I forth alone ' where westward falls the hill
And from many a village ' in the water'd valley
Distant music reached me ' peals of bells a-ringing:
The constellated sounds ' ran sprinkling on earth's floor
As the dark vault above ' with stars was spangled o'er.

Then sped my thought to keep ' that first Christmas of all
When the shepherds watching ' by their folds ere the dawn
Heard music in the fields ' and marvelling could not tell
Whether it were angels ' or the bright stars singing.

Now blessed be the towers ' that crown England so fair
That stand up strong in prayer ' unto God for our souls:
Blessed be their founders ' (said I) and our country-folk
Who are ringing for Christ ' in the belfries to-night
With arms lifted to clutch ' the rattling ropes that race
Into the dark above ' and the mad romping din.

But to me heard afar ' it was heav'nly music
Angels' song comforting ' as the comfort of Christ
When he spake tenderly ' to his sorrowful flock:
The old words came to me ' by the riches of time
Mellow'd and transfigured ' as I stood on the hill
Hark'ning in the aspect ' of th' eternal silence.

ROBERT BRIDGES.

IN DULCI JUBILO

ON a day, it was the eve of the Feast of the Holy
Angels, the Servant was in great distress of mind
and body, when he heard a heavenly song sung as it
seemed by an invisible choir of angels, and straightway
his distress was forgotten, and a voice said: "As thou
dost rejoice in the song we have sung, so too we in thy
song of the Eternal Wisdom, and this song of ours is
that which will be sung by the chosen on the day of
judgment." On the next day, it being the feast itself,
while he was meditating on what he had heard, there
appeared to the Servant a radiant youth of noblest
bearing with others his fellows, of whom he was the
princely leader. And this youth came right graciously to

8

him and told him that they had been sent by God to bring him happiness in his suffering. And he took the Servant by the hand and bade him join their dance. Then the youth sang to him a merry carol of the infant Jesus, which runs:

In dulci jubilo
Singet und sit vro!
Aller unser wonne
Layt in presipio,
Sy leuchtit vor dy sonne
Matris in gremio
Qui Alpha es et O,
Qui Alpha es et O!

In dulci jubilo
Sing ye, and gladness show!
See our bliss reclining
In præsepio,
The very sun outshining
Matris in gremio
Qui Alpha es et O,
Qui Alpha es et O!

O Jhesu parvule,
Noch dir ist mir so we:
Trosta myr myn gemute,
O puer optime!
Durch allir iunefrauwen gute,
Princeps gloriæ
Trahe me post te,
Trahe me post te!

O Jesu parvule,
I yearn for thee alway:
Grant my heart may hold Thee,
O puer optime!
Through her that did enfold Thee,
Princeps gloriæ
Trahe me post te,
Trahe me post te!

Ubi sunt gaudia?
Nyndert me even da,
Do dy vogelin singen
Nova cantica,
Und do dy schelchen klingen
In regis curia
Eya qualia
Eya qualia!

Ubi sunt gaudia?
If not in Heaven afar,
There where birds go singing
Nova cantica,
And there where bells go ringing
In regis curia
Eia qualia
Eia qualia!

Mater et filia
Ist iunefrau Maria
Wir woren ger vortorben
Per nostra crimina
Nu hot sy uns irworben
Celorum gaudia
O quanta gracia
O quanta gracia!

Mater et filia
Is maiden Maria
Doomed were we sore stained
Per nostra crimina
Till she for us regained
Cœlorum gaudia
O quanta gratia
O quanta gratia!

and the youth made a three-fold repetition of the words:
Ergo merito, etc. Thus was the song received by the
Servant of the Eternal Wisdom, from whom it has been
handed down to us.

B. HENRY SUSO, O.P. (1300–1366).

FOR THE VIGIL

I. POTAGE DE FRUMENTY

TAKE clene qwete [wheat] and bray hit wele in
morter, that the holles gone alle of, and then seth
hit that hit breke in faire watur, and then do thereto gode
brothe and cowe mylk, or mylk of almondes, and colour
hit wythe saffron, and take raw yolkes of eyren [eggs]
and bete hom wel in a vessell, and do in the pot, but
let hit not boyle aftur; and serve hit forthe.

II. FURMENTIE

TAKE qwete streyned, that is for to say, brosten, and
alay hit with gode swete mylk, and boyle hit, and stere
hit well, and put therto sugre; and colour hit with
saffron; and for a lorde put no brothe thereto, but put
therto a few yolkes of eyren beten, and stere hit wel
that hit quayle noght; and when it is sothen serve hit
forthe.

XIVth–XVth Century; Arundel MS.

THE TERRIBLE REMONSTRANCE

THE House spent much Time this Day about the
businesse of the Navie, for settling the Affairs at
Sea, and before they rose, were presented with a
terrible Remonstrance against *Christmas*-day, grounded
upon divine Scriptures: 2 Cor. v. 16; 1 Cor. xv. 14, 17;
and in honour of the *Lord's*-day, grounded on these

scriptures: John xx. 1; Rev. i. 10; Psalms cxviii. 24; Lev. xxiii. 7, 11; Mark xv. 8; Psalms lxxxiv. 10; in which *Christmas* is called *Anti-Christ's*-masse, and those *Masse-mongers* and *Papists* who observe it, &c.

In consequence of which, Parliament spent some Time in Consultation about the Abolition of *Christmas*-day, pass'd Orders to that Effect, and resolv'd to sit on the following Day, which was commonly called *Christmas*-day.

The *Flying Eagle* Gazette, London;

24 December, 1652.

CHRISTMAS EVE CEREMONY

I

COME guard this night the Christmas pie,
That the thief, though ne'er so sly,
With his flesh-hooks don't come nigh
    To catch it
From him, who all alone sits there
Having his eyes still in his ear,
And a deal of nightly fear,
    To watch it.

II

WASSAIL the trees, that they may bear
You many a plum and many a pear:
For more or less fruits they will bring,
As you do give them wassailing.

ROBERT HERRICK (1591–1674).

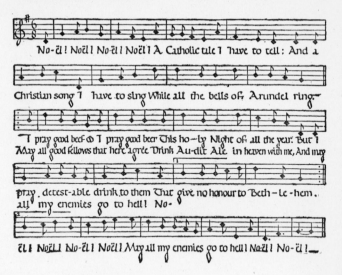

NOEL! Noël! Noël! Noël!
A Catholic tale have I to tell:
And a Christian song have I to sing
While all the bells in Arundel ring.

I pray good beef and I pray good beer
This holy Night of all the year,
But I pray detestable drink for them
That give no honour to Bethlehem.

May all good fellows that here agree
Drink Audit Ale in heaven with me,
And may all my enemies go to hell!
Noël! Noël! Noël! Noël!
May all my enemies go to hell!
Noël! Noël!

HILAIRE BELLOC.

12

TO all unto whom these letters shall come, We, the Official and Special Commissary of the reverend Lord and Father in Christ, Dom. GUILLERMUS, by Divine grace Bishop of Paris, charged especially by the said reverend Father in Christ to inquire into crimes and derelictions committed in this Town, City, and Diocese of Paris and elsewhere where crimes may be discovered, and personally to apprehend, punish, and correct delinquents taken in the said Town, City, and Diocese, extend salutation in Our Lord. We hereby give notice that We, at the instance and request of the venerable Faculty of Theology of Our maternal University of Paris, have ordered the following report to be extracted from the register of prisoners in Our Court of Paris:

Master Guy Tabarie, clerk, brought from the Châtelet in Paris, where he has been held since the 26th day of June, in the year of our Lord 1458, on the charge that he and his accomplices did break and enter and abstract from the sacristy of the chapel of the College of Navarre in Paris the sum of five hundred gold crowns, the property of the said Faculty:

On Wednesday, the fifth day of July, the said clerk, being sworn on the Holy Gospels, made confession and declares it to be true, and deposes that in the week of Christmas of last year (*circa festum Nativitatis Domini ultimate lapsum*) he met Master François Villon and one Colin des Cayeux, whom he never saw before but once, in company with the said Master François, who ordered him to make ready a supper for them in the tavern called the *Mule* before St. Mathurin's church, and that he accordingly did so. And they supped in this place, there being with them a certain monk named Dom Nicolaus of Picardy, and one Petit-Jehan, whom the accused does not know. And he deposes that after supper the said Master François, Colin des Cayeux, and Dom Nicolaus forced him to swear to reveal nothing of what he was about to see or hear, and to accompany them; but they did not tell him what this might be. And he deposes that after this they went together to a house formerly occupied by Master Robert de Saint Simon, into which they entered one after the other over a low wall, and there took off their cloaks and entered the said College of Navarre by climbing a high wall giving into the court of the said College, with the help of a ladder which they took in the house. And he deposes that he, the accused, did not enter the said College, but stayed in the house until they came forth again. And he deposes that when they entered the said College the time was ten o'clock at night or thereabout, and when they came forth it was nearly midnight; and that they told him that they were the richer by a hundred gold crowns, and showed him a small bag of coarse cloth in which there was gold (but he cannot say how much), saying that if he said anything they would murder him; and in order to ensure his silence they gave him ten crowns which he, the accused, took and kept. The remainder they shared among themselves, making him stand aside, and then approached him, saying there were two good crowns for dinner to-morrow. He deposes nevertheless that he heard afterwards that the sum they shared was much greater, and that the next day he told them that they had taken more than they had declared to him; and that they answered that this was true, and that each of them had had a hundred crowns.

Examined as to where they took the money, he deposes that he does not know, unless it was in the said College, but in what place he does not know, even by hearsay.

Examined as to whether the locks were broken or picked, he deposes that he heard nothing from them, neither saw any picklocks in their possession; but he deposes that he has heard that the said Colin des Cayeux is a notable lock-picker (*fortis operator crochetorum*) but that the said Petit-Jehan, his associate, is even more so, although he has never known the aforesaid to have committed any other burglary than the said burglary.

Examined as to a theft perpetrated by him and his companions in the chamber of a religious of the house of Augustinians in Paris, he deposes that he knows nothing of it, and was not there. He deposes further that when the said theft was committed he himself was held in Our prisons in the matter of a fight between him and one Casin Cholet.

Examined as to whether he ever said anything about the aforesaid theft to one Master Pierre Marchant, he denies it.

Examined as to whether he ever told the said Master Marchant that he got out of Our prisons by means of money stolen from one Friar Guillaume Coiffier, he denies it.

Examined as to whether he ever heard it said by his associates, or said himself, that they tried to break into the Church of St. Mathurin and were prevented by the barking of dogs, he denies it.

Examined as to whether he ever said that the said Master François Villon was setting out for Angers to view a certain churchman there who was very rich, and that if his report was favourable the companions were to proceed there to rob him, he denies it.

Examined as to whether they broke into the College of Navarre in any other way than that already described, he says No.

Examined as to whether he accompanied them, he denies it, saying that he went with them only to the house of Master Robert de Saint Simon aforesaid, and waited for them there.

Examined as to the manner in which they broke the locks of the chapel sacristy of the said College, he says he does not know, as he was not present.

Examined as to the length of time he has known the above-named, he says he has known Master François

Villon a long time, but never saw the said Petit-Jehan before, and the said Colin des Cayeux only in the company of the said Master Villon.

Examined as to whether he was paid anything out of the money provided by this burglary, he says that the said Colin des Cayeux told him that he gave one Petit-Thibault four crowns for this expedition; and afterwards he heard that the said Petit-Thibault had been implicated in this burglary: but he will not say anything else to his prejudice.

     •   •   •   •   •   •

Examined as to the manner in which entry was made into the College of Navarre, he says, after some prevarication, that he heard from Master François Villon that it was done by means of picklocks.

Examined again as to whether he was present, he denies it, saying that he stayed in the house of Master de Saint Simon aforesaid to guard the cloaks.

Examined as to his share of the booty, he says he received only ten crowns, and says that the said Master Villon and the other associates told him that as he was not present during the burglary he could not receive as much as those who had participated.

On account of his refusal to confess more, by wilful stubbornness, he was removed and taken to the Painted Chamber and placed upon the little rack, on which he persisted in refusing to confess. Thence he was taken and placed upon the great rack (*applicato magno tretello*) and further examined, and requested to be released from the said punishment, promising to reveal the whole truth; and on being taken down and placed outside, of his free will made a further confession. He says that he was told by the said Master François Villon that the said associates broke into the College of Navarre and there took a bag, which they filled with a large sum of money, and that each of them got eighty gold crowns for his share, but they did not show it to him, the accused. And more than this he would not say. He was therefore placed once more in Our prisons, the venerable magistrates present being Master Estienne de Montigny, Master Robert Tuleu, Doctors in Canon Law, Master Simon Chappitault, Master Denys Commitis, Master François Ferrebourg, Master François de Vaccarie, Licentiate in Canon Law, and several others. In testimony of which We have ordered the Seal of Our Court, with Our own seal, to be appended to these letters. Dated the 22nd day of July in the year of Our Lord 1458.

(Signed): TRUISY.

Archives Nationales, Documents of the College of Navarre, 22 July, 1458.

NOWEL! NOWEL!

UPON the morwe, whan that it was day,
To Britaigne tooké they the righté way,—
Aurelius and this magicien bisyde,
And been descended ther they wolde abyde;
And this was, as thise bookés me remembre,
The coldé, frosty sesoun of Decembre.

Phebus wox old, and hewéd lyk latoun,
That in his hooté declynacioun
Shoon as the burnéd gold, with stremés brighte;
But now in Capricorn adoun he lighte,
Where as he shoon ful pale, I dar wel seyn.
The bittré frostes with the sleet and reyn
Destroyéd hath the grene in every yerd:
Janus sit by the fyr with double berd,
And drynketh of his bugle horn the wyn;
Biforn hym stant brawn of the tuskéd swyn,
And "*Nowel*" crieth every lusty man.

GEOFFREY CHAUCER, *The Frankeleyns Tale.*

I. CHRISTMAS CAROL PUNCH

(For twenty persons)

DISSOLVE a quarter of a pound of sugar in a pint of boiling water, and pour into a China bowl, which may be one decorated with some formal or pleasing pattern, as fancy may dictate, or piety direct. Add the juice of two lemons, with the rinds, half a pint of ginger brandy, one bottle of Jamaica rum, a few sticks of cinnamon, a handful of cloves, and six orange slices.

Allow to simmer, and serve hot in punch glasses. A silver ladle is customary.

Recipe by H. McElhone.

II. MULLED ALE

MAKE some ale quite hot, and add a little grated nutmeg or mixed spice. For each quart of ale beat up half a dozen eggs and mix with a little cold ale, then pour the hot into it and empty from vessel to vessel several times to prevent curdling, for the space of a *Pater* and five *Aves*.

Stir over the fire till sufficiently thick, add a piece of butter or a dash of brandy, and serve with dry toast.

R. M.

A NEW ENGLAND MISS

DEC. 24th, 1771. Eder Whitwell told my aunt that this winter began as did the winter of 1740. How that was I don't remember but this I know that to-day is by far the coldest we have had since I have been in New England. (N.B. All run that are abroad.) Last Sabbath being rainy I went to & from meeting in Mr. Soley's chaise. I dined at unkle Winslow's the walking being so bad I rode there and back to meeting. Every drop that fell froze, so that yesterday morning to this time the appearance has been similar to the description I sent you last winter. The walking is so slippery

18

& the air so cold, that aunt chuses to have me for her scoller these two days. And so to-morrow will be a holiday, so the pope and his associates have ordained, my aunt thinks not to trouble Mrs. Smith with me this week. I began a shift at home yesterday for myself, it is pretty forward. Last Saturday was seven-night my aunt Suky was delivered of a pretty little son, who was baptized by Dr. Cooper the next day by the name of Charles. I knew nothing of it till noonday, when I went there a-visiting. Last Thursday I din'd & spent the afternoon at unkle Joshua's, I should have gone to lecture with my aunt and heard Mr. Hunt preach, but she would not wait till I came from writing-school. Miss Atwood, the last of our boarders, went the same day. Miss Griswold & Miss Meriam, having departed some time agone. I forget whether I mention'd the recept of Nancy's present. I am obliged to her for it. The Dolphin is still whole. And like to remain so.

December 27th. This day the extremity of the cold is somewhat abated. I keept Christmas at home this year & did a very good day's work, aunt says so. How notable I have been this week I shall tell you by and by.

Diary of ANNA GREEN WINSLOW, aged 11,
of Boston, Mass.

Wolcum, Yol, thou mery man
In worchepe of this holy day!

WOLCUM be thou, hevene king,
  Wolcum, born in one morwening,
Wolcum, for hom we xal sing,
    Wolcum, Yol!

Wolcum be ye, Stefne and Jon,
Wolcum, Innocents everychon,
Wolcum, Thomas, marter one,
    Wolcum, Yol!

Wolcum be ye, Good Newe Yere,
Wolcum, Twelfthe Day, both in fere,
Wolcum, seintes lefe and dere,
    Wolcum Yol!

Wolcum be ye, Candylmesse,
Wolcum be ye, qwyn of blyss,
Wolcum bothe to more and lesse,
    Wolcum, Yol!

Wolcum be ye that arn here,
Wolcum alle and mak good chere,
Wolcum alle another yere,
    Wolcum, Yol!
      Sloane MS., XVth Century.

HEIGH-HO! THE HOLLY!

1

MR. *SPECTATOR,*
    I am a young woman, and have my
Fortune to make, for which Reason I come constantly
to Church to hear divine Service, and make Conquests;
but one great Hindrance in this my Design is, that our

Clerk, who was once a Gardener, has this Christmas so
over-decked the Church with Greens, that he has quite
spoil'd my Prospect, insomuch that I have scarce seen
the young Baronet I dress at these three Weeks, though
we have both been very Constant at our Devotions, and
do not sit above three Pews off. The Church, as it is
now equipped, looks more like a Green-house than a
Place of Worship; the middle Isle is a very pretty Shady
Walk, and the Pews look like so many Arbours on each
Side of it. The Pulpit itself has such Clusters of Ivy,
Holly, and Rosemary about it, that a light Fellow in
our Pew took Occasion to say, that the Congregation
heard the Word out of a Bush, like *Moses*. Sir *Anthony
Love's* Pew in particular is so well hedg'd, that all my
Batteries have no Effect. I am obliged to shoot at Random
among the Boughs, without taking any Manner of Aim.
Mr. *Spectator*, unless you will give Orders for removing
these Greens, I shall grow a very aukward Creature at
Church, and soon have little Else to do there but say
my Prayers. I am in Haste,

Dear Sir,

Your most obedient Servant,

Jenny Simper.

II

MR. *SPECTATOR*,
        I am Clerk of the Parish from whence
Mrs. *Simper* sends her Complaint, in your yesterday's
Spectator. I must beg of you to publish this as a publick
Admonition to the aforesaid Mrs. *Simper*, otherwise all
my honest Care in the Disposition of the Greens in the
Church will have no Effect: I shall therefore with your
Leave lay before you the whole Matter. I was formerly,
as she charges me, for several Years a Gardener in the
County of *Kent*; but I must absolutely deny, that it is

out of any Affection I retain for my old Employment
that I have placed my Greens so liberally about the
Church, but out of a Particular Spleen I conceived
against Mrs. *Simper*, and others of the same Sisterhood,
some Time ago. As to herself, I had one Day set the
hundredth Psalm, and was singing the first Line in order
to put the Congregation into the Tune, she was all the
While curtsying to Sir *Anthony*, in so affected and
indecent a Manner, that the Indignation I conceiv'd
made me forget myself so far, as from the Tune of that
Psalm to wander into *Southwell*-tune, and from thence
into *Windsor*-tune, still unable to recover myself, until
I had with the utmost Confusion set a new one. Nay,
I have often seen her rise up and smile, and curtsy to
one at the Lower End of the Church, in the midst of
a *Gloria-Patri*; and when I have spoke the Assent to
a Prayer with a long *Amen*, uttered with a Decent Gravity,
she has been rolling her Eyes about in such a Manner,
as plainly shew'd, however she was moved, it was not
towards an Heavenly Object. In fine, she extended her
Conquests so far over the Males, and rais'd such Envy
in the Females, that what between Love of those, and
the Jealousy of these, I was almost the only Person
that looked in a Prayer-book all Church-time. I had
several Projects in my Head to put a Stop to this Growing Mischief; but as I have long lived in *Kent*, and
there often heard how the *Kentish* men evaded the
Conquerour, by carrying green Boughs over their Heads,
it put me in Mind of practising this Device against
Mrs. *Simper*. I find I have preserv'd many a Young
Man from her Eye-shot by this Means; therefore humbly
pray the Boughs may be fix'd, until she shall give
Security for her Peaceable Intentions.

Your humble Servant,
Francis Sternhold.
RICHARD STEELE (1671–1729).

WE have all read what happened between the opposing armies, and how it came unexpected, undesigned, and yet willed with all the unconscious force of their natures. Not once or twice but again and again we hear of this sudden change upon the night of Christmas Eve, how there was singing upon one side answered by the other, and how the men rose and advanced to meet each other as if they had been released from a spell. Everyone who tells of it speaks also of his own wonder as if he had seen a miracle; and some say that the darkness became strange and beautiful with lights as well as music, as if the armies had been gathered together there not for war but for the Christmas feast. . . . The Prussian thinks that if only he is brutal enough he will cease to be ridiculous. When will Germany cease to be a monster of his creation? When will she regain the humanity of those soldiers of hers who made friends with ours on Christmas Day? We cannot tell; but we can at least refrain from delaying that time by telling her, and believing ourselves, that she is no longer human to us, that her crimes are inexpiable, and that Europe is committed to an everlasting blood-feud with her. That is not what our soldiers say; they were ready to forgive at the Christmas truce; they sang their hymns of peace, and at the sound of them war seemed unreal, and soldiers were no longer soldiers, but men.

A. CLUTTON-BROCK (in *The Times*).

. . . AND ANOTHER

WHEN this was reported to me I issued immediate orders to prevent any recurrence of such conduct, and called the local commanders to strict account, which resulted in a good deal of trouble.

FIELD-MARSHAL LORD FRENCH.

LONDON, *Dec.* 24, 1710. You will have a merryer Christmas-Eve than we here. I went up to Court before church, and in one of the rooms, there being but little company, a fellow in a red coat without a sword came up to me, and after words of course, askt me how the ladies did. I askt what ladies? He said, Mrs. Dingley and Mrs. Johnson: Very well, said I, when I heard from them last: and pray, when came you from thence, sir? Said he, I never was in Ireland; and just at that word lord Winchelsea comes up to me, and the man went off: as I went out I saw him again, and recollected him; it was Vedeau with a pox. . . . When I came from church I went up to Court again, where sir Edm. Bacon told me the bad news from Spain, which you will hear before this reaches you; as we have it now, we are undone there, and it was odd to see the whole countenances of the Court changed so in two hours. Lady Mountjoy carried me home to dinner, where I staid not long after, and came home early, and now am got into bed, for you must always write to your MD's in bed, that's a maxim.

> Mr. White and Mr. Red, write to MD when abed;
> Mr. Black and Mr. Brown, write to MD when you're down;
> Mr. Oak and Mr. Willow, write to MD on your pillow.

What's this? faith I smell fire; what can it be? this house has a thousand stinks in it. I think to leave it on Thursday, and lodge over the way. Faith I must rise, and look at my chimney, for the smell grows stronger; stay—I have been up, and in my room, and found all safe, only a mouse within the fender to warm himself, which I could not catch. I smelt nothing more, but now in my bed-chamber I smell it again; I believe I have singed the woolen curtain, and that's all, though I cannot smoak it. Presto's plaguy silly tonight; an't he? Yes, and so he be. Ay, but if I should wake and see fire. Well; I'll venture; so good-night, &c.

25. Pray, young women, if I write so much as this every day, how will this paper hold a fortnight's work, and answer one of yours into the bargain? You never think of this, but let me go on like a simpleton. I wish you a merry Christmas, and many, many a one with poor Presto at some pretty place. . . .

26. By the lord Harry I shall be undone here with Christmas-boxes. The rogues at the coffee-house have raised their tax, every one giving a crown, and I gave mine for shame, besides a great many half-crowns, to great men's porters, &c.

30. Morning. The weather grows cold, you sauce-boxes. Sir Andrew Fountain, they bring me word, is better. I'll go rise, for my hands are starving while I write in bed.—Night. . . . Well, but when shall we answer this letter, No. 8, of MD's? Not till next year, faith. . . . Pray, pray, Dingley, let me go to sleep; pray, pray, Stella, let me go slumber, and put out my wax-candle.

31. Morning. It is now seven, and I have got a fire, but am writing a-bed in my bed-chamber. 'Tis not shaving day, so I shall be ready to go before church to Mr. St. John, and to-morrow I will answer our MD's letter.

> Would you answer MD's letter,
> On New Year's-day you'll do it better;
> For when the year with MD 'gins,
> It without MD never lins.

(These proverbs have always old words in them; *lins* is leaves off.)

> But if on New-year you write nones,
> MD then will bang your bones.—

But Patrick says I must rise.—Night. I was early this morning with secretary St. John, and gave him a memorial to get the queen's letter for the First-Fruits, who has promised to do it in a very few days. He told me he had been with the Duke of Marlborough, who was lamenting

his former wrong steps in joining with the Whigs, and said he was worn out with age, fatigues, and misfortunes. I swear it pityed me; and I really think they will not do well in too much mortifying that man, although indeed it is his own fault. He is covetous as hell, and ambitious as the Prince of it: he would fain have been general for life, and has broken all endeavours for Peace, to keep his greatness and get money. . . .

January 1, 1711. Morning. I wish my dearest pretty Dingley and Stella a happy new-year, and health, and mirth, and good stomachs, and Fr's company. Faith, I did not know how to write Fr. I wondered what was the matter; but now I remember I always write pdfr. Patrick wishes me a happy New-year, and desires I would rise, for it is a good fire, and faith 'tis cold. I was so politick last night with MD, never saw the like. Get the *Examiners,* and read them; the last nine or ten are full of the reasons for the late change, and of the abuses of the last ministry; and the great men assure me they are all true. I must rise and go see sir Andrew Fountain; but perhaps to-night I may answer MD's letter; so good-morrow, my mistresses all, good-morrow.

> I wish you both a merry new year,
> Roast beef, minced pyes, and good strong beer,
> And me a share of your good cheer;
> That I was there, or you were here,
> And you are a little saucy dear.

Good-morrow again, dear sirrahs. . . .

DEAN SWIFT, *Journal to Stella.*

I

I SYNG of a Mayden
    That is makeles;
Kyng of all kynges
    To her Sone che ches.

He cam al so stylle
    Where his moder was,
As dewe in Aprylle
    That fallyt on the gras.

He cam al so stylle
    To his moder's bowr,
As dewe in Aprille
    That fallyt on the flour.

He cam al so stylle
    Where his moder lay,
As dewe in Aprille
    That fallyt on the spray.

Moder and maydyn
    Was never non but che;
Wel may swych a lady
    Godes moder be.

                    Sloane MS., XVth Century.

27

There is no___ rose of swich ver—tu   As is the
rose that bare Jhe—su___.   That is no   rose   of
swich ver—tu___   As is—the rose that bare Jhe-su.
Al————le———lu———————————ia—

THERE is no rose of swich vertu
As is the rose that bare Jhesu.
Alleluia.

For in this rose conteined was
Hevene and erthe in litel space,
Res miranda.

Be that rose we may weel see
There be o God in persones three,
Pares forma.

The aungeles sungen the schepherdes to
Gloria in excelsis Deo.
Gaudeamus.

Leve we all this werdly merthe,
And folwe we this joyful berthe.
Transeamus.

XVth Century. MS., Trinity College,
Cambridge.

MAN be merry, I thee rede,
But beware what mirthes thou make;
Christ is clothed in thy weed
And He is made man for thy sake.

He came from His Father's seat,
Into this world to be thy make;
Man beware how thou him treat,
For He is made man for thy sake.

Look thou mercy ever cry,
Now and alway, rathe and late;
And He will set thee wonder high,
For He is made man for thy sake.

Late XVth Century.

THE FIRST CRIB (1223)

NOW three years before his death it befell that he
was minded, at the town of Greccio, to celebrate
the memory of the Birth of the Child Jesus, with all
the added solemnity that he might, for the kindling of
devotion. That this might not seem an innovation, he
sought and obtained licence from the Supreme Pontiff,
and then made ready a manger, and bade hay, together
with an ox and an ass, be brought unto the place. The
Brethren were called together, the folk assembled, the
wood echoed with their voices, and that august night
was made radiant and solemn with many bright lights,
and with tuneful and sonorous praises. The man of
God, filled with tender love, stood before the manger,
bathed in tears, and overflowing with joy. Solemn
Masses were celebrated over the manger, Francis, the
Levite of Christ, chanting the Holy Gospel. Then he
preached unto the folk standing round the Birth of the

King in poverty, calling Him, when he wished to name Him, the Child of Bethlehem, by reason of his tender love for Him. A certain knight, valorous and true, Messer John of Greccio, who for the love of Christ had left the secular army, and was bound by closest friendship unto the man of God, declared that he beheld a little Child right fair to see sleeping in that manger, Who seemed to be awakened from sleep when the blessed Father Francis embraced him in both arms. This vision of the knight is rendered worthy of belief, not alone through the holiness of him that beheld it, but is also confirmed by the truth that it set forth, and withal proven by the miracles that followed it. For the ensample of Francis, if meditated upon by the world, must needs stir up sluggish hearts unto the faith of Christ, and the hay that was kept back from the manger by the folk proved a marvellous remedy for sick beasts, and a prophylactic against divers other plagues, God magnifying by all means His servant, and making manifest by clear and miraculous portents the efficacy of his holy prayers.

ST. BONAVENTURE, *Life of St. Francis of Assisi* (1263).

AT THE SHEEPSTEALER'S

ℂ, *Wakefield Second Nativity Play*

FIRST SHEPHERD.	MAK, THE SHEEP-STEALER.
SECOND SHEPHERD.	GYLL, HIS WIFE.
THIRD SHEPHERD.	

The three Shepherds arrive to search Mak's house.

Mak. Now if ye have suspouse to Gyll or to me,
Come and ryp our house, and then may ye see
      Who had her,
    If I any sheep got,

Either cow or stott,
And Gyll my wife rose not
Here since she laid her.
As I am both true and leal, to God here I pray
That this be the first meal I shall eat this day.
First Shepherd. Mak, as I have weal, arise thee, I say;
"He learned timely to steal, that could not say nay."
Gyll.   I swelt.
Out thieves from my once;
Ye come to rob us for the nonce.

[*The Shepherds search the house, Gyll scolding them
and keeping them away from her child's cradle.*

Third Shepherd. All work we in vain: as well we may go.
But hatters!
I can find no flesh;
Hard nor nesh,
Salt nor fresh,
But two tome platters.
Gyll. No, so God me bless, and give me joy of my
child.
Third Shepherd. In good time be his steps, and happy
they be.
But who was his gossips, tell now to me.
Mak. So fair fall their lips.
First Shepherd. [*Aside.*]   Hark now, a lee!
Mak.   So God them thank,
Parkin, and Gibbon Waller, I say,
And gentle John Horne, in good fay,
He made all the garray,
With the great shank.

[*The Shepherds retire baffled, but as they go a sudden
thought strikes them, and they return to Mak's
house.*

Third Shepherd. Mak, with your leave, let me give your
bairn
But six pence.

Mak.　　　Nay, go 'way: he sleepys.

Third Shepherd. Methink he peepys.

Mak.　　　When he wakens he weepys.

　　　　　　I pray you go hence.

　　　　　　　　[The Third Shepherd goes to the cradle.

Third Shepherd. Give me leave him to kiss, and lift up
　　the clout.

　　What the devil is this? He hath a long snout!

First Shepherd. He is marked amiss. We wait ill about.

Second Shepherd. Ill spun weft, I wis, aye cometh foul out.

　　　　　　Aye so!

　　　　　　He is like to our sheep!

Second Shepherd. This was a quaint gaud, and a far cast,
　　It was a high fraud.

Third Shepherd.　　　Yea sirs, was 't.

　　Let us burn this bawd and bind her fast,

　　　　　　A false skawd hangs at the last;

　　　　　　　　So shall thou.

　　　　　　Will ye see how they swaddle

　　　　　　His for feet in the middle?

　　　　　　Saw I never in a cradle

　　　　　　A hornèd lad ere now!

　　*[Mak and his wife swear the occupant of the cradle is
　　their offspring, and Gyll says it must be a changeling.*

First Shepherd. This is a false work. I would fain be
　　wroken:

　　　　　　Get a weapon.

Gyll.　　　He was taken by an elf;

　　　　　　I saw it myself.

　　　　　　When the clock struck twelve

　　　　　　Was he mis-shapen.

Second Shepherd. Ye two are right deft, same in a stead.

Third Shepherd. Since they maintain their theft, let us
　　do them to dead.

Mak. If I trespass eft, gird off my head.

　　With you will I be left.

First Shepherd. Sirs, do my rede
    For this trespass,
  We will neither ban nor flyte,
    Fight nor chyte,
    But seize him tight,
    And cast him in canvas.

 [*They seize Mak and toss him, and return towards their fold.*

First Shepherd. Lord, how I am sore, in point for to tryst;
 In faith I may no more, therefore will I rest.

Second Shepherd. As a sheep of sevenscore, he weighed in my fist.

Third Shepherd. Now I pray you,
    Lig down on this green.

First Shepherd. On these thefts yet I mean.

Third Shepherd. Whereto should ye tene?
    Do as I say you.

 Angelus cantat " Gloria in Excelsis"; postea dicat:

Angelus. Rise, herdmen heynd, for now is he born
  That shall take from the fiend, that Adam had lorn;
  That warlock to sheynd, this night is he born.
  God is made your friend; now at this morn
    He behests.
    To Bedlem go see,
    There lies that free
    In a crib full poorly,
    Betwixt two beasts.

First Shepherd. This was a quaint stevyn that ever yet I heard.
 It is a marvel to nevyn thus to be scared.
 Of God's son of hevyn, he spoke up word.
 All the wood like the levin, methought that he gard
    Appear.

Second Shepherd. Say, what was his song? Heard ye not
    how he cracked it?

  Three breves to a long.

Third Shepherd.   Yea, marry he hacked it.

  Was no crochet wrong, nor no thing that lacked it.

Second Shepherd. To Bedlem he bade that we should
    gang;

  I am full feared that we tarry too lang.

Third Shepherd. Be merry and not sad; of mirth is our
    sang,

  Everlasting glad, our road may we fang,

           Without noise.

First Shepherd. Hie we thither quickly;

      If we be wet and weary,

      To that child and that lady

      We have it not to slose.

            [*They set off on the road to Bethlehem.*

                XIIIth–XVth Century.

THE SEARCH

JHESU es thy name. A! A! that wondyrfull name! A!
that delittabyll name! This es the name that es above
all names. . . . I yede abowte be covaytyse of riches
and I fand noghte Jhesu. I satt in companyes of worldly
myrthe and I fand noghte Jhesu. . . . Therefore I
turnede by anothire waye, and I ran abowte be Poverte,
and I fand Jhesu pure, borne in the worlde, laid in a
crybe and lappid in clathis.

    RICHARD ROLLE OF HAMPOLE (1290–1349).

NOËL

LE ciel est noir, la terre est blanche.
  Cloches, carillonnez gaîment!
Jésus est né; la Vierge penche
Sur lui son visage charmant.

Pas de courtines festonnées
Pour préserver l'Enfant du froid;
Rien que les toiles d'araignées
Qui pendent des poutres du toit.

Il tremble sur la paille fraîche,
Ce cher petit enfant Jésus,
Et pour l'échauffer dans sa crèche
L'âne et le bœuf soufflent dessus.

La neige au chaume pend ses franges,
Mais sur le toit s'ouvre le Ciel,
Et, tout en blanc, le chœur des anges
Chante aux bergers: "Noël! Noël!"

THÉOPHILE GAUTIER (1811–1872).

THE WONDER

WIT hath wonder and kind ne can
How maiden is mother and God is man
Leave thy asking and believe that wonder
For might hath mastery and skill goeth under.

Laus Deo.
(From the Balliol MS.).

THE MIRACLE IN THE FOREST

L'Annonce faite à Marie; Act III. sc. iii.

Violaine (raising her finger). Listen!
[*Silence. A distant, almost imperceptible, sound of bells.*
Mara. I hear nothing.
Violaine. The Christmas bells, the bells announcing
midnight Mass!
O Mara, a little Child is born to us!
Mara. Then give me back mine.
[*Trumpets in the distance.*
Violaine. What is that?

35

Mara. It is the King going to Reims. Have you not heard
    of the road the peasants have cut through the forest?
    (And they can keep all the wood they cut).
    It is a little shepherdess who guides the King through
      the middle of France
    To Reims, to be crowned there.
Violaine. Praised be God, Who does these wonderful
    things!

                [Again the sound of bells, very distinct.

Mara. How loud the bells ring the *Gloria!*
    The wind blows this way.
    They are ringing in three villages at once.
Violaine. Let us pray, with all the universe!
    You are not cold, Mara?
Mara. I am cold only in my heart.
Violaine. Let us pray. It is long since we celebrated
    Christmas together.

    Fear nothing. I have taken your grief upon myself.
    Look! and that which you have given me lies close
    against my heart.

    Do not weep! This is not the time to weep, when the
    Salvation of all mankind is already born.

                [Bells in the distance, less clear.

Mara. The snow has stopped, and the stars are shining.
Violaine. Look! Do you see this book?
    The priest who visits me now and then left it with me.
Mara. I see it.
Violaine. Take it, will you? and read me the Christmas
    Office, the First Lesson of each of the three Nocturns.

                [Mara takes the book and reads.

PROPHECY OF ISAIAH

At the first time the land of Zabulon and the land of
Nephthali was lightly touched: and at the last the way of the
sea beyond the Jordan of the Galilee of the Gentiles was
heavily loaded.

36

The people that walked in darkness have seen a great light: to them that dwelt in the region of the shadow of death light is risen. . . .

For a child is born to us, and a son is given to us and the government is upon his shoulder: and his name shall be called Wonderful, Counsellor, God the Mighty, Father of the World to come, the Prince of Peace.[1]

Violaine (raising her face). Listen!

[*Silence.*

[*Voices of Angels, heard only by Violaine.*

Choir. HODIE NOBIS DE CÆLO PAX VERA DESCENDIT, HODIE PER TOTUM MUNDUM MELLIFLUI FACTI SUNT CÆLI.

A Voice. HODIE ILLUXIT NOBIS DIES REDEMPTIONIS NOVÆ, REPARATIONIS ANTIQUÆ, FELICITATIS ÆTERNÆ.

Choir. HODIE PER TOTUM MUNDUM MELLIFLUI FACTI SUNT CÆLI.

[*Violaine lifts her finger in warning. Silence. Mara listens and looks uneasily.*

Mara. I hear nothing.

Violaine. Read on, Mara.

Mara (continuing to read).

SERMON OF ST. LEO, POPE

Our Saviour, dearly beloved, was born to-day: let us rejoice. For there should be no loophole open to sorrow on the birthday of Life, which, the fear of Death being at last consumed, filleth us with the joy of Eternity promised. . . . Let the sinless exult, insomuch as his palm is at hand; let the sinful rejoice . . .

[*Suddenly a brilliant and prolonged sound of trumpets very near. Shouts resound through the forest.*

---

[1] This, and the homilies following, have been abbreviated here.

37

Mara. The King! The King of France!

[*Again and again the blare of trumpets, unutterably piercing, solemn, and triumphant.*

Mara (*in a low voice*). The King of France who goes to Reims!

[*Silence.*

Violaine!

[*Silence.*

Do you hear me, Violaine?

[*Silence. She goes on with the reading.*

. . . let the sinful rejoice, insomuch as forgiveness is offered to him. Let the Gentile be of good cheer, because he is bidden to share life. For the Son of God, according to the fulness of this time, which the inscrutable depth of the Divine counsel hath disposed, took on Himself the nature of mankind so that He might reconcile it to its Maker, and that this deviser of death, Satan, by Her whom he vanquished might be in his turn conquered.

[*Voices of Angels, heard only by Violaine, as before.*

Choir. O MAGNUM MYSTERIUM ET ADMIRABILE SACRAMENTUM UT ANIMALIA VIDERINT DOMINUM NATUM JACENTEM IN PRÆSEPIO! BEATA VIRGO CUJUS VISCERA MERUERUNT PORTARE DOMINUM CHRISTUM.

A Voice. AVE, MARIA, GRATIA PLENA, DOMINUS TECUM.

Choir. BEATA VIRGO CUJUS VISCERA MERUERUNT PORTARE DOMINUM CHRISTUM.

[*Pause.*

Mara. Violaine, I am not worthy to read this book!

Violaine, I know I am too hard, and I am sorry for it: I wish I could be different.

Violaine. Read, Mara. You do not know who sings the responses. [*Silence.*

Mara. [*With an effort takes up the book, and reads in a trembling voice:*]

38

THE HOLY GOSPEL ACCORDING TO ST. LUKE

> *[They both rise.*

At that time there went forth a decree from Cæsar Augustus, that the whole world should be enrolled. (And the rest.)

> *[They sit down.*

HOMILY OF SAINT GREGORY, POPE

> *[She stops, overcome by emotion. The trumpets sound a last time in the distance.*

Mara.

Forasmuch as by the grace of God we are this day thrice to celebrate the solemnities of the Mass, we may not now speak at length on the Gospel that hath just been read. But the birth of our Redeemer bids us address you at least in a few words. . . . For Bethlehem means the House of Bread, and Jesus Christ saith of Himself: I am the Living Bread descended from Heaven. Therefore had the place in which our Lord was born been called the House of Bread in order that He who was to feed our hearts with internal satiety should there appear in the substance of flesh.

Voices of Angels.

> *Choir.* BEATA VISCERA MARIÆ VIRGINIS QUÆ PORT-
> AVERUNT ÆTERNI PATRIS FILIUM; ET BEATA
> UBERA QUÆ LACTAVERUNT CHRISTUM DOMINUM.
> QUI HODIE PRO SALUTE MUNDI DE VIRGINE NASCI
> DIGNATUS EST.

> *A Voice.* DIES SANCTIFICATUS ILLUXIT NOBIS;
> VENITE, GENTES, ET ADORATE DOMINUM.

> *Choir.* QUI HODIE PRO SALUTE MUNDI DE VIRGINE
> NASCI DIGNATUS EST.

> *[Long silence.*

Voices of Angels. *[Again, almost imperceptible.]*

> *Choir.* VERBUM CARO FACTUM EST ET HABITAVIT IN
> NOBIS: ET VIDIMUS GLORIAM EJUS, GLORIAM QUASI
> UNIGENITI A PATRE, PLENUM GRATIÆ ET VERITATIS.

A Voice. OMNIA PER IPSUM FACTA SUNT ET SINE IPSO FACTUM EST NIHIL.

Choir. ET VIDIMUS GLORIAM EJUS, GLORIAM QUASI UNIGENITI A PATRE, PLENUM GRATIÆ ET VERITATIS.

A Voice. GLORIA PATRI ET FILIO ET SPIRITUI SANCTO.

Choir. ET VIDIMUS GLORIAM EJUS, GLORIAM QUASI UNIGENITI A PATRE, PLENUM GRATIÆ ET VERITATIS.
> [*Long silence.*

Violaine. [*Cries out suddenly in a stifled voice.*] Ah!

Mara. What is it?
> [*With her hand Violaine makes her a sign to be silent.
> —Silence.—The first flush of dawn appears.*
>
> *Violaine puts her hand under her cloak as if to fasten her dress.*

Mara. Violaine, I see something moving under your cloak!

Violaine (*as if awakening little by little*). Is it you, Mara? Good-morning, sister. I feel on my face the breath of the new-born day.

Mara. Violaine! Violaine! Is it your arm that stirs? Again I see something moving.

Violaine. Peace, Mara. It is Christmas Day, when all joy is born.

Mara. What joy is there for me unless my child lives?

Violaine. And for us, too—a little child is born to us!

Mara. In the name of the living God, what are you saying?

Violaine. "Behold, I bring you glad tidings. . . ."

Mara. Your cloak—it moves again!
> [*The little bare foot of a baby, moving lazily, appears in the opening of the cloak.*

Violaine. "Because a man is born into the world!"
> [*Mara falls upon her knees, with a deep sigh, her forehead on her sister's knees. Violaine caresses her.*

40

Violaine. Poor sister! she weeps. She, too, has known too much sorrow.

> [*Silence. Violaine kisses Mara's head.*

Take it, Mara. Would you leave the child with me always?

Mara. [*She takes the child from under the cloak and looks at it wildly.*] It lives!

Violaine. [*She walks out of the cave a few steps upon the heather. By the first light of the bitter cold morning can be seen first the pines and birches, hoary with frost, then, at the end of an immense snow-covered plain, seeming very small on the top of its hill but clearly etched in the pure air, the five-towered silhouette of Monsanvierge.*] Glory to God!

Mara. It lives!

Violaine. Peace on earth to men.

Mara. It lives! It lives!

Violaine. It lives, and we live.

And the face of the Father appeared on the earth renewed and comforted.

Mara. My child lives!

Violaine (*lifting her finger*). Listen!　　　　　　[*Silence.*

I hear Angelus ringing at Monsanvierge.

> [*She makes the sign of the Cross and prays. The child awakes.*

Mara (*whispering*). It is I, Aubaine! dost know me?

> [*The child moves and whimpers.*

What is it, my joy? What is it, my treasure?

> [*The child opens its eyes, looks at its mother, and begins to cry. Mara looks closely at it.*

Violaine!

What does this mean? Its eyes were black.

Now they are blue like yours!　　　　　　[*Silence.*

Ah!

And what is this drop of milk I see on its lips?

PAUL CLAUDEL.

Of a rose, a lovely rose,
Of a rose is al myn song

LESTENYT, lordyngs, bothe elde and yinge,
How this rose began to sprynge;
Swych a rose to myn lykynge
    In al this wor(l)d ne knowe I non.

The Aungil cam fro hevene tour
To grete Marye with gret honour,
And seyde sche xuld bere the flour
    That xulde breke the fynds bond.

The flour sprong in heye Bedlem,
That is bothe bryght and schen,
The rose is Mary hevene qwyn,
    Out of here bosum the blosme sprong.

The ferste braunche is ful of myght,
That sprang on Crystemesse nyght,
The sterre schon over Bedlem bryght
    That is bothe brod and long.

The secunde braunche sprong to helle,
The fendys power doun to felle:
Therein myht non sowle dwelle;
    Blyssid be the time the rose sprong!

The thredde braunche is good and swote,
It sprang to hevene crop and rote,
Therein to dwellyn and ben our bote;
    Every day it schewit in prysts hond.

Prey we to her with gret honour,
Che that bar the blyssid flowr,
Che be our helpe and our socour
    And schyd us fro the fyndes bond.

            Sloane MS., XVth Century.

CRISMAS Day we'll keepe thus: At four in the morning our trumpeters all doe flatt their trumpetts, and
begin at our Captain's Cabin, and thence to all the
officers' and gentlemen's Cabins; playing a levite at
each cabin door, and bidding good morrow, wishing a
merry Crismas. After they goe to their station, viz. on
the poope, and sound three levitts in honour of the
morning. At ten we goe to prayers and sermon; text
Zacc. ix. 9. Our Captain had all his officers and gentlemen to dinner with him where wee had excellent good
fayre: a ribb of beefe, plumb-puddings, minct pyes, &c.,
and plenty of good wines of severall sorts; dranke healths
to the King, to our wives and friends, and ended the
day with much civill myrth.

> Diary of the Rev. HENRY TEONGE,
> Naval Chaplain.

WITCH DANCE AT SALEM

AS for the Spectres that visited and afflicted Mercy
Short, there were, on the twenty-fifth of December
[1692] it was, that Mercy said, They were going to have a
Dance; and immediately those that were attending her,
most plainly Heard and Felt a Dance, as of Barefooted
People, upon the Floor; whereof they are willing to make
oath before any Lawful Authority. If I should now
venture to suppose, That the Witches do sometimes
come in person to do their Mischiefs, and yett have the
horrible skill of cloathing themselves with Invisibilities,
it would seem Romantic. And yett I am inclinable to
think it, upon Reasons more than tis here a Place to
mention. But in my Opinion, Tis not more Incredible,
or Inscrutable, than what I am going to Relate; namely
That although we have all the Demonstration a Reasonable man can desire, that Mercy Short could not in the
least measure Hear, when wee were perhaps Half an
Hundred of us together singing of a psalm in the Room;

nevertheless, at that very Time, shee could Hear a little Knock of a little Child at the Door. I say, the Philosophy that can give an Account for the One of these may do it for t'other too!

From A Brand pluck'd out of the Burning, by COTTON MATHER.

VIE DE BOHÈME

IT was Christmas Eve, and towards evening the Latin Quarter assumed its own peculiar character. From four in the afternoon the Mont-de-Piété, the old clothes stores, and the second-hand bookshops had been besieged by a noisy crowd which later in the evening surged into the pork butchers', the cookshops, and the grocers'. The shop-assistants, even if they had had the hundred hands of Briareus, could not have coped with the swarming mob fighting over their provisions. At the baker's there were queues as if it were a famine. The wine-merchants got rid of the results of three vintages, and a skilful statistician would have been hard put to it to calculate the number of ham-knuckles and sausages sold at the celebrated Borel's in the Rue Dauphine. In this one evening Daddy Cretaine, known as "Rolls," exhausted three editions of his butter-cake. All night joyous noises floated from the houses, with their glowing windows, and the atmosphere of a fair filled all the Quarter.

That night towards ten o'clock, Marcel and Rodolphe returned home moodily enough. Going along the Rue Dauphine they had seen the crowd in a provision-merchant's, and had lingered a moment in front of his windows, tantalised by the sight of so many fragrant works of art. The two Bohemians, as they gazed, had all the appearance of that personage in the Spanish romance who made hams melt to nothing by merely looking at them.

"That," said Marcel, indicating a superb bird displaying through its rosy transparent skin the truffles of Périgord with which it was stuffed, "is called a truffled turkey. I have seen impious creatures eat a thing like that without first kneeling to it," added the painter, casting on the turkey a look capable of roasting it.

"And what is your opinion concerning this modest leg of Southdown mutton?" inquired Rodolphe. "What a colour! You might say it had just been unhooked from the porkshop in that picture of Jordaëns! Leg of mutton is the favourite food of the gods and of Madame Chandellier, my godmother."

"Cast an eye over this fish," answered Marcel, pointing at some trout. "Those are the cleverest swimmers in the aquatic world. These little fellows who look like nothing at all could make a nice income by feats of strength, if you realise that they can climb a perpendicular torrent as easily as you and I could accept a supper invitation or two. I've nearly eaten them already."

"That large fruit lower down, with a golden cone and foliage like a panoply of native sabres, is called a pineapple—the pippin of the tropics," Rodolphe informed him.

"It leaves me cold," replied Marcel. "In the matter of fruit, I'd rather have this piece of beef, or that ham, or that little knuckle in the jelly-armour, transparent as amber."

"You are right," said Rodolphe. "Ham is the friend of man, when he's got any. I should not reject that pheasant over there, nevertheless."

"I agree, I agree. It is a dish for crowned heads."

And they moved on, jostling all along their way the joyous procession streaming forth to toast Momus, Bacchus, Comus, and all the little festive gods in -us, asking each other who was this Lord Gamache whose wedding everyone was celebrating with such a profusion

of cheer. Marcel was the first to remember the date and the day.

"It's Christmas Eve!" he said.

"Do you remember what we were doing this time last year?" asked Rodolphe.

"I do. At the Café Momus. Barbemuche stood the racket. I could never have imagined such a delicate girl as Phémie could hold so much sausage."

"What bad luck Momus won't let us in any more," sighed Rodolphe.

"Alas!" answered Marcel. "The years fly past, and no two are alike."

"Could you do a *réveillon*?"

"With whom and what?" asked the painter.

"With me."

"And the necessary gold?"

"Wait a minute," said Rodolphe. "I am going into this café. There are some men I know inside, playing big stakes. I'll borrow a few sesterces from a favourite of chance and bring along something to wash down a sardine or two and a pig's foot."

"Go along, then," said Marcel. "I'm as hungry as a dog. I'll wait for you here."

Rodolphe went into the café and found a friend who, having just won three hundred francs in ten rounds at *bouillotte*, made it a privilege to lend the poet forty sous, which he handed over in that bad temper which accompanies the gambling fever. At any other time, and elsewhere than around a green cloth, he would probably have made it at least forty francs.

"Well?" Marcel demanded, as the poet came out.

"Here's the takings," said Rodolphe.

"A crumb and a spot," observed Marcel.

With this modest sum they found the means of procuring bread, wine, pork, tobacco, light and fire, and returned to the small hotel where each had a room. Marcel's, which

46

served as his studio, was the larger, and was chosen for the feast. The friends together spread the table for their common meal. But when they were seated at their little table, near a hearth on which bad damp wood burned away without flame or heat, the ghost of the vanished past came in, a melancholy guest, and sat between them.

HENRY MURGER (1822–1861).

TWELFTH NIGHT, 1605

PERSONS in the *Masque of Blacknesse*, personated at the Court at White-Hall; which, beside the singular Grace of Musick and Dances, had the Success in the Nobilitie of Performance, as nothing needs to the Illustration, but the Memorie by Whom it was personated.

The Persons	The Names	The Symbols
The QUEENE Co. of BEDFORD	Euphoris Aglaia }	A golden Tree, laden with Fruit.
La. HERBERT Co. of DERBY	Diaphane Eucampse }	The figure *Icosaedron* of Cristal.
La. RICH Co. of SUFFOLK	Ocyte Kathare }	A paire of naked Feet in a River.
La. BEVILL La. EFFINGHAM	Notis Psychrote }	The SALAMANDER simple.
La. El. HOWARD La. Sus. VERE	Glycyte Malacia }	A Cloud full of Raine dropping.
La. WORTH La. WALSINGHAM	Baryte Periphere }	An Urne sphered with Wine.

The Names of the OCEANIÆ *were,*

Doris	Cydippe	Beroe	Ianthe
Petræa	Glauce	Acaste	Lycoris
Ocyrhoe	Tyche	Clytia	Plexaure.

BEN JONSON (1573–1637).

THE merry *Christmas* Carnival being now come on, when the good *Housewife* makes her husband eat his Dinner upon a *Trencher*, to preserve her New Scower'd Plates in their shining *Beauty*, and pinch'd the Guts of her Servants for the preceeding Week, that her Windows might be splendidly adorn'd with Superstitious *Greens*, and that her *Minc'd-Pyes* and *Plumb Porridge* might be richer than her Neighbours: we wander'd about like a couple of Runaway Prentices, having confin'd ourselves to no particular Port, *Uncertainty* being our *Course*, and meer *Accident* our *Pilot*. Every Street we pass'd thro' smelling as strong of Roast-Beef and Rosemary, as *Pye-Corner* does of Pig and Pork, in the Wicked Season of St. *Bartholomew*. Every Ale-House we came at was *Seranaded* with a Drum to thunder their Rattle-Headed Customers into a good Humour of spending their Pence like *Asses*, which they got like *Horses*. Every now and then we came to a common *Vaulting-School*, where peeping in we saw drunken *Tarpaulins* and their Taudry Trulls, Dancing to a *Scotch* Bagpiper, or a blind Fidler; and at least seventeen Strumpets to one that had *Modesty* enough in her Looks to be thought otherwise. Sometimes meeting in the Street with a Boats Crew, just come on Shore, in search of those Land Debaucheries which the Sea denies 'em; looking like such Wild, Staring, Gamesome, Uncouth Animals, that a Litter of Squab *Rhinocerosses*, drest up in Humane Apparel, could not have made to me a more ungainly Appearance. Every Post they came next was in Danger of having its Head broke; for every one as he pass'd by, would give the Senseless Block a Bang with his Cudgel, as if they wish'd every Post they met with to be either the *Purser* or the *Boat-swain*. The very *Dogs* in the street, I observ'd, shun'd 'em with as much Fear as a Loitering Vagrant wou'd a Gang of *Press-Masters*, being so caution'd against their Ill Usage by the Stripes they have formerly receiv'd, that as soon as ever he sees a *Seaman*, away runs the poor

Cur with his Tail between his Legs. I could not forbear
Reflecting on the Prudence of those Persons, who send
their *Unlucky Children* to *Sea* to *Tame* and *Reform* 'em,
which I am well satisfied, is like sending a *Knave* into
Scotland to learn *Honesty*; a *Fool* into *Ireland* to learn
Wit; or a *Clown* into *Holland* to learn *Breeding*.

By the Time we had made these Observations and
Reflections on those *Maritime* kind of *Monsters*, who had
little more to show that they were Men, than that they
Walk'd Upright, we were straggl'd into *Wapping*; and
being pretty well tired with our Walk, we went into a
Publick-House to Refresh our selves with a *Sneaker of
Punch*, which most likely to prove the the best Liquor
that end of the Town cou'd afford us. The first Figure
that accosted us at our Entrance, was a Female *Wap-
pineer*, whose Crimson *Countenance* and *Double Chin*,
contain'd within the Borders of a *White Callico-Hood*,
made her Fiery Face look, in my fancy, like a round
Red-Hot Iron glowing in a *Silver Chavendish*; the rest of
her Body being in proportion to her *Head*, bore so
Corpulent a *Grace*, that had a Bag of *Cotton*, or *Wooll-
Pack*, been Lac'd into a Pair of Stays, adorn'd with
Petticoats, and put upon *Stilts*, it would have made a
Figure of such Similitude to her Person, that the best
Wax-worker or *Carver* in *Christendom*, could not have
represented her in either of their *Arts*, with truer Dimen-
sions, or greater Likeness.

My Friend having a Sword on, I observed to him she
was most respectful, asking him in a Voice as hoarse as
a *Boatswain*, *What will you please to Drink, Noble Captain?*
After we had answer'd her Question, she had soon
prepar'd us a little Bowl of Spiritual *Diapente*, which,
for want of better, we were forc'd to dispence with. Up
in the Chimney Corner sat a great hulking Fellow smoaking a short Pipe of Stinking *Tobacco*, looking as Melan-
cholly upon the Fire as a Female Wretch does upon a

*c   49

Smith-field Pile, when she is brought to be burnt for *High-Treason*. By and by in comes my Landlady, and like a true Lover of *Industry*, began to Read him a Lecture against *Laziness*, tormenting the Ears of the poor dejected *Water-Rat*, with a severe Reprehension, after the following Manner. *Why, how do you think*, John, *in your Conscience, I am able to maintain you in this Lazy Life you lead ? Thou knowest I have no Money, God help me, but what I Work for, as any Woman in the Parish, therefore*, John, *it behoves thee to consider I am not able to let thee lye in this Condition. Why, what a Rope ails you, Mother* (reply'd the Fellow), *Why, would you have the Conscience to turn me a Drift now I have spent all my Money on Board you, before I have got me another Voyage? You are as hasty with a Body to turn him out, as a Boatswain in a Storm. Why, but* John (reply'd the Landlady) *dost think to get a Voyage by Smoaking in the Chimney Corner? No* (says John) *but how do you think a Man can look out without a Penny in his Breeches? I swear by the* Purser's Honesty, *I had as live step up to Furl the Main-Sail in a Gust of Wind, without a Knife in my Pocket.* To which reply'd the old Beldam, *Why, I would not have thee think what I speak is out of any Ill Will to thee; for as far as I am able: here, there is Six-pence for thee, and Prithee*, John, *go and look out, and don't fling it away Idlely: For consider these hard Times, 'tis a great deal of Money.* He takes the Six-pence, thanks her; and thus she continues, *There are several Ships going out, bound to the* West-Indies, *that want Men; and I know thou art as able a Seaman as ever walk'd between* Stem *and* Stern *of a Ship, that any Commander will be glad to Enter thee. As to that, Mother,* says he, *I can speak a proud Word for my self; there is ne'er a Part of a Seaman, from the* Splicing *of a* Cable *to the* Cooking *of the* Kettle, *but what I know as well as the* Boatswain. *Well, Mother, wish me good Luck, I'll try what I can do, as the* Gunner *said to the* Cooks

Daughter. She wish'd he might Prosper in his Endeavours, and away he went.

I could not but reflect on the unhappy Lives of these *Salt-Water* kind of *Vagabonds*, who are never at Home, but when they're at Sea, and always are Wandering when they're at Home; and never contented but when they're on Shore: they're never at Ease till they've receiv'd their Pay, and then never satisfied till they have spent it.

The London Spy (1700).

SNOWS OF YESTERYEAR

I OFTEN think with gratitude of the famous Mr. Nelson Lee—the author of I don't know how many hundred glorious pantomimes—walking by the summer wave at Margate, or Brighton perhaps, revolving in his mind the idea of some new gorgeous spectacle of faëry, which the winter shall see complete. He is like Cook at midnight (*si parva licet*). He watches and thinks. He pounds the sparkling sugar of benevolence, the plums of fancy, the sweetmeats of fun, the figs of—well, the figs of fairy fiction, let us say, and pops the whole in the seething cauldron of Imagination, and at due season serves up the PANTOMIME.

Very few men in the course of nature can expect to see *all* the pantomimes in one season, but I hope to the end of my life I shall never forego reading about them in that delicious sheet of *The Times* which appears on the morning after Boxing Day. Perhaps reading is even better than seeing. The best way, I think, is to say you are ill, lie in bed, and have the paper for two hours, reading all the way down from Drury Lane to the Britannia at Hoxton.

WILLIAM MAKEPEACE THACKERAY (1811–1863).

THE first time that Mercutio fell upon the English stage there fell with him a gay and hardly human figure; it fell, perhaps finally, for English drama. That manner of man—Arlecchino, or Harlequin—had outlived his playmates, Pantaleone, Brighella, Colombina, and the Clown. A little of Pantaleone survives in old Capulet, a little in the father of the Shrew, but the life of Mercutio in the one play, and of the subordinate Tranio in the other—both Harlequins—is less quickly spent, less easily put out, than the smouldering of the old man. Arlecchino frolics in and out of the tragedy and comedy of Shakespeare until he thus dies in his lightest, his brightest, his most vital shape, Mercutio.

Arlecchino, the tricksy and shifty spirit, the contriver, the busybody, the trusty rogue, the wonder-worker, the man in disguise, the mercurial one, lives on buoyantly in France to the age of Molière. He is officious and efficacious in the skin of Mascarille and Ergaste and Scapin; but he tends to be a lackey, with a reference rather to Antiquity and the Latin Comedy than to the Middle Ages, as on the English stage his mere memory survives differently to a later age in the person of 'Charles, his friend.' What convinces me that he virtually died with Mercutio is chiefly this—that this comrade of Romeo's lives so keenly as to be fully capable of the death that he takes at Tybalt's sword-point; he lived indeed, he dies indeed. Another thing that marks a close of a career of ages is his loss of his long customary good luck. Who ever heard of Arlecchino unfortunate before, at fault with his sword-play, overtaken by tragedy? His time had surely come. The gay companion was to bleed; Tybalt's sword had made a way. 'Twas not so deep as a well nor as wide as a church-door, but it served.

Ariel fulfils his office, and is not of one kind with those he serves. Is there a memory of Harlequin in that delicate figure? Something of the subservient immortality, of the light indignity proper to Pantaleone, Brighella, Arlecchino, Colombina, and the Clown hovers away from the stage when Ariel is released from the trouble of human things.

Immortality, did I say? It was immortality until Mercutio fell. And if some claim be made to it still because Harlequin has transformed so many scenes for the pleasure of so many thousand children since Mercutio died, I must reply that our modern Harlequin is no more than a marionnette: he has returned whence he came. A man may play him, but he is — as he was first of all—a doll. From dollhood Arlecchino took life, and so promoted flitted through a thousand comedies, only to be again what he first was; save that as once a doll played the man, so now a man plays the doll. It is but a memory of Arlecchino that our children see, a poor statue or image endowed with mobility rather than with life.

With Mercutio vanished the light heart that had given to the serious ages of the world an hour's refuge from the unforgotten burden of responsible conscience; the light heart assumed, borrowed, made dramatically the spectator's own. We are not serious now, and no heart now is quite light, even for an hour.

ALICE MEYNELL († 1922).

DECEMBER THE TWENTY-NINTH

[*St. Thomas of Canterbury*]

A a a a nunc gaudet Ecclesia

LESTENYTZ lordyngs both grete and smale
I xal you telyn a wonder tale
How holy cherche was brow(t) in bale
    Cum magna injuria
The greteste clerk of al this lond
Of Cauntyrbery ye understond

53

Slawyn he was (by) wykkyd hond
Demonis potentia
Knytes kemyn fro Hendry kyng
Wykkyd men, with-oute lesyng
Ther they dedyn a wonder thing
Ferventes insania
They sowtyn hym al abowtyn,
Withine the paleys and withoutyn
Of Jhesu Cryst hadde they non dowte
In sua malicia
They openyd here mowthis wonder wyde
To Thomeys they spokyn mekyl pryde
Here, tretour, thu xalt abyde
Ferens mortis tedia
Thomas answerid with mylde chere
If ye wil me slon in this manere
Let hem pasyn alle tho arn here
Sine contumelia
Beforn his aunter he knelyd adoun
Ther they gunne to paryn his crown
He sterdyn the braynys up and doun
Optans celi gaudia
The turmentowrs abowtyn sterte,
With dedly wondys thei gunne him hurte,
Thomas deyid in moder cherche
Pergens ad celestia
Moder, clerke, wedue, and wyf
Worchepe ye Thomeys in al your lyf
For lii poyntes he les his lyf
Contra regis consilia.

Sloane MS., XVth Century.

Dec. 24th, 1818.

MY dear Coleridge,—I have been in a state of incessant hurry ever since the receipt of your Ticket. It found me incapable of attending you, it being the night of Kenney's new Comedy, which has utterly failed. You know my local aptitudes at such a time; I have been a thorough rendezvous for all consultations. My head begins to clear up a little, but it has had Bells in it. Thank you kindly for your ticket, though the mournful prognostic which accompanies it certainly renders its permanent pretensions less marketable; but I trust to hear many a course yet. You excepted Christmas week, by which I understood *next week*; I thought Christmas Week was that which Christmas Sunday ushered in. We are sorry it never lies in your way to come to us; but, dear Mahomet, we will come to you. Will it be convenient to all the good people at Highgate, if we take a Stage up, *not next Sunday*, but the following, viz., 3rd January, 1819? Shall we be too late to catch a skirt of the old out-goer? How the years crumble from under us! We shall hope to see you before then; but, if not, let us know if *then* will be convenient. Can we secure a Coach home?

Believe me ever yours,

C. L.

I have but one holiday, which is Christmas Day itself nakedly; no pretty garnish and fringes of St. John's Day, Holy Innocents, &c., that used to bestud it all around in the Calendar. *Improbe labor!* I write six hours every day in this candle-light fog-den at Leadenhall.

CHARLES LAMB to Samuel Taylor Coleridge.

MRS. MARKHAM ON CHRISTMAS

Mary (*settling down comfortably*). And now, dear Mamma, you will tell us something about Christmas, as you promised.

Mamma. Well, my dear, I suppose I must, because the season of Good Will and Peace on Earth is approaching; but I confess I prefer to instruct you children in the workings of our Constitution, the justice of our Laws and the beautiful adaptations of our Social System, which is the pride and envy of the world.

Tommy. Yes, dear Mamma, and on the foreign policy of our beloved country and its dealings with inferior races. I vow and protest but for your instruction——

Mary. Do stop him, Mamma! We shall never get to Christmas if he goes on like this.

Tommy. Stop yourself! I was only thanking Mamma for her intensely interesting information.

Mary. You weren't! You were using long words. You love the sound of your own voice.

Mamma. Children! Children! This will never do! Here we are nearer, every day, to the great feast and Boxing Day succeeding it, and it is shocking to mar its holy calm with wrangling and cursing.

Tommy. But, Mamma! I didn't curse. I didn't even say——

Mary. Oh! Mamma, he's going to say that dreadful word again!

Mamma (*sharply*). Quiet! [*She smoothes her skirts.*] I desire you, I *command* you both to sit silent while I describe to you the origin and character of Christmas. . . . Christmas, my dears, is the mid-winter feast of us English Folk and one to which we have always been lovingly attached. Our Saxon Forefathers knew it as Yule-tide and would hold Wassail in Hall with song and foaming cups of Mead.

Tommy (*very interested*). What is Mead, Mamma?

Mamma. Mead, my dear, is a fermented liquor made with Honey.

Tommy. Supposing I were to take some Honey and Hot Water, Mamma, and . . .

Mary (*interrupting him*). Was it intoxicating, Mamma?

Mamma. No doubt it was mildly exhilarating as befitted occasions of rejoicing, but not strictly speaking intoxicating.

Mary. It would be horrible to think of them getting drunk!

Tommy. Who?

Mamma. She is speaking of our Saxon Forefathers, Tommy. We must remember that they were ruder than we are, for we all get better as time goes on, but they were of the same sturdy stuff as we are and had the same self-control and decency, so I am sure they never got drunk—a horrible idea, as you rightly say.

Mary. Why did they sit in the Hall, Mamma? Why did they not drink in the Dining Room?

Mamma. My dear, in those days the Hall *was* the Dining Room. Everyone took dinner in the Hall.

Tommy. What an extraordinary place to dine in!

Mamma. Yet so it was: and all classes—Lords and Ladies and guests and servants all dined together.

Mary (*starting*). Oh! Mamma! Incredible! Do you really mean that the maids, like our Anne and Evangeline, came upstairs and ate with Gentlemen and Ladies, and even Lords?

Mamma. Yes, my dear: it was indeed the case. But as I have told you, they were still in a rude condition, so perhaps there was not so much difference between the Upper and Lower Classes as there is to-day.

Mary. What does Lady mean, Mamma?

Mamma. Wise men tell us that it means "Loaf Giver."

Mary. How do they know, Mamma?

Mamma. They do not tell us, my dear, and it would ill become us to inquire. We must humbly accept their information—and there is much else of the kind. For instance, Book comes from the habit of writing on Beech Bark, and "Horse" is derived from a word meaning "Mare," while Beef comes from Ox. [*A long silence.*]

Tommy (after a further pause). Well! Well!

Mary. Pray, Mamma, why do we hang holly and other evergreens about the House and even in Church at Christmas?

Mamma. As an accompaniment to our festivity, my dear, I suppose, or perhaps as a sign of our rejoicing. It is a most ancient custom.

Mary (doubtfully). I see; and the same with Christmas Trees.

Mamma. No. Those are of recent introduction and come, like most good things, from Germany. They were brought into England by Albert the Good.

Tommy. Pray, who was this foreign potentate, Mamma?

Mamma (sighing). Ah! My children! He is no longer even a name to your generation! To mine he was a sacred memory, and dear Granny actually saw him with her own eyes.

Tommy (persisting). Yes! But who was he, Mamma?

Mamma. He was a German Prince, the Husband of our Great Queen Victoria.

Mary. Great Heavens! I never knew Queen Victoria ever had a husband!

Mamma. Of course she had, my dear, but he died, alas! comparatively early in life.

Tommy. Why was he so good, Mamma?

Mamma. Because he had a good mother. She was also

a very clever woman, as German women so often are,
and had many brilliant friends attending her: among
others a Mr. Meyer, from whom little Albert may have
acquired his fine taste in pictures.

Mary. Was he handsome, Mamma?

Mamma. Strikingly so, I believe. But I can only judge
from his monuments, which hardly do him justice. . . .
Well, then, he it was who grafted the Christmas Tree
on to our dear old English Christmas. He also introduced Fish Knives.

HILAIRE BELLOC.

THE POET IS GAY

I

IN the old Scythe-Bearer's festal days [Saturnalia] over
which the dice-box reigns as king, you, O Rome, wearing your cap of licence, permit me, I think, to trifle in
lightsome verse. You have smiled: then I, too, am not
forbidden. Away, far away, ye pallid Cares! Let me
speak whatever comes to mind, without morose cogita-
tion. Boy, blend cups of half and half, such as Pythag-
oras offered to Nero! blend, Dindymus, *et plus vite que
ça!* I can do nothing sober, but when I drink I am
impelled by fifteen poet-power!

II

I have written things that Cato's wife and the bleak
Sabine dames might read; but I wish this little book to
laugh from end to end, and to be naughtier than all my
little books. Let it be drenched in wine, and not blush
to be stained with rich Cosmian unguents. Yet remember,
Apollinaris, these are verses of the Saturnalia. This little
book does not express my own morals.

MARTIAL (A.D. ? 41–? 104).

CHRISTMAS Day.—We caught the 10.20 train at Paddington, and spent a pleasant day at Carrie's mother's. The country was quite nice and pleasant, although the roads were sloppy. We dined in the middle of the day, just ten of us, and talked over old times. If everybody had a nice, *un*interfering mother-in-law, such as I have, what a deal of happiness there would be in the world. Being all in good spirits, I proposed her health; and I made, I think, a very good speech.

I concluded, rather neatly, by saying: "On such an occasion as this—whether relatives, friends, or acquaintances—we are all inspired with good feelings towards each other. We are of one mind, and think only of love and friendship. Those who have quarrelled with absent friends should kiss and make it up. Those who happily have *not* fallen out, can kiss all the same."

I saw tears in the eyes of both Carrie and her mother, and must say I felt very flattered by the compliment. That dear old Reverend John Panzy Smith, who married us, made a most cheerful and amusing speech, and said he should act on my suggestion respecting the kissing. He then walked round the table and kissed all the ladies, including Carrie. Of course one did not object to this; but I was more than staggered when a young fellow named Moss, who was a stranger to me, and who had scarcely spoken a word through dinner, jumped up suddenly with a sprig of mistletoe, and exclaimed: "Hulloh! I don't see why I shouldn't be on in this scene." Before one could realise what he was about to do, he kissed Carrie and the rest of the ladies. Fortunately the matter was treated as a joke, and we all laughed; but it was a dangerous experiment, and I felt very uneasy for a moment as to the result. I subsequently referred to the matter to Carrie, but she said: "Oh, he's not much more than a boy." I said that he had a very large moustache for a boy. Carrie replied: "I didn't say he was not a nice boy."

December 28.—Lupin, on coming down to breakfast,

said to his mother: "I have not put off Daisy and Frank, and should like them to join Gowing and Cummings this evening." I felt very pleased with the boy for this. Carrie said in reply: "I am glad you let me know in time, as I can turn over the cold leg of mutton, dress it with a little parsley, and no one will know it has been cut." She further said she would make a few custards, and stew some pippins, so that they would be cold by the evening.

Finding Lupin in good spirits, I asked him quietly if he really had any personal objections to either Gowing or Cummings. He replied: "Not in the least. I think Cummings looks rather an ass, but that is partly due to his patronising 'the three-and-six-one-price hat company,' and wearing a reach-me-down frock-coat. As for that perpetual velveteen jacket of Gowing's—why, he resembles an itinerant photographer."

I said it was not the coat that made the gentleman; whereupon Lupin, with a laugh, replied: "No, and it wasn't much of a gentleman who made their coats."

We were rather jolly at supper, and Daisy made herself very agreeable, especially in the earlier part of the evening, when she sang. At supper, however, she said: "Can you make tee-to-tums with bread?" and she commenced rolling up pieces of bread, and twisting them round on the table. I felt this to be bad manners, but of course said nothing. Presently Daisy and Lupin, to my disgust, began throwing bread-pills at each other. Frank followed suit, and so did Cummings and Gowing, to my astonishment. They then commenced throwing hard pieces of crust, one piece catching me on the forehead, and making me blink. I said: "Steady, please; steady!" Frank jumped up and said: "Tum, tum; then the band played."

I did not know what this meant, but they all roared, and continued the bread-battle. Gowing suddenly seized all the parsley off the cold mutton, and threw it full in my face. I looked daggers at Gowing, who replied: "I

say, it's no good trying to look indignant with your hair full of parsley." I rose from the table, and insisted that a stop should be put to this foolery at once. Frank Mutlar shouted: "Time, gentlemen, please! time!" and turned out the gas, leaving us in absolute darkness.

I was feeling my way out of the room, when I suddenly received a hard intentional punch at the back of my head. I said loudly: "Who did that?" There was no answer; so I repeated the question, with the same result. I struck a match, and lighted the gas. They were all talking and laughing, so I kept my own counsel; but after they had gone I said to Carrie: "The person who sent me that insulting post-card at Christmas was here to-night."

GEORGE and WEEDON GROSSMITH.

A REPROOF FOR KING ARTHUR

AT this time (A.D. 521) that great Monarch Arthur, with his Clergy, all his Nobility, and Soldiers, kept *Christmas* in *York*, whither resorted to him the prime Persons of the Neighbourhood, and spent the latter End of *December* in Mirth, Jollity, Drinking and the Vices that are too often the Consequence of them; so that the Representations of the old Heathenish Feasts dedicated to Saturn were here again revived; but the Number of Days they lasted were doubled and amongst the wealthier Sort trebled; during which Time they counted it almost a Sin to treat of any serious Matter. Gifts are sent mutually from and to one another; frequent invitations pass betwixt Friends, and domestick Offenders are not punished. Our Countrymen call this Jule-tide, substituting the name of *Julius Cæsar* for that of *Saturn*. The Vulgar are yet persuaded that the Nativity of Christ is then celebrated, but mistakenly; for 'tis plain they imitate the Lasciviousness of *Bacchanalians*, rather than the memory of *Christ*, then, as they say, born.   *History of York*, 1785.

62

A LORDLY DISH

At a Feeste-Royall Pecokkes shall be dight on this manere.

TAKE and flee off the skynne with the fedurs tayle and the nekke, and the hed thereon; then take the skyne with all the fedurs, and lay hit on a table abrode; and strawe thereon grounden comyn; then take the pecokke, and roste him, and endore hym with raw yolkes of egges; and when he is rosted take hym of, and let hym cool awhile, and take hym and sowe hym in his skyn, and gilde his combe, and so serve hym forthe with the last cours.

XIVth–XVth Century, Arundel Collection.

THE MARVEL OF THE SWORD

THEN stood the realm in great jeopardy long while, for every lord that was mighty of men made him strong, and many weened to be king. Then Merlin went to the Archbishop of Canterbury, and counselled him for to send for all the lords of the realm, and all the gentlemen of arms, that they should to London come by Christmas, upon pain of cursing; and for this cause, that Jesus, that was born on that night, that he would of his great mercy show some miracle, as he was come to be King of mankind, for to show some miracle who should be rightways king of this realm. So the Archbishop, by the advice of Merlin, sent for all the lords and gentlemen of arms

63

that they should come by Christmas even unto London.
And many of them made them clean of their life, that
their prayer might be the more acceptable unto God.
So in the greatest church of London, whether it were
Paul's or not the French book maketh no mention, all
the estates were long or day in the church for to pray.
And when Matins and the first Mass was done, there
was seen in the church-yard, against the high altar, a
great stone four square, like unto a marble stone, and in
the midst thereof was like an anvil of steel a foot on high,
and therein stuck a fair sword naked by the point, and
letters there were written in gold about the sword that
said thus:

WHOSO PULLETH OUT THIS SWORD OF THIS STONE AND
ANVIL, IS RIGHTWISE KING BORN OF ALL ENGLAND.

Then the people marvelled, and told it to the Archbishop. I command, said the Archbishop, that ye keep
you within your church, and pray unto God still; that
no man touch the sword till the high Mass be all done.
So when the Masses were done all the lords went to
behold the stone and the sword. And when they saw the
scripture, some assayed; such as would have been king.
But none might stir the sword nor move it. He is not
here, said the Archbishop, that shall achieve the sword,
but doubt not God will make him known. But this is
my counsel, said the Archbishop, that we let purvey ten
knights, men of good fame, and they to keep this sword.
So it was ordained, and then there was made a cry, that
every man should essay that would, for to win the sword.
And upon New Year's day the barons let make a jousts
and a tournament, that all the knights that would joust
or tourney there might play, and all this was ordained
for to keep the lords and the commons together, for the
Archbishop trusted that God would make him known
that should win the sword. So upon New Year's day,

when the service was done, the barons rode unto the
field, some to joust and some to tourney, and so it
happened that Sir Ector, that had great livelihood about
London, rode unto the jousts, and with him rode Sir
Kay his son, and young Arthur that was his nourished
brother; and Sir Kay was made knight at All Hallowmass
afore. So as they rode to the jousts-ward, Sir Kay had
lost his sword, for he had left it at his father's lodging,
and so he prayed young Arthur for to ride for his sword.
I will well, said Arthur, and rode fast after the sword,
and when he came home, the lady and all were out to
see the jousting. Then was Arthur wroth, and said to
himself, I will ride to the church-yard, and take the
sword with me that sticketh in the stone, for my brother
Sir Kay shall not be without a sword this day. So when
he came to the church-yard, Arthur alit and tied his horse
to the stile, and so he went to the tent, and found no
knights there, for they were at jousting; and so he
handled the sword by the handles, and lightly and
fiercely pulled it out of the stone, and took his horse and
rode his way until he came to his brother Sir Kay, and
delivered him the sword. And as soon as Sir Kay saw the
sword, he wist well it was the sword of the stone, and so
he rode to his father Sir Ector, and said: Sir, lo here is
the sword of the stone, wherefore I must be king of this
land. When Sir Ector beheld the sword, he returned
again and came to the church, and there they alit all
three, and went into the church. And anon he made
Sir Kay to swear upon a book how he came by that sword.
Sir, said Sir Kay, by my brother Arthur, for he brought
it to me. How gat ye this sword? said Sir Ector to Arthur.
Sir, I will tell you. When I came home for my brother's
sword, I found nobody at home to deliver me his sword,
and so I thought my brother Sir Kay should not be
swordless, and so I came hither eagerly and pulled it
out of the stone without any pain. Found ye any knights

about this sword? said Sir Ector. Nay, said Arthur.
Now, said Sir Ector to Arthur, I understand ye must
be king of this land. Wherefore I, said Arthur, and for
what cause? Sir, said Ector, for God will have it so,
for there should never man have drawn out this sword,
but that he shall be rightways king of this land. Now let
me see whether ye can put the sword there as it was, and
pull it out again. That is no mastery, said Arthur, and so
he put it in the stone, therewithal Sir Ector essayed to
pull out the sword and failed.

Now assay, said Sir Ector unto Sir Kay. And anon
he pulled at the sword with all his might, but it would
not be. Now shall ye essay, said Sir Ector unto Arthur.
I will well, said Arthur, and pulled it out easily. And
therewithal Sir Ector knelt down to the earth, and Sir
Kay. Alas, said Arthur, my own dear father and brother,
why kneel ye to me? Nay, nay, my lord Arthur, it is not
so, I was never your father nor of your blood, but I
wot well ye are of an higher blood than I weened ye
were. And then Sir Ector told him all, how he was
bitaken him for to nourish him, and by whose com-
mandment, and by Merlin's deliverance.

.　　.　　.　　.　　.

Therewithal they went unto the Archbishop, and told
him how the sword was achieved, and by whom; and on
Twelfth Day all the barons came thither, and to essay
to take the sword, who that would essay. But there afore
them all, there might none take it out but Arthur.

SIR THOMAS MALORY, *Morte d'Arthur* (1470).

THE PROVENÇAL LOG

FOR my father, who was so faithful to ancient custom,
the feast of the year was Christmas Eve. That day
the farm-labourers left off work early, and my mother
gave each of them, in a napkin, a splendid *galette* (pastry-

cake) *à l'huile*, a roll of nougat, a bunch of dried figs, a cheese from our own flocks, a celery salad, and a bottle of old wine. And then the servants went off in every direction to "place the Log" in their own country and their own homes. Those who stayed behind at the Farm were the unfortunates who had no family; and sometimes relatives, an old bachelor, perhaps, would arrive at nightfall, saying:

"Merry Christmas! I've come to place the Log with all of you."

Then all together we went in a joyous crowd to find the Christmas Log, which—the tradition was strict— had to be a fruit-tree. We lugged it back to the Farm, all in line, the eldest at one end and I, the youngest, at the other; thrice we paraded it round the kitchen; and then, as we arrived again in front of the hearthstone, my father solemnly poured over the Log a glass of old wine, saying:

> "Allégresse! Allégresse!
> Mes beaux enfants, que Dieu nous comble d'allégresse!
> Avec Noël tout bien vient!
> Dieu nous fasse la grâce de voir l'année prochaine,
> Et, sinon plus nombreux, puissions-nous n'y pas être moins!"

And crying all together "*Allégresse! Allégresse! Allégresse!*" — "Happiness! Happiness! Happiness!" — we placed the Log in position on the fire-dogs; and as the first tiny flame darted from it,

> "A la bûche
> Boute feu!"

recited my father, crossing himself. And then we all went to supper.

Oh, the holy table! Holy in truth, with the whole family gathered round it, at peace and happy! In place of the hanging lamp which lighted us all the year round, three tall candles burned on the table that night; if a wick bent towards anyone it was a bad omen. At either end of the table shone a plateful of green corn, placed in water to sprout on the feast of St. Barbara. On the triple white cloth appeared, each in turn, the consecrated dishes—snails, which everyone extracted from the shell with a long nail; fried cod and mullet with olives; shrimps; celery with pepper and vinegar sauce; followed by a heap of dainties reserved for this Feast, flat cakes *à l'huile*, raisins, almond nougat, the apples called *pommes de Paradis*, and above all the great *Pan calendau*, the Christmas Loaf, quartered crosswise, which was never attacked until a quarter of it had been religiously handed to the first poor person who passed that way.

The wait for midnight Mass was long this night; and we gathered round the hearth, talking of our ancestors and praising their deeds.

FRÉDÉRIC MISTRAL (1830–1914).

WHITE RUSSIAN CAROL

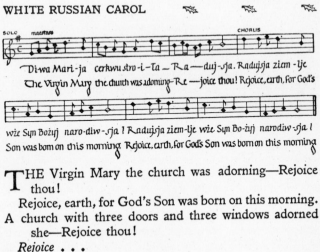

THE Virgin Mary the church was adorning—Rejoice thou!
Rejoice, earth, for God's Son was born on this morning.
A church with three doors and three windows adorned she—Rejoice thou!
Rejoice . . .

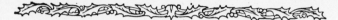

In at the first window the sun it came leaping—Rejoice
thou!
Rejoice . . .
Through the next window the moon it shone brightly—
Rejoice thou!
Rejoice . . .
In through the third an angel came flying—Rejoice thou!
Rejoice . . .
From that angel's tear the Danube's overflowing—Rejoice
thou!
Rejoice . . .
And there on the Danube a boat it is floating—Rejoice
thou!
Rejoice . . .
And see, in that boat a young Cossack is sailing—Rejoice
thou:
Rejoice . . .
He's whittling his arrows and painting his bow now—
Rejoice thou!
Rejoice . . .

> Traditional, trans. H. E. Kennedy
> and S. Uminska.

DECLINE OF AN ORATOR

BOSTON, Dec. 25th, 1778. A feverish disorder which
gave me a poor night prevented my going to church or
meeting, for Christmas is observed in both and the streets
are more orderly than they are on Sunday. Mr. Wickes
Green & Bliss dined with me & my son & wife & Dr.
O'Brien. Mr. Weekes says that when the plan of Government recommended by the House to the Towns for
consideration came before the town of Boston, Otis
appeared and spake so well against it that he prevented
its passing as otherwise it would have done and it was
put off to another day when they chose Otis Moderator
and he spake so well on introducing the subject that it

was rejected by a great majority. He dressed himself very decently on that occasion but soon after returned to his sordid dress & demeanour about the streets.

Diary of THOS. HUTCHINSON,
Governor of Massachusetts.

CHRIST IN THE CRADLE

LOOK, how He shakes for cold!
How pale His lips are grown!
Wherein His limbs to fold
Yet mantle has He none.
His pretty feet and hands
(Of late more pure and white
Than is the snow
That pains them so),
Have lost their colour quite.
His lips are blue
Where roses grew,
He's frozen everywhere:
All the heat He has
Joseph, alas!
Gives in a groan; or Mary in a tear.

HON. PATRICK CAREY (1623–1657).

THE HAPPY ENGLISH

THE lewid peple than algates agre,
And caroles singen everi' Criste masse tyde,
Not with schamefastenes bot jocondle,
And holey bowghes aboute; and al asydde
The brenning fyre hem eten, and hem drinke,
And laughen mereli, and maken route,
And pype, and dansen, and hem rage; ne swinke,
Ne noe thynge els, twalue daye' thei wolde not.

Ludus Corporis Xti, XIVth Century.

AN EPIPHANY GAMBOL

❡ *Twelfth Night,* Act II. sc. iii.

Olivia's house.

Enter Sir Toby and Sir Andrew.

Sir To. Approach, Sir Andrew: not to be a-bed after midnight is to be up betimes; and 'diluculo surgere,' thou
know'st,—

Sir And. Nay, by my troth, I know not: but I know, to
be up late is to be up late.

Sir To. A false conclusion: I hate it as an unfilled can.
To be up after midnight and to go to bed then, is early:
so that to go to bed after midnight is to go to bed betimes. Does not our life consist of the four elements?

Sir And. Faith, so they say; but I think it rather consists
of eating and drinking.

Sir To. Thou'rt a scholar; let us therefore eat and drink.
Marian, I say! a stoup of wine!

Enter Clown.

Sir And. Here comes the fool, i' faith.

Clo. How now, my hearts! did you never see the picture
of 'we three'?

Sir To. Welcome, ass. Now, let's have a catch.

Sir And. By my troth, the fool has an excellent breast.
I had rather than forty shillings I had such a leg, and
so sweet a breath to sing, as the fool has. In sooth,
thou wast in very gracious fooling last night, when
thou spokest of Pigrogromitus, of the Vapians passing

the equinoctial of Queubus: 'twas very good, i' faith. I sent thee sixpence for thy leman: hadst it?

Clo. I did impeticos thy gratillity; for Malvolio's nose is no whipstock: my lady has a white hand, and the Myrmidons are no bottle-ale houses.

Sir And. Excellent! why, this is the best fooling, when all is done. Now, a song.

Sir To. Come on; there is sixpence for you: let's have a song.

Sir And. There's a testril of rae too: if one knight give a—

Clo. Would you have a love-song, or a song of good life?

Sir To. A love-song, a love-song.

Sir And. Ay, ay: I care not for good life.

Clo. [*Sings.*]

> O mistress mine, where are you roaming?
> O, stay and hear; your true love's coming,
>   That can sing both high and low:
> Trip no further, pretty sweeting;
> Journeys end in lovers meeting,
>   Every wise man's son doth know.

Sir And. Excellent good, i' faith.

Sir To. Good, good.

Clo. [*Sings.*]

> What is love? 'tis not hereafter;
> Present mirth hath present laughter;
>   What's to come is still unsure:
> In delay there lies no plenty,
> Then come kiss me, sweet and twenty,
>   Youth's a stuff will not endure.

Sir And. A mellifluous voice, as I am true knight.

Sir To. A contagious breath.

Sir And. Very sweet and contagious, i' faith.

Sir To. To hear by the nose, it is dulcet in contagion. But shall we make the welkin dance indeed? shall we rouse the night-owl in a catch that will draw three souls out of one weaver? shall we do that?

Sir And. An you love me, let's do't: I am a dog at a catch.

Clo. By 'r lady, sir, and some dogs will catch well.

Sir And. Most certain. Let our catch be, "Thou knave."

Clo. "Hold thy peace, thou knave," knight? I shall be constrained in't to call thee knave, knight.

Sir And. 'Tis not the first time I have constrained one to call me knave. Begin, fool: it begins "Hold thy peace."

Clo. I shall never begin if I hold my peace.

Sir And. Good, i' faith. Come, begin.   [*Catch sung.*

Enter Maria.

Mar. What a caterwauling do you keep here! If my lady have not called up her steward Malvolio and bid him turn you out of doors, never trust me.

Sir To. My lady's a Cataian, we are politicians, Malvolio's a Peg-a-Ramsey, and "Three merry men be we." Am not I consanguineous? am I not of her blood? Tillyvally. Lady! [*Sings.*] "There dwelt a man in Babylon, lady, lady!"

Clo. Beshrew me, the knight's in admirable fooling.

Sir And. Ay, he does well enough if he be disposed, and so do I too: he does it with a better grace, but I do it more natural.

Sir To. [*Sings*] "O, the twelfth day of December,"—

Mar. For the love o' God, peace!

Enter Malvolio.

Mal. My masters, are you mad? or what are you? Have you no wit, manners, nor honesty, but to gabble like tinkers at this time of night? Do you make an alehouse of my lady's house, that ye squeak out your coziers' catches without any mitigation or remorse of voice? Is there no respect of place, persons, nor time in you?

Sir To. We did keep time, sir, in our catches. Sneck up!

Mal. Sir Toby, I must be round with you. My lady bade me tell you, that, though she harbours you as her kinsman, she's nothing allied to your disorders. If you can separate yourself and your misdemeanours, you are welcome to the house; if not, an it would please you to take leave of her, she is very willing to bid you farewell.

Sir To. "Farewell, dear heart, since I must needs be gone."

Mar. Nay, good Sir Toby.

Clo. "His eyes do show his days are almost done."

Mal. Is't even so?

Sir To. "But I will never die."

Clo. Sir Toby, there you lie.

Mal. This is much credit to you.

Sir To. "Shall I bid him go?"

Clo. "What an if you do?"

Sir To. "Shall I bid him go, and spare not?"

Clo. "O no, no, no, no, you dare not."

Sir To. Out o' tune, sir: ye lie. Art any more than a steward? Dost thou think, because thou art virtuous, there shall be no more cakes and ale?

Clo. Yes, by Saint Anne, and ginger shall be hot i' the mouth too.

Sir To. Thou'rt i' the right. Go, sir, rub your chain with crums. A stoup of wine, Marie!

Mal. Mistress Mary, if you prized my lady's favour at any thing more than contempt, you would not give means for this uncivil rule: she shall know of it, by this hand.   [*Exit.*

WILLIAM SHAKESPEARE (1564–1616).

WHAT MIGHT HAVE BEEN

ON the 6th of January 1662 that indefatigable play-goer Mr. Pepys recorded in his diary: "After dinner to the Duke's House, and there saw *Twelfth Night* acted well, though it be but a silly play and not related at all

74

to the name." The final court of literary appeal—the general consent of the cultivated caste in modern Europe—has not confirmed Pepys' sentence on the "silly play"; but when he speaks of it as "not related at all to the name" he makes a palpable hit, or at least indicates a lost opportunity. John Downes, writing a century after the play was composed, says that "it was got up on purpose to be acted on Twelfth Night." And this fact, if fact it be, only makes it more tantalising that the plot, the action, and the characters should bear no relation to the title. Shakespeare is Catholic as the sea is salt. Did not the very word "Catholicism" suggest to Matthew Arnold's mind "the pell-mell of all the men and women of Shakespeare's plays"? Shakespeare painted the daily life of a rich and free humanity, with the Mass, and all that the Mass represents, as its sun and centre. It is a permissible exercise of literary fancy to imagine the delightful combination of love and frolic and festivity which he might have woven round the traditional observance of Twelfth Night, when in Baron's Hall and minstrel-gallery the mirth of Christmas reached its topmost and final note, but not till, in the Mass of the Epiphany, men had once again paid their homage to the story of the Star. *Vidimus stellam Ejus in Oriente, et venimus adorare Eum.*

But it is idle to speculate on what Shakespeare might have done. What he actually did had in it enough of wonder and astonishment to satisfy John Milton, and what satisfied Milton may well suffice for our less heroic age. Only the title, *Twelfth Night*, haunts and tantalises us, and sets us dreaming of the immortal music in which Shakespeare, had he so willed, might have told the story and meaning of the Star.

Rt. Hon. G. W. E. Russell.

O SWEETEST Night! my mind I ne'er can wean
From thoughts of thee, in which the Heavens do rain
Huge showers of grace: the hillocks flow with sweets,
And from the mountains milk and honey sweats.
O sweetest Night! my starvèd soul doth die
To have a full draught of thy ambrosy.
Tertullian gravely said: "Some goods there are
As well as evils, which e'en oppress and bear
Us to the ground." The wonders of this Night
Are such, to find our God in such a plight:
That hardly such a bastard soul is found
Who sends not knees and heart to kiss the ground.

MYLES PINKNEY, priest (1599–1674).

CHRISTMAS SONG

℄ *by a Monk of Tours.*

DEUS Pater Filium,
O natale gaudium!
Deus Pater Filium
Proprium donavit.
O natale gaudium!
Dominus regnavit.

Habet vaticinium,
O natale gaudium!
Habet vaticinium
Suum psalmus David.
O natale gaudium!
Dominus regnavit.

Abraham fidelium,
O natale gaudium!
Abraham fidelium
Pater exultavit.
O natale gaudium!
Dominus regnavit.

76

ADORATION OF THE MAGI

From a French Breviary of the XVth Century

Ecce sicut lilium,
O natale gaudium!
Ecce sicut lilium
Justus germinavit.
O natale gaudium!
Dominus regnavit.

XIIIth Century.

CAROL OF THE NUNS OF CHESTER

Qui cre-a-vit ce-lum lul-ly lul-ly lu.— Nasci-tur in stabulo

by-by by-by by— Rex qui re-git se-cu-lum lul-ly lul-ly lu.—

QUI creauit celū   lully lully lu
Nascitur in stabulo   byby byby by
Rex qui regit seculum   lully lully lu

Joseph emit panniculū   lully lully lu
Mater inuolit puerū   byby byby by
Et ponit in presepio   lully lully lu

Inter animalia   byby byby by
Jacit mūdi gaudia   lully lully lu
Dulcia sup. omnia   byby byby by

Lactat Mater filiū   lully lully lu
Osculatur paruulum   byby byby by
Et adorat dominū   lully lully lu

77

Roga mater filiū   byby byby by
Ut det nobis gaudiū   lully lully lu
In perenni gloria   byby byby by

In sempiterna sæcula   lully lully lu
In eternū et ultra   byby byby by
Det nobis sua gaudia   lully lully lu

From the MS. *Processional* of St. Mary's,
Chester (*c.* 1425).

MEDITATION ON THE FEAST

DERE frēdes. As we may heare and se all holy churche
maketh mynde and mencion of the great myrth and
melody of the blessed byrth of oure lorde Jhesu Chryst
very god and man that was this daye borne of his mother
Mary in socour of all mankynde, and in especyal for
thre causes. Fyrste to give peace to men of good wyll,
and to lyght them that were in derkenes of synne, and to
draw us with love to hym. Than as for the fyrste cause
he was borne to gyve man peace of good wyll, I may well
prove this. For whan he was borne aungels songe thus
(Gloria in excelsis deo) Joye be to god in heven, and peace
in erth to mankynde of good wyll. At mydnyght our
lorde was borne, for by kynde all thyngs was in peace
and rest, in shewynge that he was and is (Princeps pacis)
Prince of Peace, and came to make peace bytwene god
and man, and bytwene aungel and man, and bytwene
man and man, and for to be true mediator bytwene
god and man, he toke nature and kynde of bothe, and was
bothe very god and man, and by his mediacyon he knytte
the love of god to man, so sadly that the father of heven
spared not hym that is his owne sone, but sent hym downe
in to this worlde to bye mankynde with his precyous blode
through his great mekenes to the joye of paradyse that
man had lost by covetyse of unbuxomnes, for it is a

78

synne that aungelles doth hate greatly. Therfore they
kepte the gates of paradyse and wolde let no soul come
in to paradyse tyll they sawe theyr lorde and soverayne
borne of mankynde and take flesshe of the blessed
virgin Mary his most beloved mother. And then anone
for love of our lorde the aungels did mankynde worshyp &
spake goodly to mankynde, as to ye shepherdes that kepte
theyr shepe in the countree by. They had them go to the
cite of Bethleem, & there they sholde fynde a chylde
borne and layde in a cratche, and bad them do hym
worshyp, and so they did, and ever syth aungels have
ben frendly to man and lowly, and have done reverence
to mankynde, for the incarnacyon of our lorde Jesu
Chryst. Than he made peace bytwene aungels & man.
Also he made peace bytwene man and man, for agaynst
the tyme that our lorde wolde be borne he made so greate
peace, that in all ye worlde there as kyngdomes & coun-
trees were at debate & warres eche with other unto the
tyme of our lordes byrth. Then there was so great peace
that a man that was called Octavyan emperour of Rome,
& he had ye gouvernaunce of all ye worlde, for all the
worlde was subjecte to Rome, and it dured xxx yeres,
in so moche that there was a commaundement sent out
from Rome in to all the worlde commaundynge yt all
maner of people sholde go to the cite that he drew
lygnage of & laye a peny on his heed, & offre it up in
knowlegynge yt he was subjecte to the emperour of
Rome. Than must Joseph our ladyes husband nedes go
to the cite of Bethlem to offre with other people, but for
he had no money to offre he toke an oxe with hym to sell
at the cite, to make money to do his duty with. But for
he durst not leve our lady behynde hym for she was nere
her tyme, and therfore he set her upon an asse and toke
her with hym. And so whan they came to the cite of
Bethleem, it was so full of people that Joseph and our
lady myght have no lodgynge, but turned in to a caban

that was made bytwene two houses there as the people
of the countree set theyr horses and theyr asses and other
beestes whan they came in to the towne to the market,
and there they found a cratche with hey, & they set the
oxe and the asse therto, and so there they taryed all that
nyght. And whan it was a lytel before mydnyght, our
lady bad Joseph go in to the towne and loke for her a
mydwyfe, for the tyme was come that she sholde be
delyvred. And so whyle that Joseph was in the towne for
the mydwyfe, our lady was delyvred, and she lapped her
sone in clothes and layde hym in the cratche before the
oxe and the asse, anone they knew theyr lorde, and fell
downe on theyr knees & worshypped hym, and ete no
more of yᵉ hey. Than anone after came Joseph with two
mydwyves, Yebell and Salome, and Yebell founde that
our lady was a clene mayden and cryed and sayd (Virgo
peperit filium) A mayde hath borne a chylde. Than
Salome wolde not byleve it, but anone went to our lady
and buystously handled our lady (Probare vellet) And she
wolde prove it, and even therwith her hands dryed up.
Than came an aungell to her and badde her go and touche
the chylde. And so she did, & anone she was hole. Than
went Joseph and dyd his offrynge with other people,
and kept our lady in the same caban whyle she was in
chylde bedde. Thus ye may understand that Chryst
gyveth peace to all people that be of good wyll, and calleth
them to his chyldren. And in veryfyynge of this the fyrst
masse that is songe that daye in holy chyrche is songe
soone after mydnyght and begynneth thus (Dominus
dixit ad me filius meus es tu ego hodie genui te) Our
lorde sayth to me thou art my sone. Our lorde calleth
hym his sone and his chylde that loveth hym in rest and
peace & whan he departeth out of this worlde he wyll
brynge hym to everlastynge rest and peace. And he that
wyll not have here no rest and peace shall go to everlastynge payne, there as is never no rest & peace nor

never shal be but everlasting woo. Thus he gyveth peace
to men of good wyll. He lyghtneth them that lyketh hym.
Hereby good men ye shall understand that Chryst
healeth not onely them that were blynde in soule and
combred with derknes of synfull lyvynge. For as saint
Austyn sayth, whan our lorde sholde be borne, the worlde
was full of derknes, and specyally of the synne of lechery,
and of the synne agaynst kynde, in so moche that he had
almoost lefte to be borne of mankynde, wherfore all
those yᵗ dyd synne agaynst kynde that tyme, they dyed
sodeynly throughout all yᵉ worlde, in shewynge how
horryble and abomynable that synne is in the syght of
almyghty god. Than loked they full derke in synne that
had theyr thoughtes alwaye in synne and evill lyvynge,
and had full greate nede to be lyghtned, wherfore Chryst
was borne at mydnyght and turned the derknes of the
nyght in to the daye light, and lyghtned all them that
ever were covered and combred with derknes of synne.
Also the same tyme that our lorde was borne (as many
doctors sayen) Chryst apered in a bryght sterre to the
kynges of the east, and badde them go to Bethleem &
worshypp a lytell chylde that sholde be kynge of the jews,
that was there newe borne. And so they dyd, and ever
the sterre shewynge before them tyll they came thyder.
Thus he lyghtned them that before were full derke in
synne, for these kyngs were paynyms before, and byleved
in mawmettes and in false goddes, and after they byleved
in Chryst and were holy lyvers, and now be at Coleyne.
Thus the byrth of our lord Jesu Chryst made many a
man loke full bryght that tofore were full derke in synne.
For he is full derke in his soule that ever setteth his herte,
mynde and thought in the prosperite, worshyp and welfare
of this worlde, and that maketh them so inwardly blynde
& so ignoraunt, that they have no fealynge of the greate
and inestymable grace of ghoostly syght, but ben made
blynde and abused with the transytory rychesse of this

worlde, and for covetyse therof they commytte usury,
and so they gete theyr good, and have no desire to yᵉ
rychesse of heven, ne to se the lyght that is there. For
suche thynges as mannes herte is most on, that he maketh
his god. For to destroy all such mawmettry of synne our
lorde was borne. Than King herode pursued our lorde
and wolde have slayne hym. Than his mother bare hym
in to Egypte, as an aungell bad Joseph and sayd (Accipe
puerum et matrem ejus et fuge in egyptum) Take the
chylde and his mother and flee in to Egypte. And as
soone as he came thyder all yᵉ mawmettes that were in
that lande fell downe to the grounde, doynge to understande that he was come in to the worlde that sholde
cast down the mawmettry of all maner synne and evyll
lyvyng, as pryde, and covetyse, and all maner of falsehede
that is used now a dayes, and therfore take hede how that
lorde that made all maner thynge of nought, and is lorde
of all lordes, where he was borne in a poore place and in
poore araye, & of a poore mayden gyvynge ensample
to all chrysten people to set nought by the worshyp,
rychesse & vanyte of this worlde. For have a man never
so grete worshyp and never so moche rychesse, yet he
leveth it here. And shal bere no more with hym but his
good dedis. Therfor our lorde shewed many thynges in
his byrthe, lyghtned many one yᵗ here byfore were ful
blynde. In tokenynge hereof the seconde masse this daye
is sayd in the dawnynge whan the nyght and the daye
departed. The whiche begynneth thus (Lux fulgebit
hodie) yᵗ is this moche to saye, Lyght shall shyne today
upon us, for the fader of heven sendeth the grace of the
ghoostly lyght to all crysten people that byleve truly
that our lorde was borne verey god and man of his
moder Mary verey moder and mayden. Thus they that
byleve truly in oure lord Jhesu Cryst & his moder mary
sette full lytyll by the vanyte of this worlde. But put all
theyr hope and trust in Cryste. Thus yᵉ byrthe of our

lorde Jhesu cryste lyghtened many one yt before loked
full yll, also he drew us to hym with love. For childern
drawe to hem that maketh moche of hem, & playe with
hem. Thus our lorde Jhesu crist was borne a childe, to
draw mannys love to hym for while a childe is yonge,
and withoute synne, he is more amyable and more
lovyng thene whan he is at mannys age, and is past Inno-
cency with doynge. Sythen the love is not only for his
bewte, but for ye clennesse of his soule, and also for the
goodnesse. Eche man is bounde for to drawe to hym, &
doo hym worshyp, as dyd Octavyan the Emporour of
Rome, that pleysed soo moche his people of his Empyre
of Rome, that they wolde have worshypped hym, as for
her god. But the Emporour was wyse and wyst well,
that he was but a man as an other was, & durst not take
that upon hym. But anone he sent after Sybyll the sage
& asked her wheder sholde ony after hym be borne that
shold be gretter than he. Thenne at mydday Sybyll loked
in ye sonne & there she sawe a cercle of gold about ye
sonne (Et in medio circuli virgo pulcerrima cum puero)
and in ye myddys of the cyrcle a fayre mayden & a childe
in her arme with a crowne of golde. And whan Sybyll
hadde shewed this to the Emporour she sayde to hym.
This childe shal be gretter than thou arte, or ever were,
or ever shall be. And therfore doo hym worshyp and
reverence. Thenne anone the Emporour toke encense
and dyde worshyp to hym. And charged all the people
to doo ye same and to calle ye childe her god, and hym
but a mann as other were. Thus all crysten people may
lerne to doo worshyp and service to this childe this day.
And therfore the iii masse this day is sayd at mydday, in
tokenynge yt cristen peple shold come and offre in the
worshyp of this childe and his moder, and shew hem
servaunt and subgect to hym and knowleche this childe
for her lord & her god. And eche man sholde come to
hym for love and not for drede. And therfore ye office

of yᵉ masse this daye begynneth thus (Puer natus est nobis) A childe is borne to us, he sayth, and not a man. For all cristen people sholde be bolde and not aferde to come to hym to have grace, for he is ful of grace, and redy to gyve mercy to theym that aske it mekely, with dew reverence. He is ever redy to gyve mercy and grace. In tokenyng that same day that Cryste was borne in Bethlem, a well of water in Rome tourned and ranne oyle all that daye shewyng that the well of grace and mercy was born that day that shold gyve mercy and grace to alle theym that wolde come to hym and aske mercy and grace, and that ye shal here by ensample.

> From a Homily of JOHN MIRKUS, monk
> of Gloucester Abbey; from *The
> Festiall*, 1482.

TWO SPANISH PASTORALS

I

SHEPHERD, shepherd, hark that calling!
Angels they are, and the day is dawning.

What is this ding-dong,
  Or loud singing is it?
Come, Bras, now the day is here
  The Shepherdess we'll visit.
Shepherd, shepherd, hark that calling!
Angels they are, and the day is dawning.

O is this the Alcalde's daughter,
  Or some lady come from far?
She is the daughter of God the Father,
  And she shines like a star.
Shepherd, shepherd, hark that calling!
Angels they are, and the day is dawning.

84

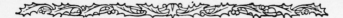

II

To-day a shepherd and our kin,
  O Gil, to ransom us is sent,
  And He is God Omnipotent.

For us hath He cast down the pride
  And prison-walls of Satanas;
  But he is of the kin of Bras,
  Of Menga, also of Llorent!
  O is not God omnipotent?

Why, I have seen Him born, pardi,
  And of a most sweet shepherdess.
  —If He is God, how can he be
With such poor folk as these content?
—See'st not He is Omnipotent?

Give over idle parleying,
  And let us serve Him, you and I,
  And since He came on earth to die,
  Let us die with Him too, Llorent;
  For He is God Omnipotent.

St. Teresa of Jesus (1515–1582):
  tr. Arthur Symons.

AS I UP ROSE

> *Moder, white as lylie flour,*
> *Your lulling lassyt myn langour.*

A S I up rose in one morning,
  My thowt was on a mayde ying
Che songe aslepe with her lulling
  Here dere sone, our Saviour.

As che him tok al in here lap,
He tok that maydyn be the pap,
And tok therof a right god nap,
  And sok his fille of that licour.

85

To his moder than he gan say,
 "For this mylk me muste day;
It is myn kynde therwith to play,
 My swete moder, myn paramour."

That mayde frely gan to sing,
And in here song che made murnynge,
That her sone, that is our kynge
 Xuld sched his blod with gret dolour.

"Your wepyng, moder, greveth me sore;
But I wold deye, ye wern forlore.
Do wey, moder, and wepe no more!
 Your lulling lassit myn langour."
 Sloane MS., XVth Century.

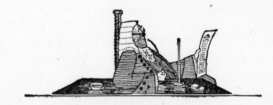

CHRISTMAS WITH SIR ROGER

—Ævo rarissima nostro
Simplicitas——
 OVID, *Ars Amor.*, I. 241.
 And brings our old Simplicity again.
 DRYDEN.

I WAS this Morning surprised with a great Knocking
at the Door, when my Landlady's Daughter came up
to me, and told me, that there was a Man below desired
to speak with me. Upon my asking her who it was, she
told me it was a very grave elderly Person, but that she
did not know his Name. I immediately went down to
him, and found him to be the Coachman of my worthy

86

Friend Sir *Roger de Coverley*. He told me that his Master came to Town last Night, and would be glad to take a Turn with me in Gray's-Inn Walks. As I was wondering in myself what had brought Sir *Roger* to Town, not having lately received any Letter from him, he told me that his Master was come up to get a Sight of Prince *Eugene,* and that he desired I would immediately meet him.

I was no sooner come into Gray's-Inn Walks, but I heard my old Friend upon the Terrace hemming twice or thrice to himself with great Vigour, for he loves to clear his Pipes in good Air, to make use of his own Phrase, and is not a little pleased with any one who takes notice of the Strength which he still exerts in his Morning Hems.

Our Salutations were very hearty on both Sides, con-sisting of many kind Shakes of the Hand, and several affectionate Looks which we cast upon one another. After which the Knight told me my good Friend his Chaplain was very well, and much at my Service, and that the Sunday before he had made a most incomparable Sermon out of Dr. *Barrow.* I have left, says he, all my Affairs in his Hands, and being willing to lay an Obligation upon him, have deposited with him Thirty Marks, to be distributed among his poor Parishioners.

He then proceeded to acquaint me with the Welfare of Will *Wimble.* Upon which he put his Hand in his Fob, and presented me in his Name with a Tobacco-stopper, telling me that Will had been busy all the beginning of the Winter in turning great Quantities of them; and that he made a Present of one to every Gentleman in the Country who has good Principles, and smoaks. He added, that poor *Will* was at present under great Tribulation, for that Tom *Touchy* had taken the Law of him for cutting some Hazel-Sticks out of one of his Hedges.

Among other Pieces of News which the Knight brought from his Country-seat, he informed me that

Moll *White* was dead; and that about a Month after her Death the Wind was so very high, that it blew down the End of one of his Barns. But for my own Part, says Sir *Roger*, I do not think that the old Woman had any Hand in it.

He afterwards fell into an Account of the Diversions which had passed in his House during the Holidays; for Sir *Roger*, after the laudable Custom of his Ancestors, always keeps open House at Christmas. I learned from him that he had killed eight Fat Hogs for this Season, that he had dealt about his Chines very liberally amongst his Neighbours, and that in particular he had sent a String of Hogs'-puddings with a Pack of Cards to every poor Family in the Parish. I have often thought, says Sir *Roger*, it happens very well that Christmas should fall out in the Middle of Winter. It is the most dead uncomfortable Time of the Year, when the poor People would suffer very much from their Poverty and Cold, if they had not good Chear, warm Fires, and Christmas Gambols to support them. I love to rejoice their poor Hearts at this Season, and to see the whole Village merry in my great Hall. I allow a double Quantity of Malt to my Small Beer, and set it a-running for twelve Days to every one that calls for it. I have always a Piece of Cold Beef and Mince-pye upon the Table, and am wonderfully pleased to see my Tenants pass away a whole Evening in playing their innocent Tricks, and smutting one another. Our Friend Will *Wimble* is as merry as any of them, and shews a thousand Roguish Tricks upon these Occasions.

I was very much delighted with the Reflexion of my old Friend, which carried so much Goodness with it. He then launched out into the Praise of the late Act of Parliament for securing the Church of *England*, and told me with great Satisfaction, that he believed it already began to take Effect, for that a rigid Dissenter who chanced

to dine at his House on Christmas-day, had been observed
to eat away very plentifully of his Plumb-porridge.

Having passed away the greatest Part of the Morning
in hearing the Knight's Reflexions, which were partly
private, and partly political, he asked me if I would
smoke a Pipe with him over a Dish of Coffee at *Squire's*.
As I love the old Man, I take Delight in complying with
every Thing that is agreeable to him, and accordingly
waited on him to the Coffee-house, where his venerable
Figure drew upon us the Eyes of the whole Room. He
had no sooner seated himself at the upper End of the
high Table, but he called for a clean Pipe, a paper of
Tobacco, a Dish of Coffee, a wax Candle, and the Supplement, with such an Air of Chearfulness and Good-
humour, that all the Boys in the Coffee-room, who seemed
to take Pleasure in serving him, were at once employed
on his several Errands, insomuch that nobody else could
come at a Dish of Tea, until the Knight had got all his
Conveniencies about him.

JOSEPH ADDISON (1672–1719).

TO MAKE A DISH OF SNOW

TAKE a pottle of sweet thick Cream, and the white
of eyght Egs, and beate them altogether, with a
spoone, then put them into your cream with a dishfull
of Rosewater, and a dishfull of Sugar withall, then take
a sticke and make it clene, and then cut it in the end
foursquare, and therewith beat all the aforesaid things
together, and ever as it ariseth take it off, and put it in
to a Cullender, this doone, take a platter and sette an
Apple in the midst of it, stick a thicke bush of Rosemary
in the Apple. Then cast your Snow upon the Rosemary
and fill your platter therewith, and if you have wafers
cast some withall, and so serve them forthe.

From *A Booke of Cookerie*, 1594.

AND once, in winter, on the causeway chill
  Where home through flooded fields foot-travellers go,
  Have I not pass'd thee on the wooden bridge
Wrapt in thy cloak and battling with the snow,
    Thy face towards Hinksey and its wintry ridge?
    And thou hast climb'd the hill
And gain'd the white brow of the Cumnor range;
    Turn'd once to watch, while thick the snowflakes fall,
    The line of festal light in Christ Church hall—
Then sought thy straw in some sequester'd grange.

MATTHEW ARNOLD (1822–1888).

THE DUTCHMAN ARRIVES

℃, An Account of His Majesty K. James II.'s
Going from *White-Hall*. December 18, 1688.

THE night before, being the 17th, and the day after
  his Majesty's returne from Feversham, his Majesty
going to bed at his usual time, I went to see all the doors
leading to the bedchamber made fast, which is the duty
of the Page in Waiting, and then went to bed, being then
about 12 a clocke. I had been but little in bed before my
man came up to me and said: My Lord Middleton is
come to the back-stairs and would speak with you. At
which I putt on some cloaths and went down to his
Lordship, who told me he must speak with the King.
Upon which I took a light in my hand and went towards
the bedchamber, but at the back-stairs-door, going into
the drawing-room, where I left English centinels when
I went to bed, I now found Dutch, who made some difficulty in letting us pass. When we came to the bed-
chamber-door, I prayd his Lordship to stay till I had
acquainted the Lord in Waiting; which his Lordship
did. I went in and told Lord Ailesbury, who answerd,
Let him in. When we came to the bed-side, the curtains

being opened, his Majesty was fast asleep. My Lord Middleton kneeled down by the bed-side, and called, Sir; at which his Majesty awaked.

My Lord told the King that there were some Lords from the Prince of Orange that had sent him word they must needs speak with his Majesty that night.

After some little pawse, the King said, Must they come to night? Cannot they stay till to morrow?

LORD M. Sir, I tell your Majesty what they sent to me.

KING. Where are they, my Lord?

LORD M. Indeed, Sir, I do not know.

KING. Well, let them come, my Lord.

Upon which my Lord going away, I drew the curtains close again and lighted my Lord into the drawing-room; when my Lord going on said, Mr. Man, you must not goe to bed; you hear what the King saith. I staid about halfe an hour, and then came my Lord with the Lords Hallifax, Shrewsbury, and Delamere. When they came to the King's bed-side, the Lord H. from under an open cover pulled out another open paper, which he gave to his Majesty, who read the same to him. After which he said to the Lords,

KING. Ham-House is but a little house and not bigg enough; besides there's no furniture in it.

LORD D. Sir, there's care taken for that.

LORD H. Which way will your Majesty goe? By land, or by water?

KING. I do not know yet.

LORD H. Your Majesty sees the Prince of Orange desires you will be gone before 12 to morrow.

KING. Yes, yes, my Lord; there's time enough for that. But the King said it over again, that Ham-House was not bigg enough; I cannot have any of my people about me.

LORD H. Your Majesty sees the P. of Orange desires you will be gone before 12 to morrow.

KING. Well, well, my Lord, I'll give order time enough.

Upon which the Lords going away, the King called my Lord Middleton to him. Upon which my Lord calls to me to call back the Lords; the King would speak with them. When they came,

The King said, Ham-House was by much too little; and that it was not possible for him to be there, and said he had rather goe to Rochester; there were some of his Foot-Guards.

LORDS. Your Majesty sees we cannot say anything to that.

KING. Well, but you may send to the Prince of Orange; he is not so far off, he is but at Sion.

LORDS. Looking upon one another for a small time, one of them broke silence, and said, Then, if your Majesty pleases, wee'l send to the Prince of Orange.

KING. Ay, pray do.

Then the Lords withdrew, and as I was going out of the bed-chamber his Majesty calls to me, and bid me call him at 7 of the clocke, which was halfe an hour sooner than he had given order for when he went to bed. As soon as his Majesty was out of his bed, he bidd me send to the Meuse [Mews] and to have his coaches and pads be got ready, and there to stay till further order. Which I did. Then his Majesty bidd me send for all his barges, and bidd them to be at the Privy-Stairs by nine of the clock. At 10 or thereabouts, an order came from the Prince of Orange that his Majesty might goe to Rochester. Upon which his Majesty ordered me to take some watermen and carry his strong-boxes into his barge; which I did. But in going down the staires the Dutch centinels stopt me. I told them in French, That they were the King's goods, and must goe into his barge. One of them answered me in French, It was no matter, if the King himselfe came, he should not pass, for he had orders to

the contrary. Upon which I went back into the bed-chamber and complained to Count Solmes; who seemed to be very angry with the officer that commanded, and gave other orders.

The Pepys Correspondence, 1679–1700.

DRINKING SONG

⁋ On the Excellence of Burgundy Wine.

MY jolly fat host with your face all a-grin,
Come, open the door to us, let us come in.
A score of stout fellows who think it no sin
If they toast till they're hoarse, and they drink till they
    spin,
      Hoofed it amain,
      Rain or no rain,
   To crack your old jokes, and your bottles to drain.

Such a warmth in the belly that nectar begets
As soon as his guts with its humour he wets,
The miser his gold, and the student his debts,
And the beggar his rags and his hunger forgets.
      For there's never a wine
      Like this tipple of thine
From the great hill of Nuits to the River of Rhine.

Outside you may hear the great gusts as they go
By Foy, by Duerne, and the hills of Lerraulx,
But the rain he may rain, and the wind he may blow,
If the Devil's above there's good liquor below.
      So it abound,
      Pass it around,
   Burgundy's Burgundy all the year round.

HILAIRE BELLOC.

℄ A Dialogue between Mrs. *Custome*, a Victuallers Wife neer *Cripplegate*, and Mrs. *New-come*, a Captains Wife, living in *Reformation*-alley neer *Destruction*-street.

M. New-come. What, have you a feast here suddenly, that you are so Decking, Adorning, and Trimming up your house with this fine Rosemary and Bayes.

M. Custome. No truely, here is no Feasting, but what doth fall out according to the Time.

M. New. Time; pray now what Time?

M. Cust. Why *Christmas*, woman; have you forgot it? Indeed these Wars and Jars would almost make one forget their Christen name, if they were not often called on to put one in remembrance.

M. New. What, will you keepe *Christmas* in spite of Authoritie?

M. Cust. What Authoritie? I am sure my Father and Mother had the greatest authoritie over me since I was borne, and other authoritie I knew none before I was married, and now it seems I am under a crabb'd Husbands Authoritie, and besides him I will be subject to none, and I am sure he is as strong for *Christmas*, as the greatest of our Ancestors.

M. New. Why then you count the *Parliament* no authoritie?

M. Cust. I hope Gossip you are not come to pick Quarrells with me in my owne House? What doe you mean, in telling me of the *Parliament*?

M. New. I mean the two Houses of *Parliament* which have jumped together in one Opinion, for the putting-downe and destroying of this *Romish* Beast *Christmas*; for which they are to be commended.

M. Cust. It is a strange Thing; let the Devill never so cunningly hide his head, we shall know him by his cloven Foot; nor let the Asse never so craftily hide his feet, yet we may know him by his Eares. I see you are

of the New Faction, and a great Student in *Spittle-Colledge*; but that is nothing to me: yet what do you mean by calling *Christmas* a *Romish* Beast?

M. New. To leave all manner of Circumstance, which is not pertinent to our Subject in hand—

M. Cust. By'r Lady neighbour, I think you are one of these new Teachers, you handle your Matter so excellent; but I trouble you, pray proceed.

M. New. The word (*Christmas*) if learnedly weighed in it we shall find matter of Dangerous consequence: As

   1. If we consider what the word or name is.

   2. If we consider who gave him this Name.

   3. Where he was Christned or had the Name given him.

   4. By what authoritie they gave him this Name.

Of which I shall proceed in Order, according to my weak abilitie: And first for the word: *Christmas*, is a word which deciphers a Scorpion, which is a venomous Beast, which carries a sting at his Tayle, and so doth *Christmas*: for the word *Masse* is a sting in the tayle of that *Romish* Beast: Secondly, we must consider who gave him this Name, that was his God-fathers and God-mothers; from whence ariseth this doubtful question—who they were, and that was Pope *Boniface*, Pope *Fireface*, and Pope *Joane*; but by reason of their non-residence here in *England*, the Bishops took that office upon them and stood as s—n Gossips: Thirdly the place where, this is by the learned held in great Dispute, but I beleeve in his infancie he was Sickly; and therefore he was twice christned, that is to say, at home here in *England* and confirmed at *Rome*, the mother-Church of all such Antichristian Heresies; but I shall be over-tedious, therefore I will come to the fourth Devision, and that is by what Authoritie they doe these things: this will take up a great Deale of time to open and explaine unto you, if I should doe

it to Purpose; therefore I will omit it, onely certifying you this much, that there is no Power under the Sun that hath any Authoritie to erect or build up, neither to destroy and pull downe any thing, save what is in the will of the two Houses of *Parliament*.

M. Cust. That word waked me, indeed I was asleep; what, you say that the *Parliament* hath power to pull down *Christmas*; I pray then what will they put up in the room on't, Stage-Playes, dancing upon the Ropes; and *Hocus-Pocus*.

The Epilogue

Christmas is the welcommest Time,
　　That does come through the Yeare;
For't maketh many joyfull hearts
　　And fills the World with Cheare.

Now Tom and Tib, and lustie Jack
　　The time in Mirth doe passe;
And each in kitchen or the Hall
　　Is towsing of his Lasse.

As long as there the fragrant Fire
　　Doth spit out its fierce Flames
There is no ceasing of their Mirth
　　Nor period to their Games.

But now the Log of Logs is burnt,
　　The Hall-chimney leaves smoaking;
Good folkes farewell, for I will stay
　　No longer in it poaking.

Women will have their Will, or, Give Christmas his Due. London, 1642.

A PARISIAN MINIATURE

EN ce temps que j'ay dit devant,
Sur le Noël, morte saison,
Que les loups se vivent de vent
Et qu'on se tient en sa maison,
Pour le frimas, pres du tison,
Me vint ung vouloir de brisier
La tres amoureuse prison
Qui souloit mon cuer debrisier.

FRANÇOIS VILLON (1431–14—?).

NATIVITY, IN THE MODE OF SPAIN

THERE is at the end of the church [the Dominican
church at Cadiz] a chapel thrusting some four or five
feet beyond the thickness of the wall; in this there has
been contrived a large niche filled with several figures.
In the centre is the Child Jesus in his cradle, and at his
side our Lady dressed from head to foot like a young
married girl, her tresses plaited behind her head and
covered with gold lace. Her magnificent clothing is
changed according to the season and the festival; at
her waist hangs a superb rosary. Saint Anne, on the
other side of the cradle, is dressed like an old lady in a
great robe of black velvet with gold lace; she is seated
on a tabouret, in the manner of the country, and holds
a rosary in her hand. Saint Joseph, at her side, is also
dressed in the Spanish mode, in breeches, doublet, and
a cloak of black damask, with the *golilla* [stock], silk
stockings, and black morocco shoes with a rose of the

same colour. His hair is parted on the side and powdered,
he has great spectacles on his nose, a flat hat under his
left arm, a long rapier, and a dagger, with a large rosary
in his right hand. Finally, in the same chapel there are
two other saints vested like bishops, mitre on head,
crozier in one hand and rosary in the other.

The first time I said Mass in this chapel, which is
dark, I hardly knew what to think of these personages,
for their faces and figures are so natural that if they were
on a level with the altar I should have taken them for
human beings. For it is not a habit with us in France
to dress the saints in modern clothes.

JEAN-BAPTISTE LABAT, O.P. (1663–1738).

FESTAL COCKCROW

SOME say, that ever 'gainst that season comes
Wherein our Saviour's birth is celebrated,
This bird of dawning singeth all night long:
And then, they say, no spirit can walk abroad;
The nights are wholesome; then no planets strike,
No fairy takes, nor witch hath power to charm,
So hallowed and so gracious is the time.

WILLIAM SHAKESPEARE.

ASPIRATION

OH, give me an old-fashioned Christmas card,
With hostlers hostling in an old inn yard,
With church bells chiming their silver notes,
And jolly red squires in their jolly red coats,
And a good fat goose by the fire that dangles,
And a few more angels and a few less angles.
Turn backward, Time, to please this bard,
And give me an old-fashioned Christmas card.

OGDEN NASH.

IT was the Winter wilde,
　While the Heav'n-born-childe,
　　All meanly wrapt in the rude manger lies;
Nature in aw to him
Had doff't her gawdy trim,
　　With her great Master so to sympathize:
It was no season then for her
To wanton with the Sun her lusty Paramour.

Only with speeches fair
　She woo's the gentle Air
　　To hide her guilty front with innocent Snow,
And on her naked shame,
Pollute with sinfull blame,
　　The Saintly Vail of Maiden white to throw,
Confounded, that her Makers eyes
Should look so neer upon her foul deformities.

But he her fears to cease,
　Sent down the meek-eyd Peace,
　　She crown'd with Olive green, came softly sliding
Down through the turning sphear
His ready Harbinger,
　　With Turtle wing the amorous clouds dividing,
And waving wide her mirtle wand,
She strikes a universall Peace through Sea and Land.

No Warr, or Battails sound
Was heard the World around,
　　The idle spear and shield were high up hung;
The hookèd Chariot stood
Unstain'd with hostile blood,
　　The Trumpet spake not to the armèd throng,
And Kings sate still with awfull eye,
As if they surely knew their sovran Lord was by.

But peacefull was the night
Wherin the Prince of light
   His raign of peace upon the earth began:
The Windes with wonder whist,
Smoothly the waters kist,
   Whispering new joyes to the milde Ocean,
Who now hath quite forgot to rave,
While Birds of Calm sit brooding on the charmèd wave.

The Stars with deep amaze
Stand fixt in stedfast gaze,
   Bending one way their pretious influence,
And will not take their flight,
For all the morning light,
   Or Lucifer that often warn'd them thence;
But in their glimmering Orbs did glow,
Untill their Lord himself bespake, and bid them go.

And though the shady gloom
Had given day her room,
   The Sun himself with-held his wonted speed,
And hid his head for shame,
As his inferiour flame,
   The new enlightn'd world no more should need;
He saw a greater Sun appear
Then his bright Throne, or burning Axletree could bear.

The Shepherds on the Lawn
Or ere the point of dawn
   Sate simply chatting in a rustick row;
Full little thought they than,
That the mighty Pan
   Was kindly com to live with them below;
Perhaps their loves, or els their sheep,
Was all that did their silly thoughts so busie keep.

When such musick sweet
Their hearts and ears did greet,
    As never was by mortall finger strook,
Divinely-warbled voice
Answering the stringèd noise,
    As all their souls in blisfull rapture took:
The Air such pleasure loth to lose,
With thousand echo's still prolongs each heav'nly close.

Nature that heard such sound
Beneath the hollow round
    Of Cynthia's seat, the Airy region thrilling,
Now was almost won
To think her part was don,
    And that her raign had here its last fulfilling;
She knew such harmony alone
Could hold all Heav'n and Earth in happier union.

At last surrounds their sight
A Globe of circular light,
    That with long beams the shame-fac't night array'd,
The helmèd Cherubim
And sworded Seraphim,
    Are seen in glittering ranks with wings displaid,
Harping in loud and solemn Quire,
With unexpressive notes to Heav'ns new-born Heir.

Such musick (as 'tis said)
Before was never made,
    But when of old the sons of morning sung,
While the Creator Great
His constellations set,
    And the well-ballanc't world on hinges hung,
And cast the dark foundations deep,
And bid the weltring waves their oozy channel keep.

Ring out ye Crystall sphears,
Once bless our human ears,
   (If ye have power to touch our senses so)
And let your silver chime
Move in melodious time;
   And let the Base of Heav'ns deep Organ blow
And with your ninefold harmony
Make up full consort to th'Angelike symphony.

For if such holy Song
Enwrap our fancy long,
   Time will run back, and fetch the age of gold,
And speckl'd vanity
Will sicken soon and die,
   And leprous sin will melt from earthly mould,
And Hell it self will pass away,
And leave her dolorous mansions to the peering Day.

Yea Truth, and Justice then
Will down return to men,
   Th'enameld Arras of the Rain-bow wearing,
And Mercy set between,
Thron'd in Celestiall sheen,
   With radiant feet the tissued clouds down stearing,
And Heav'n as at som festivall,
Will open wide the Gates of her high Palace Hall.

But wisest Fate sayes no,
This must not yet be so,
   The Babe lies yet in smiling Infancy,
That on the bitter Cross
Must redeem our loss;
   So both himself and us to glorifie:
Yet first to those ychain'd in sleep,
The wakefull trump of doom must thunder through the
    deep,

With such a horrid clang
As on mount Sinai rang
   While the red fire, and smouldring clouds out brake:
The agèd Earth aghast
With terrour of that blast,
   Shall from the surface to the center shake;
When at the worlds last session,
The dreadfull Judge in middle Air shall spread his
   throne.

And then at last our bliss
Full and perfect is,
   But now begins; for from this happy Day
Th'old Dragon under ground
In straiter limits bound,
   Not half so far casts his usurpèd sway,
And wrath to see his Kingdom fail,
Swindges the scaly Horrour of his foulded tail.

The Oracles are dumm,
No voice or hideous humm
   Runs through the archèd roof in words deceiving.
Apollo from his shrine
Can no more divine,
   With hollow shreik the steep of Delphos leaving.
No nightly trance, or breathèd spell,
Inspire's the pale-ey'd Priest from the prophetic cell.

The lonely mountains o're,
And the resounding shore,
   A voice of weeping heard, and loud lament;
From haunted spring, and dale
Edg'd with poplar pale,
   The parting Genius is with sighing sent,
With flowre-inwov'n tresses torn
The Nimphs in twilight shade of tangled thickets mourn.

In consecrated Earth,
And on the holy Hearth,
   The Lars, and Lemures moan with midnight plaint,
In Urns, and Altars round,
A drear, and dying sound
   Affrights the Flamins at their service quaint;
And the chill Marble seems to sweat,
While each peculiar power forgoes his wonted seat.

Peor, and Baalim,
Forsake their Temples dim,
   With that twise-batter'd god of Palestine,
And moonèd Ashtaroth,
Heavn's Queen and Mother both,
   Now sits not girt with Tapers holy shine,
The Libyc Hammon shrinks his horn,
In vain the Tyrian Maids their wounded Thamuz mourn.

And sullen Moloch fled,
Hath left in shadows dred,
   His burning Idol all of blackest hue,
In vain with Cymbals ring,
They call the grisly king,
   In dismall dance about the furnace blue;
The brutish gods of Nile as fast,
Isis and Orus, and the Dog Anubis hast.

Nor is Osiris seen
In Memphian Grove, or Green,
   Trampling the unshowr'd Grasse with lowings loud:
Nor can he be at rest
Within his sacred chest,
   Naught but profoundest Hell can be his shroud,
In vain with Timbrel'd Anthems dark
The sable-stolèd Sorcerers bear his worshipt Ark.

He feels from Juda's Land
The dredded Infants hand,
   The rayes of Bethlehem blind his dusky eyn;
Nor all the gods beside,
Longer dare abide,
   Not Typhon huge ending in snaky twine:
Our Babe to shew his Godhead true,
Can in his swadling bands controul the damnèd crew.

So when the Sun in bed,
Curtain'd with cloudy red,
   Pillows his chin upon an Orient wave,
The flocking shadows pale,
Troop to th'infernall jail,
   Each fetter'd Ghost slips to his severall grave,
And the yellow-skirted Fayes
Fly after the Night-steeds, leaving their Moon-lov'd
   maze.

But see the Virgin blest,
Hath laid her Babe to rest.
   Time is our tedious Song should here have ending,
Heav'ns youngest teemèd Star
Hath fixt her polisht Car,
   Her sleeping Lord with Handmaid Lamp attending:
And all about the Courtly Stable,
Bright-harnest Angels sit in order serviceable.

                         JOHN MILTON (1608–1674).

December 24, 1484.

❡ *To my right worshipful husband, John Paston.*

RIGHT worshipful husband, I recommend me unto you: please it you to weet that I sent your eldest son to my Lady Morley, to have knowledge of what sports were used in her house in Christmas next following after the decease of my lord her husband; and she said that there were none disguisings, nor harping, nor luting, nor singing, nor none loud disports; but playing at the tables, and chess, and cards; such disports she gave her folks leave to play and none other.

I pray you that ye will assure to you some man at Caister to keep your buttery, for the man that ye left with me will not take upon him to breve daily as ye commanded; he saith he hath not used to give a reckoning neither of bread nor ale till at the week's end, and he saith he wot well that he should not condeneth [give satisfaction], and therefore I suppose he shall not abide, and I trow ye shall be fain to purvey another man for Symond, for ye are never the nearer a wise man for him.

I am sorry that ye shall not at home be for Christmas.

I pray you that ye will come as soon as ye may; I shall think myself half a widow, because ye shall not be at home, &c. God have you in his keeping. Written on Christmas even.

By your servant and bedeswoman,

MARGERY PASTON.

The Paston Letters (1424–1505).

A CHRISTMAS BOX

REWARD to the servauntes at Crystemas, with their aprons xxs. Reward to the Clerk of the Kechyn, xiij s, iiij d. Reward to the Baily of the husbandry vis. viijd. Reward to the Keeper of the Covent Garden, vis. viijd.

From the Accounts of Dame Agnes Merett, Cellaress of Syon Convent at Isleworth, 1537–8.

1643. Dec. 28. Colonel Nathaniell Fines, one of the first that appeared in this rebellion, was in a Court of Warre at *St. Albans* by his fellow rebels sentenced to be hanged for a coward.

Dec. 29. The stately Screene of copper richly gilt set up by King Henry VII. in his chapel at *Westminster*, was by order of the Houses reformed, That is to say broken downe and sold to Tinkers.

1644. Dec. 24. Sir Will. Vaughan, Governor of Shrawarden Castle for His Majesty, fell on a party of rebels at *Welch Poole* commanded by Sir John Price, killed some, wounded others, took 47 prisoners, 64 horse and many Armes.

England's Iliad, 1645.

FUGUE FOR STRINGS

JUST before the clock struck twelve, they lighted the lanterns and started. The moon, in her third quarter, had risen since the snowstorm; but the dense accumulation of snow-cloud weakened her power to a faint twilight, which was rather pervasive of the landscape than traceable to the sky. The breeze had gone down, and the rustle of their feet, and tones of their speech, echoed with an alert rebound from every post, boundary-stone, and ancient wall they passed, even where the distance of the echo's origin was less than a few yards. Beyond their own slight noises nothing was to be heard, save the occasional howl of foxes in the direction of Yalbury Wood, or the brush of a rabbit among the grass now and then, as it scampered out of their way.

Most of the outlying homesteads and hamlets had been visited by about two o'clock; they then passed across the Home Plantation towards the main village. Pursuing no recognised track, great care was necessary in walking lest their faces should come in contact with the low-hanging boughs of the old trees, which in many spots formed dense overgrowths of interlaced branches.

"Times have changed from the times they used to be," said Mail, regarding nobody can tell what interesting old panoramas with an inward eye, and letting his outward glance rest on the ground, because it was as convenient a position as any. "People don't care much about us now! I've been thinking, we must be almost the last left in the county of the old string-players. Barrel-organs, and they next door to 'em that you blow wi' your foot, have come in terribly of late years."

"Ah!" said Bowman, shaking his head; and old William, on seeing him, did the same thing.

"More's the pity," replied another. "Time was—long and merry ago now!—when not one of the varmits was to be heard of; but it served some of the choirs right. They should have stuck to strings as we did, and keep out clar'nets, and done away with serpents. If you'd thrive in musical religion, stick to strings, says I."

"Strings are well enough, as far as that goes," said Mr. Spinks.

"There's worse things than serpents," said Mr. Penny. "Old things pass away, 'tis true; but a serpent was a good old note: a deep rich tone was the serpent."

"Clar'nets, however, be bad at all times," said Michael Mail. "One Christmas—years agone now, years—I went the rounds wi' the Dibbeach choir. 'Twas a hard frosty night, and the keys of all the clar'nets froze—ah, they did freeze!—so that 'twas like drawing a cork every time a key was opened; the players o' 'em had to go into a hedger and ditcher's chimley-corner, and thaw their clar'nets every now and then. An icicle o' spet hung down from the end of every man's clar'net a span long; and as to fingers—well, there, if ye'll believe me, we had no fingers at all, to our knowledge."

"I can well bring back to my mind," said Mr. Penny,

"what I said to poor Joseph Ryme (who took the tribble part in High-Story Church for two-and-forty year) when they thought of having clar'nets there. 'Joseph,' I said, says I, 'depend upon't, if so be you have them tooting clar'nets you'll spoil the whole set-out. Clar'nets were not made for the service of Providence; you can see it by looking at 'em,' I said. And what cam o't? Why, my dear souls, the parson set up a barrel-organ on his own account within two years o' the time I spoke, and the old choir went to nothing."

"As far as look is concerned," said the tranter, "I don't for my part see that a fiddle is much nearer heaven than a clar'net. 'Tis farther off. There's always a rakish, scampish countenace about a fiddle that seems to say the Wicked One had a hand in making o'en; while angels be supposed to play clar'nets in heaven, or som'at like 'em, if ye may believe picters."

"Robert Penny, you were in the right," broke in the eldest Dewy. "They should ha' stuck to strings. Your brass-man, is brass—well and good; your reed-man, is reed—well and good; your percussion-man, is percussion —good again. But I don't care who hears me say it, nothing will speak to your heart wi' the sweetness of the man of strings!"

"Strings for ever!" said little Jimmy.

"Strings alone would have held their ground against all the new-comers i' creation." ("True, true!" said Bowman.) "But clar'nets was death." ("Death they was!" said Mr. Penny.) "And harmoniums," William continued, in a louder voice, and getting excited by these signs of approval, "harmoniums and barrel-organs" ("Ah!" and groans from Spinks) "be miserable—what shall I call 'em—miserable—"

"Sinners," suggested Jimmy, who made large strides like the men, and did not lag behind like the other little boys.

"Miserable machines for such a divine thing as music."
"Right, William, and so they be!" said the choir with earnest unanimity.

THOMAS HARDY (1840–1928).

A SONG AGAINST BORES

Make we mery bothe more and lasse
For now ys the tyme of Crystymas.

LETT no man cum into this hall,
Grome, page, nor yet marshall,
But that sum sport he bryng withall;
    For now ys the tyme of Crystymas!

Yff that he say he can not sing,
Some oder sport then let him bring,
That yt may please at thys festyng;
    For now ys the tyme of Crystymas!

Yff he say he can nowght do,
Then for my love aske hym no mo,
But to the stokkis then lett hym go;
    For now ys the tyme of Crystymas!

Balliol MS.; Commonplace Book of
Richard Hill, 1500–35.

ON THE TURKEY

A Turkey Aladoub.

TAKE a Turkey, cut off the penions, and leggs, and break the brest bone, lard it with large pieces of Bacon, round in a piece of browne butter and spice, put it in high season'd gravey and let it stew until it is tender, than take it out of the broth into ye dish, take all the fatt of ye Broth if possible browne some butter and

straine y^e broth into it, three anchoves, and an Onion shred very fine, about a dozen spoonfulls of white Wine, some Morslley truffles, sweet breads cut in dice, pallatts sliced thin, mushrooms, and Forcedmeats, the juice of a Lemon, and a good piece of butter, give them a boyle together, pour them over the Turkey, garnish it with patties, when you first put it in rub the pann with a clove of Garlike, you may stuff the brest with forced meat and likewise ye Belley, let the sauce be very thick and very high seasoned.

XVIIth Century.

TO MAKE BENICRZ

TAKE six spoonfulls of Flower, grate in a little nutt-meg, mix it with milk as thick as for Pancakes, add a little Sack and a little salt, put a little fresh butter in the pann, pour it out into the pann very thin, just harden it, do not let it be browne, when they are all fryed put them in a Mortar and beat them a quarter of an hour, then break in one egg beat it some time, and then put in another, so till you have put in six eggs (to the six spoonfulls of Flower, it must be beating an hour and half, the more you beat it the better it is) then flower a pye plate and spread it thin all over, so keep it for y^or use. When you use it take a sauspan of Beefe suet, let it be boyled hott, then cut them off with a whole bone into the Liquor, when they are brown they are enough, take them out of the liquor with a slice and set them in a Cullender before the fire, the sooner you serve them up the better, grate loaf Suger over them very thick and serve them up.

XVIIth Century.

℃. There follows the dialogue of the Shepherds before the stable of Betleem.

Aloris. Shepherds, we must think of everything.
    I am well advised
    We have not yet decided
    What gifts, and in what fashion,
      We will give to this Infant,
      When we see Him there.
Ysambert. Aloris, that is well said.
    We must think of it now.
Pellion. For myself, I have well decided
    What present I shall give, and a worthy one.
Rifflart. What, I pray you?
Pellion.   Guess,
    And you will hear a good answer.
Rifflart. Will you give your crook?
    Or your fine rosary?
Pellion. You have not guessed.
    My crook is too necessary,
    I can do nothing without it;
    I doubt if He will get that.
Rifflart. Will you give Him your dog?
Pellion.   Nenny,
    Who would turn my sheep home for me?
Rifflart. Then you will give Him your stale bread,
    And a great heap of chestnuts?
Pellion. Nenny.
Rifflart.   What will you give, then?
Pellion. I will give Him my flageolet,
    My new one; He cannot refuse it;
    It was never in Betlem before
    Except when a little packman carried it:
    It cost me two good deniers.
Aloris.   The gift is not mean,
    But worthy of great reward.
Ysambert. I have thought of another gift—

I will give Him a rattle
Marvellously well made,
Which goes *clic, clic*, at His ear,
At least when the Infant cries
This rattle will dry His tears,
And He will be pacified.

Aloris. I will give Him something different—
I have a fine kalendar in wood
Which tells the days and months,
Lent and the new year:
By it I can tell all feasts,
I have never found a truer;
Every saint in it has his own picture.
That will be an advantage to Him;
At least when He is old enough,
He may learn to read it.

Rifflart. It is a gift worth having,
And worthy of being given to a Count;
But for my part I am determined
To give Him this little bell
Which hangs in my hat
Ever since the time of Robin Fouet;
And with this, a very fine whirligig
Which I have in my bag.
There is no shepherd or shepherdess in the world
Who could choose a better gift
Or one more novel.

Le Grant Kalendrier des Bergiers, 1480.

CONCERNING A PIG

Twelfth Day, 1823.

THE Pig was above my feeble praise. It was a dear
pigmy. There was some contention as to who should
have the ears; but in spite of his obstinacy (deaf as these
little creatures are to advice), I contrived to get at one
of them.

It came in boots, too, which I took as a Favour. Generally these petty toes, petty toes! are missing; but I suppose he wore them to look taller.

He must have been the least of his race. His little foots would have gone into the Silver Slipper. I take him to have been a Chinese and a female. If Evelyn could have seen him, he would never have farrowed two such prodigious Volumes; seeing how much good can be contained in— how small a compass!

He crackled delicately.

I left a blank at the top of my letter, not being determined which to address it to; so Farmer and Farmer's Wife will please to divide our thanks. May your granaries be full, and your rats empty, and your chickens plump, and your envious neighbours lean, and your labourers busy, and you as idle and as happy as the Day is long!

VIVE L'AGRICULTURE!

How do you make your pigs so little?
They are vastly engaging at the age:
   I was so myself.
Now I am a disagreeable old Hog,
A middle-aged gentleman-and-a-half;
   My faculties (thank God!) are not much impaired.

I have my sight, hearing, taste, pretty perfect; and can read the Lord's Prayer in common type, by the help of a candle, without making many mistakes. Believe me, that while my Faculties last, I shall ever cherish a proper appreciation of your many kindnesses in this way, and that the last lingering relish of past favours upon my dying memory will be the smack of that little ear. It was the left ear, which is lucky. Many happy returns, not of the Pig, but of the New Year, to both! Mary, for her share of the Pig and the Memoirs, desires to send the same.

CHARLES LAMB to Mr. and Mrs.
Bruton.

SEIGNORS ore entendez a nus,
De loinz sumes venuz a wous
    Pur quere Noël;
Car lun nus dit que en cest hostel
Soleit tenir sa feste anuel
      Ahi cest iur
          Deu doint a tuz icels joie d'amurs
          Qi a DANZ NOËL ferunt honors.

NOËL beyt bein li vin Engleis
E li Gascoin e li Franceys
      E l'Angevin
NOËL fait beivre son veisin,
Si quil se dort, le chief en clin,
      Sovent le ior
          Deu doint, etc.

Seignors io vus di par NOËL
E par li sires de cest hostel
      Car benez ben:
E io primes beurai le men,
E pois apres chescon le soen
      Par mon conseil
Si io vus di trestoz *Wesseyl*
Dehaiz eil qui ne dirra *Drincheyl!*

                    XIIth Century

[*F. Douce's translation of penultimate verse.*]

Lordings, Christmas loves good drinking,
    Wines of Gascoigne, France, Anjou,
English ale that drives out thinking,
    Prince of liquors, old or new,
Every neighbour shares the bowl,
    Drinks of the spicy liquor deep,
Drinks his fill without controul,
    Till he drowns his care in sleep.

THE time draws near the birth of Christ:
The moon is hid; the night is still;
The Christmas bells from hill to hill
Answer each other in the mist.

Four voices of four hamlets round,
From far and near, on mead and moor,
Swell out and fail, as if a door
Were shut between me and the sound:

Each voice four changes on the wind,
That now dilate, and now decrease,
Peace and goodwill, goodwill and peace
Peace and goodwill, to all mankind.

.   .   .   .

The time admits not flowers or leaves
To deck the banquet. Fiercely flies
The blast of North and East, and ice
Makes daggers at the sharpen'd eaves,

And bristles all the brakes and thorns
To yon hard crescent, as she hangs
Above the wood which grides and clangs
Its leafless ribs and iron horns

Together, in the drifts that pass
To darken on the rolling brine
That breaks the coast. But fetch the wine,
Arrange the board and brim the glass;

Bring in great logs and let them lie,
To make a solid core of heat;
Be cheerful-minded, talk and treat
Of all things ev'n as he were by.

We keep the day. With festal cheer,
   With books and music, surely we
   Will drink to him, whate'er he be,
And sing the songs he loved to hear.

ALFRED, LORD TENNYSON (1809–1892).

TROLL-FEAST

℄ *Norwegian Folk-Tale.*

IN the old days there lived in Kvam a hunter named
Per Gynt. He was continually in the mountains, where
he shot bear and elk, for at that time there were more
forests on the Fjäll, and all sorts of animals lived in them.
Once, late in the year towards Christmas, when the cattle
had long been driven down from the mountain pastures,
Per Gynt decided to go up on the Fjäll again. Except
for three dairy-maids, all the herd-folk had already left
the mountains. When Per Gynt reached Hövringalm,
where he intended to spend the night in a herdsman's
hut, it was already so dark that he could not see his hand
before his eyes. The dogs began to bark violently, and
suddenly his foot struck something, and when he took
hold of it, it was cold, and large, and slippery.

"Who are you?" asked Per Gynt, for he noticed that
it moved.

"I am the Crooked One," was the answer.

"Well, crooked or straight, you will have to let me
pass," said Per Gynt, for he saw that he was going
around in a circle, and that the Crooked One was coiled
all round the hut. At these words the Crooked One
moved a little to one side, so that Per could get into the
hut. When he entered he found it as dark inside as out,

117

and while he was feeling his way about he once more struck something cold, and large, and slippery.

"And who are you now?" cried Per Gynt.

"I am the Crooked One," was the answer. And no matter where Per set his foot he could feel the coils of the Crooked One around him.

"This is a poor place to be in," thought Per. He took his firelock, went out of the hut, and felt his way along the Crooked One till he came to his head.

"And who are you, really and truly?" he asked.

"I am the Great Crooked One of Etnedal," said the monster Troll. Then Per Gynt wasted no time, but shot three bullets right through the middle of his head.

"Shoot again!" cried the Crooked One. But Per knew better, for had he shot again the bullets would have rebounded and hit him. Therefore Per and his dogs took hold of the great Troll and dragged him out of the hut, so that they might make themselves comfortable there; and the hills about rang with laughter and jeers. Then Per made a fire and hung a soup kettle on it; but the fire smoked so terribly that he could hardly keep his eyes open, and so he made a loophole in the wall. Suddenly up came a Troll and thrust his nose through the loophole; his nose was so long that it reached over to the fireplace.

"Here is my smeller," said the Troll. "Take a good look!"

"Here is a taste of the soup I cook!" said Per Gynt; and he poured the whole kettleful over the nose. The Troll rushed off lamenting loudly; and from all the heights around came laughter and derision and calls of

"Gyri Soupsmeller! Gyri Soupsmeller!"

Then all was quiet; but before very long the noise and tumult outside began again, and Per, looking out, saw a wagon drawn by bears; the great Troll was loaded upon it, and off they went with him up the Fjäll. Suddenly a pailful of water came pouring down the chimney, smothering the fire, and Per was in the dark. Laughter and jeers came from every corner, and a voice said: "Now Per Gynt will be no better off than the dairy-maids in the hut at Val!"

Per Gynt called his dogs, locked the hut, and went on north towards Val. After covering some distance he saw a fire, as though the whole hut were ablaze, and at the same moment came upon a pack of wolves, of whom he shot some and clubbed the others to death. When he reached Val the hut was in darkness and no fire was to be seen: but there were four mountain Trolls in the hut, frightening the dairy-maids; the Trolls' names were Gust i Väre, Tron Valfjeldet, Kjöstöl Aabakken, and Rolf Eldförkungen. Gust i Väre stood on guard in the door-way. Per Gynt shot at him, but missed, and he ran away. When Per entered the hut the Trolls, who had frightened the dairy-maids nearly to death, saw who had come and began to wail, and told Eldförkungen to make a fire. At the same moment the dogs sprang on Kjöstöl Aabakken and threw him head over heels into the hearth, so that ashes and sparks flew about.

"Have you seen my snakes, Per Gynt?" cried Tron Valfjeldet; for that was what he called his wolves.

"Yes, and you shall travel the same road," cried Per Gynt, and shot him. Then he made an end of Aabakken with the butt of his firelock; but Eldförkungen fled through the chimney. Per Gynt then accompanied the dairy-maids back to their village, for they dared not stay in the hut any longer.

It was now Christmas, and Per Gynt, having heard of a farm in the Dovre country where so many Trolls were accustomed to congregate on Christmas Eve that the people who lived there had to flee and find places to stay at other farms, decided to go there: for he thought he would like to see these Trolls. He put on torn clothing,

and took with him a tame bear which belonged to him, together with an awl, some pitch, and some wire. When he reached the farm he went in and asked for shelter.

"God help us," cried the farmer, "We cannot shelter you. We have to leave the house ourselves, for the place is alive with Trolls every Christmas Eve!"

But Per thought he could manage to clear the farm of Trolls, so they told him to stay, and gave him a pig's skin in the bargain. Then the bear lay down behind the hearth, and Per took his awl, his pitch, and his wire, and made a large shoe out of the pig's skin, drawing a thick rope through it for a shoelace, having also at hand two wagon-spokes for wedges. Suddenly the Trolls arrived with fiddles and fiddlers, and began to dance and to eat their Christmas dinner on the table, some eating fried bacon, some fried frogs and toads and things of that kind; for they had brought their Christmas dinner with them. In the meantime some of them noticed the shoe Per Gynt had made, and since it was evidently intended for a large foot, all the Trolls wanted to try it on. When every one of them had thrust in his foot Per Gynt laced it, forced in a wedge, and drew the lace so tight that at last every one of them was caught and held in the shoe. But now the bear thrust forth his snout and sniffed the roast.

"Would you like some cake, little white cat?" said one of the Trolls, and threw a burning hot roasted frog into the bear's jaws.

"Thump them, Master Bruin!" cried Per Gynt: and the bear, very angry, rushed on the Trolls, raining blows and scratching on every side, Per Gynt hewed into the crowd with his spare wagon-spoke as though he meant to break their skulls. The Trolls soon had to make themselves scarce, but Per remained and feasted on Christmas fare all the week, while for many a year no more was heard of the Trolls.

P. C. ASBJÖRNSEN.

VIDES ut alta stet nive candidum
　　Soracte nec jam sustineant onus
silvæ laborantes geluque
　　flumina constiterint acuto?

Dissolve frigus ligna super foco
large reponens atque benignius
　　deprome quadrimum Sabina,
　　O Thaliarche, merum diota.

HORACE, Carm. I. 9.

[*C. S. Calverley's translation.*]

One dazzling mass of solid snow
　　Soracte stands; the bent woods fret
　　Beneath their load; and sharpest-set
With frost, the streams have ceased to flow.

Pile on great faggots and break up
　　The ice: let influence more benign
　　Enter with four-years-treasured wine,
Fetched in the ponderous Sabine cup.

SOCIAL AND PERSONAL

WE, HENRY, by the grace of God King of France and
　　England, make known and proclaim to all present
and to come that We have received the humble supplica-
tion of the blood-relations and connections of Jehan la
Fille, *dit* Vignette, labourer, lodging at St. Germain des
Prés, having a young wife and two small children, and
at present held in the prison of St. Germain des Prés.
The deponents affirm:

THAT a little time ago the said Jehan la Fille returned
from Paris to his lodging in St. Germain des Prés with
a quantity of carpentry-work, and having entered his
said lodging, recollecting that he had forgotten to get
himself a candle, he departed from his said lodging for
the purpose of borrowing one; and on returning to his
said lodging he encountered one Philipot Laurens, also

living at St. Germain des Prés, who was carrying a half-pike. And the said Jehan la Fille, being angered and enraged against the said Philipot, for that the wife of the said Jehan had previously informed him that the said Philipot had called her *"whore"* and *"mopsy,"* said in a low voice into the ear of the said Philipot that he was an evil fellow to have uttered such villainy, and a liar also; and thereupon, taking a stone in his hand, he flung it at the said Philipot and struck him on the head, so that he fell to the ground; and after this he took and snatched from him his said half-pike and beat him about the legs only some two or three times. On account of these wounds the said Philipot has lain for three weeks or thereabout in the Hostel-Dieu, where he was carried, and also in his own lodging; and since then, through lack of governance, he has passed from this life. And for this cause the said Jehan la Fille, *dit* Vignette, is held prisoner in the prison of St. Germain des Prés, in great poverty and misery, his goods having been seized and taken, and on this account he is in danger of ending his days miserably within a short space, if Our grace and mercy be not accorded him.

THEREFORE, We, having pity and compassion on him, his said wife and children, and in honour and reverence of the blessed Nativity of Our Lord Jesus Christ, on this the first day of the year do remit and pardon the said Jehan la Fille, *dit* Vignette, for the above stated act, and do sentence him to fifteen days' imprisonment on bread and water only.

AND this is hereby commanded and presented to the Provost of Paris, and to all Our justiciaries.

GIVEN at Paris, on the first day of January, the year of grace 1422 [N.S. 1423], the first of Our reign.

AND signed: For the King, by order of the Council,

OGER.

Registers of the Chancellery of France.

⁙ To my right worshipful husband, John Paston, dwelling in the Inner Temple at London, in haste.

RIGHT worshipful husband, I recommend me to you, desiring heartily to hear of your welfare, thanking God of your amending of the great disease that ye have had, and I thank you for the letter that ye sent me, for by my troth my mother and I were nought in heart's ease from the time that we wist of your sickness, till we wist verily of your amending.

My mother behested another image of wax of the weight of you, to our Lady of Walsingham, and she sent four nobles to the four Orders of friars at Norwich to pray for you, and I have behested to go on pilgrimage to Walsingham and to St. Leonard's for you; by my troth I had never so heavy a season as I had from the time that I wist of your sickness, till I wist of your amending, and yet my heart is in no great ease, nor nought shall be, till I weet that ye be very whole.

I pray you heartily that ye will vouchsafe to send me a a letter as hastily as ye may, if writing be none disease to you, and that ye will vouchsafe to send me word how your sore do. I would ye were at home, if it were your ease, and your sore might be looked to here as it is there ye be now, lever than a new gown though it were of scarlet. I pray you if your sore be whole, and so that ye may endure to ride when my father come to London, that ye will ask leave and come home when the horse should be sent home again, for I hope ye shall be kept as tenderly here as ye be at London. I may none leisure have to do write half a quarter so much as I should say to you if I might speak with you. I shall send you another letter as hastily as I may. I thank you that ye would vouchsafe to remember my girdle, and that ye would write to me at the time, for I suppose that writing was none ease to you. Almighty God have you in his keeping,

and send you health. Written at Oxnead, in right great haste.

Yours, M. PASTON.

Christmas, 1443.

My mother greet you well, and sendeth you God's blessing and hers; and she prayeth you, and I pray you also, that ye be well dieted of meat and drink, for that is the greatest help that ye may have now to your health-ward. Your son fareth well, blessed be God.

The Paston Letters.

NOËL

UNE pastourelle gentille
  Et ung bergier en ung verger
L'autr'hyer en jouant à la bille
S'entredisoient, pour abréger :
     Roger
     Bergier
     Legière
     Bergière,
  C'est trop à la bille joué ;
  Chantons Noé, Noé, Noé.

Te souvient-il plus du prophète
Qui nous dit cas de si hault faict,

Que d'une Pucelle parfaicte
Naistroit ung Enfant tout parfaict?
    L'effect
    Est faict;
    La belle
    Pucelle
A eu ung filz du ciel voué:
Chantons Noé, Noé, Noé.

CLÉMENT MAROT of Cahors (1495–1544).

CAROL OF THE FIVE JOYS OF MARY

Ay, ay, ay, ay, Gaude celi domina.

MARY, for the love of thee
  Blyth and glad may we be,
And I shall sing as ye may se,
    Tua quinque gaudia.

The fyrst joy was sent to the
When Gabryell gretyd thee
And sayd hayle Mary in chastite,
    Officiaris gravida.

The second joy was full gud
When Chryst toke both flesshe and blod
Without syn talkyng of mode,
    Enixa est puerpera.

The third joy was of gret myght
Whan Jhesu was on the Rode dight,
Dead and buried in all men's sight,
    Surrexit die tertia.

The fourth joy was without ay
When Jhesu to hell toke the way
And with him com gret aray,
    Ad cœli palacia.

The fifth joy was on holy Thursday,
Unto hevyn He took the way,
God and man, and so he ys for ay,
Ascendit super sidera.

Balliol MS., XVIth Century.

SHEPHERDS' SALUTE

℃ Wakefield Second Nativity Play.

The Shepherds arrive at Bethlehem.

First Shepherd. Hail, comely and clean; hail, young child!
Hail, maker, as I mean, of a maiden so mild!
Thou hast wared, I ween, off the warlock so wild,
The false guiler of teen, now goes he beguiled.

> Lo, He merry is!
> Lo, he laughs, my sweeting,
> A welcome meeting!
> I have given my greeting.
> Have a bob of cherries.

Second Shepherd. Hail, sovereign saviour, for thou hast us
sought!
Hail freely, leaf and flower, that all thing has wrought!
Hail, full of favour, that made all of nought!
Hail, I kneel and I cower. A bird have I brought

> To my bairn!
> Hail, little tiny mop,
> Of our creed thou art crop!
> I would drink in thy cup,
> Little day-starn!

126

Third Shepherd. Hail, darling dear, full of godheed!
  I pray thee be near, when that I have need.
  Hail! sweet is thy cheer; my heart would bleed
  To see thee sit here in so poor weed
               With no pennies.
            Hail! put forth thy dall,
            I bring thee but a ball
            Have and play thee with all,
            And go to the tennis.
Maria Mater. The Father of Heaven, God omnipotent,
  That set all on levin, his son has he sent.
  My name could he neven, and laught as he went.
  I conceived him full even, through might, as God
              meant;
            And new is he born.
            He keep you from woe;
            I shall pray him so;
            Tell forth as ye go,
            And mind on this morn.
First Shepherd. Farewell lady, so fair to behold,
  With thy child on thy knee.
Second Shepherd.   But he lies full cold,
  Lord, well is me: now we go forth, behold!
Third Shepherd. Forsooth, already it seems to be told
  Full oft.
First Shepherd. What grace we have fun. [found]
Second Shepherd. Come forth, now are we won.
Third Shepherd. To sing are we bun:
  Let take on loft.

           ❦ *Explicit pagina Pastorum.*

I

The Rev. Lawrence Lidbetter to his curate, the Rev. Arthur Starling.

DEAR Starling,—I am sorry to appear to be running away at this busy season, but a sudden call to London on business leaves me no alternative. I shall be back on Christmas Eve for certain, perhaps before. You must keep an eye on the decorations, and see that none of our helpers get out of hand. I have serious doubts as to Miss Green.—Yours,
L. L.

II

Mrs. Clibborn to the Rev. Lawrence Lidbetter.

DEAR Rector,—I think we have got over the difficulty which we were talking of—Mr. Lulham's red hair and the discord it would make with the crimson decorations. Maggie and Popsy and I have been working like slaves, and have put up a beautiful and effectual screen of evergreen which completely obliterates the keyboard and organist. I think you will be delighted. Mr. Starling approves most cordially.—Yours sincerely,
MARY CLIBBORN.

III

Miss Pitt to the Rev. Lawrence Lidbetter.

MY dear Mr. Lidbetter,—We are all so sorry you have been called away, a strong guiding hand being never more needed. You will remember that it was arranged that I should have sole charge of the memorial window to Colonel Soper—we settled it just outside the Post Office on the morning that poor Blades was kicked by the Doctor's pony. Well, Miss Lockie now says that Colonel Soper's window belongs to her, and she makes

it impossible for me to do anything. I must implore you to write to her putting it right, or the decorations will be ruined. Mr. Starling is kind, but quite useless.—Yours sincerely,

VIRGINIA PITT.

IV

Miss Lockie to the Rev. Lawrence Lidbetter.

MY dear Mr. Lidbetter,—I am sorry to have to trouble you in your enforced rest, but the interests of the church must not be neglected, and you ought to know that Miss Pitt not only insists that the decoration of Colonel Soper's window was entrusted to her, but prevents me carrying it out. If you recollect, it was during tea at Mrs. Millstone's that it was arranged that I should be responsible for this window. A telegram to Miss Pitt would put the matter right at once. Dear Mr. Starling is always so nice, but he does so lack firmness.—Yours sincerely,

MABEL LOCKIE.

V

Mrs. St. John to the Rev. Lawrence Lidbetter.

DEAR Rector,—I wish you would let Miss Green have a line about the decoration of the pulpit. It is no use any of us saying anything to her since she went to the Slade School and acquired artistic notions, but a word from you would work wonders. What we all feel is that the pulpit should be bright and gay, with some cheerful texts on it, a suitable setting for you and your helpful Christmas sermon, but Miss Green's idea is to drape it entirely in black muslin and purple, like a lying in state. One can do wonders with a little cotton-wool and a few yards of Turkey twill, but she will not understand this. How with all her *nouveau art* ideas she got permission to decorate the pulpit at all I cannot think,

but there it is, and the sooner she is stopped the better. Poor Mr. Starling drops all the hints he can, but she disregards them all.—Yours sincerely,

CHARLOTTE ST. JOHN.

VI

Miss Olive Green to the Rev. Lawrence Lidbetter.

DEAR Mr. Lidbetter,—I am sure you will like the pulpit. I am giving it the most careful thought, and there is every promise of a scheme of austere beauty, grave and solemn and yet just touched with a note of happier fulfilment. For the most part you will find the decorations quite conventional—holly and evergreens, the old terrible cotton-wool snow on crimson background. But I am certain that you will experience a thrill of satisfied surprise when your eyes alight upon the simple gravity of the pulpit's drapery and its flowing sensuous lines. It is so kind of you to give me this opportunity to realise some of my artistic self. Poor Mr. Starling, who is entirely Victorian in his views of art, has been talking to me about gay colours, but my work is done for *you* and the few who can *understand*.—Yours sincerely,

OLIVE GREEN.

VII

Mrs. Millstone to the Rev. Lawrence Lidbetter.

DEAR Rector,—Just a line to tell you of a delightful device I have hit upon for the decorations. Cotton-wool, of course, makes excellent snow, and rice is sometimes used, on gum, to suggest winter too. But I have discovered that the most perfect illusion of a white rime can be obtained by wetting the leaves and then sprinkling flour on them. I am going to get all the others to let me finish off everything like that on Christmas Eve (like varnishing-day at the Academy, my husband says), when it will all be fresh for Sunday. Mr. Starling who is proving himself such a dear, is delighted with the scheme. I hope you are well in that dreadful foggy city.—Yours sincerely,

ADA MILLSTONE.

VIII

Mrs. Hobbs, charwoman, to the Rev. Lawrence Lidbetter.

HONOURED Sir,—I am writing to you because Hobbs and me dispare of getting any justice from the so called ladies who have been turning the holy church of St. Michael and all Angels into a Covent Garden market. To sweep up all holly and green stuff I don't mind, because I have heard you say year after year that we should all do our best at Christmas to help each other. I always hold that charity and kindness are more than rubys, but when it comes to flour I say no. If you would believe it, Mrs. Millstone is first watering the holly and the lorrel to make it wet, and then sprinkling flour on it to look like hore frost, and the mess is something dreadful, all over the cushions and carpet. To sweep up ordinery dust I don't mind, more particularly as it is my paid work and bounden duty; but unless it is made worth my while Hobbs says I must say no. We draw the line at sweeping up dough. Mr. Starling is very kind, but as Hobbs says you are the founting head.—Awaiting a reply, I am, your humble servant,

MARTHA HOBBS.

IX

Mrs. Vansittart to the Rev. Lawrence Lidbetter.

DEAR Rector,—If I am late with the north windows you must understand that it is not my fault, but Pedder's. He has suddenly and most mysteriously adopted an attitude of hostility to his employers (quite

in the way one has heard of gardeners doing), and nothing will induce him to cut me any evergreens, which he says he cannot spare. The result is that poor Horace and Mr. Starling have to go out with lanterns after Pedder has left the garden, and cut what they can and convey it to the church by stealth. I think we shall manage fairly well, but thought you had better know in case the result is not equal to your anticipation.—Yours sincerely,

GRACE VANSITTART.

X

Mr. Lulham, organist, to the Rev. Lawrence Lidbetter.

DEAR Sir,—I shall be glad to have a line from you authorising me to insist upon the removal of a large screen of evergreens which Mrs. Clibborn and her daughters have erected by the organ. There seems to be an idea that the organ is unsightly, although we have had no complaints hitherto, and the effect of this barrier will be to interfere very seriously with the choral part of the service. Mr. Starling sympathises with me, but has not taken any steps.—Believe me, yours faithfully,

WALTER LULHAM.

XI

The Rev. Lawrence Lidbetter to Mrs. Lidbetter.

MY Dearest Harriet,—I am having, as I expected, an awful time with the decorations, and I send you a batch of letters and leave the situation to you. Miss Pitt had better keep the Soper window. Give the Lockie girl one of the autograph copies of my *Narrow Path*, with a reference underneath my name to the chapter on self-sacrifice, and tell her how sorry I am that there has been a misunderstanding. Mrs. Hobbs must have an extra half-crown, and the flouring must be discreetly

discouraged—on the ground of waste of food material. Assure Lulham that there shall be no barrier, and then tell Mrs. Clibborn that the organist has been given a pledge that nothing should intervene between his music and the congregation. I am dining with the Lawsons tonight, and we go afterwards to the *Tempest*, I think.— Your devoted,

L.

E. V. Lucas.

NOËL

    O N a winter's night long time ago
      (*The bells ring loud and the bells ring low*)
When high howled wind, and down fell snow,
    (Carillon, Carilla)
Saint Joseph he and Nostre Dame,
Riding on an ass, full weary came
From Nazareth into Bethlehem.
    And the small child Jesus smile on you.

And Bethlehem inn they stood before
    (*The bells ring less and the bells ring more*)
The landlord bade them begone from his door,
    (Carillon, Carilla)
"Poor folk" (says he) "must lie where they may,
For the Duke of Jewry comes this way,
With all his train on a Christmas Day."
    And the small child Jesus smile on you.

Poor folk that may my carol hear
    (*The bells ring single and the bells ring clear*)
See! God's one child had hardest cheer!
    (Carillon, Carilla)
Men grown hard on a Christmas morn;

133

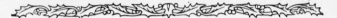

The dumb beast by and a babe forlorn,
It was very, very cold when Our Lord was born.
And the small child Jesus smile on you.

Now these were Jews as Jews must be
  (*The bells ring merry and the bells ring free*)
But Christian men in a band are we
  (Carillon, Carilla).
Empty we go, and ill be-dight,
Singing Noël on a winter's night:
Give us to sup by the warm firelight,
  And the small child Jesus smile on you.

HILAIRE BELLOC.

THE DEATH OF GALAHAD

QUANT vint au chief de l'an, a celui jor meismes que Galaad avoit porté corone, si se leva bien matin entre lui et ses compaignons. Et quant il vindrent el palés que len apeloit esperitel, si regarderent devant le saint Vessel: et voient un bel home vestu en semblance de evesque, et estoit a genolz devant la table et batoit sa coupe; et avoit entor lui si grant plenté d'angleres come se ce fust Jhesucrist meisme. Et quant il ot esté grant piece a genolz, si se leva et commença la Messe de la glorieuse Mere Dieu. Et quant vint el segré de la Messe, que il ot ostee la plateinne de desus le saint Vessel, si apella Galaad et

NOW at the year's end, and the self day after Galahad had borne the crown of gold, he arose up early and his fellows, and came to the palace, and saw tofore them the holy Vessel, and a man kneeling on his knees in likeness of a bishop, that had about him a great fellowship of angels as it had been Jhesu Christ himself; and then he arose and began a Mass of Our Lady. And when he came to the Sacring of the

li dist: "Vien avant, serjant Jhesucrist, si verras ce que tu as tant desirré a veoir." Et il se tret avant et regarde dedenz le saint Vessel. Et si tost come il i ot regardé, si comence a trembler molt durement, si tost come la mortel char commença a regarder les esperitex choses. Lors tent Galaad ses meins vers le ciel et dit: "Sire, toi ador ge et merci de ce que tu m'as acompli mon desirrier, car ore voi ge tot apertement ce que langue ne porroit descrire ne cuer penser. Ici voi ge l'a començaille des granz hardemenz et l'achoison des proeces; ici voi ge les merveilles de totes autres merveilles! Et puis qu'il est einsi, biax dolz Sires, que vos m'avez acomplies mes volontez de lessier moi veoir ce que j'ai touz jors desirré, or vos pri ge que vos en cest point ou je sui et en ceste grant joie soffrez que je trespasse de ceste terriene vie en la celestiel."

Si tost come Galaad ot fete ceste requeste a Nostre Seignor, li prodons qui devant l'autel estoit revestuz en semblance de evesques prist *Corpus Domini* sus la table et l'offri a Galaad. Et il le reçut molt humilieusement et o grant devocion.

Mass, and had done, anon he called Galahad, and said to him: Come forth the servant of Jhesu Christ, and thou shalt see that thou hast much desired to see. And then he began to tremble right hard when the deadly flesh began to behold spiritual things. Then he held up his hands toward heaven and said: Lord, I thank thee, for now I see that that hath been my desire many a day.

Now, blessed Lord, would I not longer live, if it might please thee, Lord.

And therewith the good man took our Lord's Body betwixt his hands, and proferred it to Galahad, and he received It right gladly and meekly.

Et quant il l'ot usé, li pro-dom li dit: "Sez tu," fet il, "qui je sui?"—"Sire, nenil, se vos nel me dites."—"Or saches," fet il, "que je sui Josephes, li filz Joseph d'Ari-matie, que Nostre Sires t'a envoié por toi fere compaignie. Et sez tu por quoi il m'en a plus tost envoié que un autre? Por ce que tu m'as resemblé en deus choses: en ce que tu as veues les merveilles del Saint Graal ausi come je fis, et en ce que tu as esté virges ausi come je sui; si est bien droiz que li uns virges face compaignie a l'autre."

Quant il ot dite ceste parole, Galaad vient a Perceval et le bese et puis a Boorz, si li dist: "Boorz, saluez moi monseigneur Lancelot mon pere si tost come vos le ver-roiz." Lors revint Galaad devant la table et se mist a coudes et a genolz; si n'i ot gueres demoré quant il chaï a denz sus le pavement del palés, qar l'ame li eirt ja fors del cors. Si l'en porterent li anglere fessant grant joie et beneissant Nostre Seignor.

Si tost come Galaad fu deviez avint illuec une grant merveille. Qar li dui com-paignon virent apertement que une mein vint devers le ciel; mes il ne virent pas le cors dont la mein estoit. Et

Now wotest thou what I am? said the good man. Nay, said Galahad. I am Joseph of Aramathie, the which Our Lord hath sent here to thee to bear thee fellowship; and wotest thou wherefore that he hath sent me more than any other? For thou hast resembled me in two things; in that thou hast seen the marvels of the Sangreal, in that thou hast been a clene maiden, as I have been and am.

And when he had said these words Galahad went to Per-civale and kissed him, and commended him to God; and so he went to Sir Bors and kissed him, and com-mended him to God, and said: Fair lord, salute me to my Lord, Sir Launcelot, my father, and as soon as ye see him, bid him remember of this unstable world. And therewith he kneeled down tofore the table and made his prayers, and then suddenly his soul departed to Jhesu Christ, and a great multitude of angels bare his soul up to heaven, that the two fellows might well see it. Also the two fellows saw come from heaven an hand, but they

elle vint droit au seint Vessel
et le prist, et la Lance ausi,
et l'enporta tot amont vers
le ciel, a telle eure qu'il ne
fu puis hons si hardiz qu'il
osast dire qu'il eust veu le
Seint Graal.

saw not the body. And then
it came to the Vessel, and
took it and the Spear, and
so bare it up to heaven.
Sithen was there never man
so hardy to say that he had
seen the Sangreal.

La Queste del S. Graal.
XIIIth Century.

MALORY.

OUR LADY'S LULLABY

UPON my lap my Sovereign sits,
  And sucks upon my breast;
Meanwhile, his love sustains my life,
And gives my body rest.

> *Sing lullaby, my little Boy,*
> *Sing lullaby, my life's Joy.*

When thou hast taken thy repast
Repose, my Babe, on me;
So may thy mother and thy nurse
Thy cradle also be.

> *Sing lullaby.*

My Babe, my Bliss, my Child, my Choice,
My Fruit, my Flower, and Bud,
My Jesus, and my only Joy,
The Sum of all my good.

> *Sing lullaby.*

The shepherds left their keeping sheep
For joy to see my Lamb;
How may I more rejoice to see
Myself to be the Dam.

> *Sing lullaby.*

F
137

Three Kings their treasure hither brought
Of incense, myrrh, and gold,
The Heaven's Treasure and the King
That here they might behold.

   Sing lullaby.

One sort an Angel did direct,
A Star did guide the other;
And all the fairest Son to see
That ever had a Mother.

   Sing lullaby, my little Boy,
   Sing lullaby, my life's Joy.

RICHARD VERSTEGAN (ROWLANDS), priest
(1565–1620).

GLORIA IN EXCELSIS
(or, What it Meant to Henry.)

IT was years ago, I remember, one Christmas Eve
when I was dining with friends: a lady beside me made
in the course of talk one of those allusions that I have
always found myself recognising on the spot as "germs."
The germ, wherever gathered, has ever been for me the
germ of a "story," and most of the stories straining to
shape under my hand have sprung from a single small
seed, a seed as minute and wind-blown as that casual
hint for *The Spoils of Poynton* dropped unwitting by my
neighbour, a mere floating particle in the stream of talk.
What above all comes back to me with this reminiscence

is the sense of the inveterate minuteness, on such happy occasions, of the precious particle—reduced, that is, to its mere fruitful essence. Such is the interesting truth about the stray suggestion, the wandering word, the vague echo, at touch of which the novelist's imagination winces as at the prick of some sharp point: its virtue is all in its needle-like quality, the power to penetrate as finely as possible. This fineness it is that communicates the virus of suggestion, anything more than the minimum of which spoils the operation. . . .

So it was, at any rate, that when my amiable friend, on the Christmas Eve, before the table that glowed safe and fair through the brown London night, spoke of such an odd matter as that a good lady in the north, always well looked on, was at daggers drawn with her only son, ever hitherto exemplary, over the ownership of the valuable furniture of a fine old house just accruing to the young man by his father's death, I instantly became aware, with my "sense for the subject," of the prick of inoculation; the *whole* of the virus, as I have called it, being infused by that single touch. For the action taken, and on which my friend, as I knew she would, had already begun all complacently and benightedly further to report, I had absolutely, and could have, no scrap of use; one had been so perfectly qualified to say in advance, "It's the perfect little workable thing, but she'll strangle it in the cradle, even while she pretends, all so cheeringly, to rock it; wherefore I'll stay her hand while yet there's time." I didn't of course stay her hand—there never *is* in such cases "time"; and I had once more the full demonstration of the fatal futility of Fact. The turn taken by the excellent situation—excellent, for development, if arrested in the right place, that is in the germ—had the full measure of the classic ineptitude; to which with the full measure of the artistic irony one could once more, and for the thousandth time, but take off one's hat. It was not, however, that this in the least mattered, once the seed had been transplanted to richer soil; and I dwell on that almost inveterate redundancy of the wrong, as opposed to the ideal right, in any free flowering of the actual, by reason only of its approach to calculable regularity.

If there was nothing regular meanwhile (etc. etc.)

HENRY JAMES
(1843-1916).

THE STAR SONG

A CAROL SUNG TO THE KING AT WHITEHALL

The Flourish of Music; then followed the Song.

1. Tell us, thou clear and heavenly tongue,
   Where is the Babe but lately sprung?
   Lies He the lily-banks among?

2. Or say, if this new Birth of ours
   Sleeps, laid within some ark of flowers,
   Spangled with dewlight; thou canst clear
   All doubts, and manifest the where.

3. Declare to us, bright Star, if we shall seek
   Him in the morning's blushing cheek,
   Or search the beds of spices through,
   To find Him out.
                    Star. No, this ye need not do;
   But only come and see Him rest
   A Princely Babe in's mother's breast.

Chor. He's seen, He's seen! why then a round,
   Let's kiss the sweet and holy ground;
   And all rejoice that we have found
   A King before conception crown'd.

140

THE NATIVITY : *Piero della Francesca*

4. Come then, come then, and let us bring
   Unto our pretty Twelfth-tide King,
   Each one his several offering;

Chor. And when night comes we'll give Him wassailing;
   And that His treble honours may be seen,
   We'll choose Him King, and make His mother
       Queen.

ROBERT HERRICK.

FROM THE PROVINCE OF QUEBEC

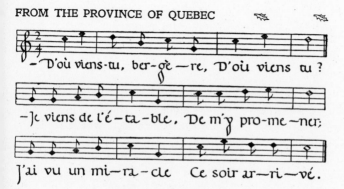

— D'où viens-tu, ber-gè—re, D'où viens tu ?

—Je viens de l'é—ta—ble, De m'y pro-me—ner;

J'ai vu un mi—ra—cle Ce soir ar—ri—vé.

Qu'as-tu vu, bergère,
    Qu'as-tu vu ?
J'ai vu dans la crèche
Un petit Enfant
Sur la paille fraîche
Mis bien tendrement.

Rien de plus, bergère,
    Rien de plus ?
Saint' Marie, sa mère,
Lui fait boir' du lait,
Saint Joseph, son père,
Qui tremble de froid.

141

Rien de plus, bergère,
    Rien de plus?
Ya le bœuf et l'âne
Qui sont par devant;
Avec leur haleine
Réchauffent l'Enfant.

Rien de plus, bergère,
    Rien de plus?
Ya trois petits anges
Descendus du ciel,
Chantant les louanges
Du Père Eternel.

XVIIth Century.

THE BURNING BABE

AS I in hoary Winter's night stood shivering in the snow,
Surpris'd I was with sudden heat which made my
    heart to glow;
And lifting up a fearful eye to view what fire was near,
A pretty Babe, all burning bright, did in the air appear;
Who, scorchèd with exceeding heat, such flood of tears
    did shed,
As though His floods should quench His flames, which
    with His tears were fed.
"Alas!" quoth He, "but newly born in fiery heat I fry,
Yet none approach to warm their hearts or feel My fire
    but I.

"My faultless breast the furnace is, the fuel, wounding
    thorns,
Love is the fire and sighs the smoke, the ashes, shames
    and scorns.
The fuel Justice layeth on and Mercy blows the coals,
The metal in this furnace wrought are men's defilèd souls,

142

For which, as now on fire I am to work them to their good,
So will I melt into a bath to wash them in My blood."
With this He vanish'd out of sight and swiftly shrunk
away,
And straight I callèd unto mind that it was Christmas Day.

VEN. ROBERT SOUTHWELL, S.J. (1561–1595).

A PRESENT FOR THE GRAND TURK

℃. *How the true tidings of the battle in Turkey was
known in the French king's house.*

SO it was, on Christmas Day sir Jaques Helly about
the hour of noon entered into Paris and so took his
lodging, and demanded where the king was; and it was
shewed him that he was at Saint-Pol's on the river of
Seine: then he went thither. There was with the king
the duke of Orleans his brother, the duke of Berry, the
duke of Burgoyne, the duke of Bourbon and the earl of
Saint-Pol, and divers other noblemen of the realm of
France, as the usage was for such noblemen to be with
the king at such high feasts. So sir Jaques Helly
entered into the court booted and spurred; as then he
was not beknown, for he had of long time haunted far
countries. He did so much that he came to the king's
chamber, and said how he came from Amurath-baquin
[Bajazet] out of Turkey, and had been at the battle before
Nicopoly, where the Christian men had lost the tourney,
and said he had letters from the earl of Nevers and from
other lords of France, such as were prisoners. Then he
was brought to the king; he kneeled down and wisely
declared his message, as well from Amurath-baquin as
from the earl of Nevers and other lords of France
prisoners in Turkey. The king gave him audience, and
he was sweetly examined of all the whole matter, and to
everything he answered so discreetly, that the king was

143

well content with him, and was right sorrowful for the damage that the king of Hungary and they had sustained. . . .

Then it was demanded of sir Jaques what jewels or presents the king might best send to Amurath-baquin and that should best please him, to the intent that the prisoners should be the better entreated. The knight answered that Amurath-baquin took great pleasure in cloths of Arras made of old ancient histories, and also, he said, he had great delight in those white falcons called gerfalcons; also he said that fine linen cloths and fine scarlets were much made of there, for of cloth of gold and silk they had plenty.

Sir John Froissart, Canon of Chimay
(1337–1410).

AT CHAINMAIL HALL

PROCEEDING to the edge of the moat, they fished up Mr. Firedamp, who had missed his way back and tumbled in. He was drawn out, exclaiming, "that he had taken his last dose of malaria in this world."

The Rev. Dr. Folliott.

Tut, man; dry clothes, a turkey's leg and rump, well devilled, and a quart of strong punch, will set all to rights.

"Wood embers," said Mr. Firedamp, when he had been accommodated with a change of clothes, "there is no antidote to malaria like the smoke of wood embers; pine embers." And he placed himself, with his mouth open, close by the fire.

The Rev. Dr. Folliott.

Punch, sir, punch; there is no antidote like punch.

Mr. Chainmail.

Well, Doctor, you shall be indulged. But I shall have my wassail-bowl nevertheless.

An immense bowl of spiced wine, with roasted apples hissing on its surface, was borne into the hall by four men, followed by an empty bowl of the same dimensions, with all the materials of arrack punch, for the divine's especial brewage. He accinged himself to the task with his usual heroism; and having finished it to his entire satisfaction, reminded his host to order in the devil. . . .

After a time, the ladies, and all the females of the party, retired. The males remained on duty with punch and wassail, and dropped off one by one into sweet forgetfulness; so that when the rising sun of December looked through the painted windows on mouldering embers and flickering lamps, the vaulted roof was echoing to a mellifluous concert of noses, from the clarionet of the waiting-boy at one end of the hall, to the double-bass of the Reverend Doctor, ringing over the empty punch-bowl, at the other.

THOMAS LOVE PEACOCK (1785–1866).

THE FALL OF THE MIGHTY

LONDON, Dec. 24, 1711. I went into the City to-day in a coach, and dined there. My cold is going. It is now bitter hard frost, and has been so these three or four days. . . . My lord privy-seal set out this day for Holland: he'll have a cold journey. I gave Patrick half a crown for his Christmas-box, on condition he would be good, and he came home drunk at midnight. I have taken a memorandum of it; because I never design to give him a groat more. 'Tis cruel cold.

25. I wish MD a merry Christmas, and many a one; but mine is melancholy: I durst not go to church to-day, finding myself a little out of order, and it snowing prodigiously, and freezing.

27. The frost still continues violently cold. Mrs.

Masham invited me to come to-night and play at cards; but our society did not part till nine. But I supped with Mrs. Hill, her sister, and there was Mrs. Masham and lord treasurer, and we stayed till twelve. He is endeavouring to get a majority against next Wednesday, when the House of lords is to meet, and the Whigs intend to make some violent addresses against a Peace, if not prevented. God knows what will become of us.

29. Saturday night. I have broke open my letter, and tore it into the bargain, to let you know that we are all safe; the queen has made no less than twelve lords to have a majority; and has turned out the Duke of Somerset. She is awaked at last, and so is lord treasurer: I want nothing now but to see the duchess [of Marlborough] out. We are all extremely happy. Give me joy, sirrahs. This is written in a coffee-house. Three of the new lords are of our Society.

30. The duke of Marlborough was at Court to-day, and nobody hardly took notice of him.

31. Our frost is broken since yesterday, and it is very slabbery; yet I walked into the city and dined, and ordered some things with the printer. . . . I hear the Duke of Marlborough is turned out of all his employ-ments: I shall know to-morrow, when I am to carry Dr. King to dine with the secretary.

January 1, 1712. Now I wish my dearest little MD many happy New-years; yes, both Dingley and Stella, aye, and Presto too, many happy new-years. I dined with the secretary, and it is true that the duke of Marl-borough is turned out of all. The duke of Ormond has got his regiment of Footguards, I know not who has the rest. . . . The queen and lord treasurer mortally hate the duke of Marlborough, and to that he owes his fall, more than to his other faults; unless he has been tampering too far with his party, of which I have not heard any particulars; however it be, the world abroad will blame us. I confess my belief that he has not one good quality in the world besides that of a General, and even that I have heard denied by several great soldiers. But we have had constant success in arms while he commanded. Opinion is a mighty matter in war, and I doubt but the French think it impossible to conquer an army that he leads, and our soldiers think the same; and how far even this step may encourage the French to play tricks with us, no man knows. I do not love to see personal resentment mix with publick affairs.

DEAN SWIFT, *Journal to Stella*.

A CHICKEN FOR A LORD

Checones in Critone for x messes.

TAKE checones [chickens] and make hom clene, and chop hom on quarters, and sethe hom, and when thai byn half sothen take hom up and pylle of the skynne, and frie hom in faire grese and dress hom up, and cast thereon pouder of gynger ande sugur; then take iii pounde of almondes, and blaunche hom, and draw up a gode thik mylke with the brothe, and other gode brothe therewith, and do hit in a pot and sethe hit; and put thereto hole clowes, maces and pynes, and let hit boyle altogedur, and in the settynge down do thereto an ounce of pouder of gynger, and medel hit wyth vynegar, and serve hit forthe, and poure the syrip thereon, and cast thereon pouder of gynger and sugur; and a hole chekyn for a lorde.

XIVth-XVth Century: Arundel Collection.

THE RESCUE OF BRANDY NAN

¶ Christmas Eve, 1713.

AS Lads and Lasses stood around
To hear my boxen Hautboy sound,
Our Clerk came posting o'er the Green
With doleful tidings of the Queen;
That Queen (he said) to whom we owe
Sweet Peace that maketh Riches flow,
That Queen who eas'd our Tax of late,
Was dead, alas!—and lay in State.

At this, in Tears was *Cic'ly* seen,
Buxoma tore her Pinners clean,
In doleful Dumps stood ev'ry Clown,
The Parson rent his Band and Gown.
For me, when as I heard that Death
Had snatch'd Queen *Anne* to *Elizabeth*,
I broke my Reed, and sighing swore
I'd weep for *Blouzelind* no more.

While thus we stood, as in a Stound,
And wet with Tears, like Dew, the Ground,
Full soon by Bonfire and by Bell
We learnt, our Liege was passing well.
A skilful Leech (so God him speed)
They said had wrought this blessed Deed;
This Leech ARBUTHNOT was yclept,
Who many a Night not once had slept,
But watch'd our gracious Sovereign still:
For who could rest when she was ill?
O, may'st thou henceforth sweetly sleep!
Shear, Swains, oh shear your softest Sheep
To swell his Couch; for well I ween
He sav'd the Realm who sav'd the Queen.

JOHN GAY (1688–1732).

1743, January 2nd. A deal of discussion is taking place touching a snuff-box worth a thousand crowns which the King has presented to Madame de Mailly, the concern displayed by Madame de la Tournelle on this occasion, and a recent interview between both ladies. They say Mme. de la Tournelle's moods occupy the King a great deal, and that she is jealous and fiery-tempered; but that nevertheless she continues to be in favour more and more.

5th. They say there have been certain misunderstandings between the King and Madame de la Tournelle, following a letter from the Duc d'Agenois.

6th. Twelfth Day. The King has presented Madame de la Tournelle with a watch which he had ordered for Madame de Mailly. The case is of lacquer, richly studded with diamonds. Madame de la Tournelle has given his Majesty for a New Year gift an almanac in a China case, bearing her monogram in diamonds.

Several burlesque Noëls and lampoons directed against the Ministers and the Government are flying about, but since the great pains taken by M. de Marville to trace the authors they appear with less facility than before.

Journal de Police sous Louis XV.

A PRESENT FROM HORACE

Strawberry-Hill, December 24, 1754.

MY dear Sir,—I received your packet of December 6th, last night, but intending to come hither for a few days, had unluckily sent away by the Coach in the morning a parcel of things for you; you must therefore wait till another bundle sets out, for the new letters of Madame Sévigné. Heaven forbid that I should have said they were bad! I only meant that they were full of family details, and mortal distempers, to which the most immortal of us are subject; and I was sorry that the prophane

should ever know that my Divinity was ever troubled
with a sore leg, or the want of money. . . .

Well! but you will want to know the contents of the
parcel that is set out. It contains another parcel, which
contains I don't know what; but Mr. C—— sent it, and
desired I would transmit it to you. There are Ray's
Proverbs in two volumes interleaved; a few seeds, mis-
laid when I sent the last; a very indifferent new Tragedy,
called Barbarossa, now running; the author unknown,
but believed to be Garrick himself; there is not one word
of Barbarossa's real story, but almost the individual
History of Merope; not one new thought, and, which is
the next material want, but one line of perfect nonsense:

And rain down Transports in the shape of Sorrow.

To complete it, the manners are so ill observed, that
a Mahometan Princess-royal is at full liberty to visit
her lover in Newgate, like the banker's daughter in
George Barnwell.

For news, I think I have none to tell you. Mr. Pitt is
gone to the Bath, and Mr. Fox to Newcastle-house;
and everybody else into the country for the holidays.

HORACE WALPOLE to Richard Bentley.

"COME, LASSES AND LADS"

PRENONS chacun sa panetière,
  Suivons Philanon le berger,
Annete-Philis sa bergère,
  Ils nous conduiront sans danger:
    Venez, Jane et Janot,
    Anne, Madelon, Collinet,
    Marion, Carlet, et Margot,
    Guillot, Jacquet, Bernardinet:
  Adorons l'Enfant tous assemble
  Pour celebrer ceste faveur.

Il nous faut adorer
Les rayons de sa charité,
Qui dans la nuict font éclairer
En nous les rais de sa bonté.

En ceste heureuse nuict,
Vierges et purs nous detestons
L'amour impur qui les seduit,
Et l'Amour des Amours chantons.
Chantons d'une amour bien grande
Cet Amour, l'Amour des Amours:
Allons luy presenter l'offrande,
Et requerir de luy secours:
Si qu'en joyeuseté,
Qu'en sons et qu'en beaux chants toujours
Soit chacun an de nous chanté
Cet Amour, l'Amour des Amours.

VAUQUELIN DE LA FRESNAYE (1535–1607).

ON CHRIST'S NATIVITY

I WOULD I were some *Bird*, or star,
Flutt'ring in Woods, or lifted far
Above this *Inne*
And rode of sin!
Then either Star or *Bird* should be
Shining or singing still to thee.

I would I had in my best part
Fit Roomes for thee! or that my heart
Were so clean as
Thy Manger was!
But I am all filth, and obscene;
Yet, if thou wilt, thou canst make clean.

HENRY VAUGHAN THE SILURIST (1622–1695).

THE chief passion of Shakespeare's life was Stratford-on-Avon. He never forgot it. Amid all the wild whirl of that London life—and it was a wild whirl then, a foaming torrent of such passions, political, sensual, emotional, intellectual, that our poor attempts at being alive in London now are pretty much as the green stuff on a duck-pond is to Niagara—he thought of the friendly fires and the good taverns and the solid, stolid, worthy people and the beloved fields. *Romeo and Juliet, Hamlet, Othello*—so many steps nearer to the haven where he would be, to the true, secure life he loved. We think our London a tremendous centre of excitement; we, who are impressed when somebody takes hold of a revue which is a failure and turns it into a revue which is a success. William Shakespeare lived in a London which was impressed when it saw live men disembowelled at Tyburn and the heads of traitor nobles spiked on London Bridge. He lived in a red-hot world; a world of terrific beauty, horror, cruelty, disgust, revelry. Our tea-party people and commentating Dons do not begin to have the elementary data—as they would say—for the understanding of Shakespeare. I do not believe many of them have read Ben Jonson's description of a voyage down Fleet Ditch; they had better not; it would make them unwell. . . .

To the horrible people who are best designated as Dons, whose idea of Heaven is an everlasting examination, it is repulsive that this young wastrel, with a possible Grammar School smattering, should have written the finest things in the world. "The Warwickshire yokel," says one of them in high contempt. And so has arisen the most marvellous folly of the world: the Baconian Hypothesis. Grave men, being first assured that shabby Bohemian fellows do not write immortalities, have committed themselves to all the wonderful lunacies of the Bilateral Cypher, have gone a little farther, and have at last found that Bacon wrote not only all Shakespeare but all the literature of his age, including Montaigne's *Essais* and Cervantes' *Don Quixote*. The last book which I read on the subject showed that *Don Quixote* should be read "*d'un qui s'ôte*"—concerning one who hides himself—Bacon, of course. Indeed, the writer proved that the alleged author, Cervantes, had an illegitimate child and was very poor: which is evidence, of course, that he could not write masterpieces. The masterpieces notoriously are all written by moral men with large banking accounts.

May this January, this Twelfth Night, bring us better sense, as we sit about our sea-coal fire.

ARTHUR MACHEN.

PLUS ÇA CHANGE . . .

JANUARY 1, 1747. Towards the end of last year there appeared in Paris the toy called a *pantin*, or jumping-jack, made in the first instance to amuse the children, but later on to amuse grown-ups. These are little figures of pasteboard with the members made separately and attached by threads, to make them dance. These puppets represent Harlequin, Scaramouch, etc., and are painted in all manner of ways; some by very good artists, among them M. Boucher, one of the most famous members of the Academy. These are very expensive, and some of them make posturings which are hardly genteel. This is the sort of stupidity which has been amusing all Paris, so that one cannot go into any house where these dolls are not dangling from every chimneypiece. People make presents of them to ladies and young girls, and they are so much the rage that this month all the shops are offering them as New Year gifts.

This is not a new invention, but simply a revival; twenty years ago it was equally a passing fashion. And

153

as always happens, when everybody has one the fashion becomes stale and dies. In order to do justice to national taste it was adjudged important to preserve a specimen of *Pantin* and *Pantine*: the little figures cost three livres, and almost before they had been bought the craze for them had faded away.

Journal of the Avocat Barbier.

FROM "THE MASQUE OF CHRISTMAS," 1616

℟ *The Court being seated,*

Enter CHRISTMAS, *with two or three of the Guard, attired in round Hose, long Stockings, a close Doublet, a high-crowned Hat, with a Brooch, a long thin Beard, a Truncheon, little Ruffes, white Shoos, his Scarfes and Garters tied cross, and his Drum beaten before him.*

WHY, Gentlemen, do you know what you doe? Ha! would you have kept me out? CHRISTMAS, old Christmas, Christmas of *London,* and Captayn Christmas? Pray you, let me be brought before my Ld. Chamberlayn, Ile not be answred else: *'Tis merry in hall, when beards wag all.*

The Truth is, I have brought a Masque here, out o' the Citty, of my own making, and do present it by a Sett of my Sons, that come out of the Lanes of *London,* good dancing Boyes all. It was intended, I confess, for *Curriers'-Hall*; but because the Weather has been open, and the Liverie were not at Leisure to see it till a Frost came, that they cannot worke, I thought it convenient, with some little Alterations, and the Groome o' the Revells hand to 't, to fit it for a higher Place; which I have done, and though I say it, another Manner of Device than your *New Yeares Night.* Bones o' bread, the King! (*seeing his Mjty.*) Son *Rowland*! son *Clem*! be readie there in a Trice: quick boyes!

Enter his SONS and DAUGHTERS (ten in Number), led in, in a string, by CUPID, who is attired in a flat Capp, and a Prentice's Coat, with Winges at his Shoulders.

MISRULE, in a velvet Capp, with a sprigg, a short Cloke, great yellow Ruffe (like a Reveller); his Torche-bearer bearing a Rope, a Cheese, and a Baskett.

CAROL, a long tawny Coat, with a red Capp, and a Flute at his Girdle; his Torche-bearer carrying a Song-booke open.

MINCED-PYE, like a fine Cook's wife, drest neat; her Man carrying a Pye, Dish, and Spoones.

GAMBOL, like a Tumbler, with a Hoope and Bells; his Torche-bearer armed with a Colt-staff and a Binding-Cloth.

POST AND PAIR, with a Pair-royal of Aces in his Hat; his Garment all done over with Pairs and Purs; his 'Squire carrying a Boxe, Cards, and Counters.

NEW YEARE'S GIFT, in a blue Coat, serving-man-like, with an Orange, and a sprigg of Rosemary gilt on his Head, his Hat full of Brooches, with a Collar of Gingerbread; his Torche-bearer carrying a March-Pane with a Bottle of Wine on either arme.

MUMMING, in a masquing pied Suit, with a Vizard; his Torche-bearer carrying the Boxe, and ringing it.

WASSEL, like a neat Sempster and Songster; her Page bearing a brown Bowle, drest with Ribbands, and Rosemary before her.

OFFERING, in a short Gowne, with a Porter's Staffe in his Hand, a Wyth borne before him, and a Bason, b his Torche-Bearer.

BABY-CAKE, drest like a Boy, in a fine long Coat, Biggin-bib, Muckender, and a little Dagger; his Usher bearing a great Cake, with a Beane and a Pease.

They enter singing.

Now God preserve, as you do well deserve,
　　Your Majesties all two there;
Your Highnesse small, with my good Lords all,
　　And Ladies, how do you do there?

Give me leave to ask, for I bring you a Masque
　　From little, little, little London,
Which saye the King likes, I have passed the Pikes,
　　If not, old Christmas is undone.

　　　　　　　　　　　　　　[*Noise without.*

BEN JONSON.

155

The scene is a public place, hung with many Orders, By-Laws, Regulations, and other Documents of State.

Enter, in ghostly form, the Lord of Misrule.

Lord of Misrule. There stood an ancient custom in the
    land
That, when the Old Year died, a wanton band
Of revellers made riot through the town
With serfs enfranchised in a master's gown.
No man had plunged his life so deep in failure
He might not act the lord in Saturnalia.
Then when the Church was heir to pagan rite
It suffered still the holiday; so dight
In wild attire of furs and foolery
The hinds assumed brief lordship and were free.
The clerk became the lawyer, while the maid
Lolled o'er a banquet by her mistress laid.
The valet then was hero to himself;
The steward took rare bottles from the shelf
To wait on kitchen-wenches: flaring beacons
Illumed the feast where curates mimed archdeacons;
The petty clerks mixed litanies with low tales
And trod with licence on the prelate's coat-tails.
Bishops might frown; their law was out of season,
Sole cleric now the Abbot of Unreason.
A Feast of Fools it was, when naught was holy
Save that the lord gave service to the lowly.
Then was my hour; a crazy potentate,
Lord of Misrule, I governed all the State.
Authority was bent to learn the feel
Of scorn and whips and fettering of steel.
The later ages with a new-found gravity
Found naught in Saturnalia but depravity
And killed the age-long ritual; so I,
For virtue's sake, was led away to die.
But even such as I can have a ghost
And beckon forth again the rebel host

Of wantons skipping in the law's despite
And mocking righteousness with ancient rite.
See where they come, the modern libertines
Freed from inspectors, curfews, spies, and fines.
The play-boys now play not at changing stations;
Their game is just escape from Regulations,
From Departmental Orders and the scowl
Of County Councillors upon the prowl.
Behold the saucy gallants of the State,
Do all things now which men hold profligate.

> *The Lord of Misrule here steps aside and there enters
> a Masque of Citizens. They dance a comely
> measure, looking round carefully to see if any
> policemen are about. One or two of the more
> desperate may fling their bowler-hats in the air or
> wave an umbrella. As they dance they chant their
> hymn of liberty.*

Oh, we are the Freemen of England.
   At least we are free for the day.
We believe that hot pies may be bought after eight,
Without permit of any Department of State!
We believe that a man can be safe in the park
Without passport or visa, although it is dark!
   Oh, we are the Freemen of England,
   And we're going remarkably gay.
[*Here the Masquers divide in two parties, one coming
   from each in turn to recount his lawless deed.*

First Citizen. Brothers, to-day I broke the Eternal Laws;
  Swollen in sin I mocked the Primal Cause
  With desperate deed, an outrage against Heaven.
  I drank a lager at ten past eleven!
Second Citizen. But what of me? To celebrate the rite,
  I practised crime most black and erudite.
  I left my motor standing in the street,
  And never bribed the policeman on the beat!

Third Citizen. Hot blood indeed! Yet mine has been no
  calmer!
  Seeking a strong sex play I found the drama
  Insufferable without a chocolate.
  Brothers, at nine o'clock I bought and ate!
Fourth Citizen. Rash venture, sir! But mine's the deed of
  honour;
  I've seen a film not licensed by O'Connor.
  And then, my courage to a tempest fanned,
  I saw the girl whom Birmingham had banned!
Fifth Citizen. I, like an anarch, full of pride and spleen,
  Quite late at night desired nicotine;
  In Saturnalian frenzy out I strode,
  Bought cigarettes, and smoked one in the road!
Sixth Citizen. Bold sinners are ye all, but hark to me
  Whose sin outranges all audacity,
  Yes, I have dared, beneath a policeman's eye,
  To look at a young woman passing by.
Seventh Citizen. The Radio Programme set my heart on
  fire
  (A Talk on Turtles and the Girl Guides' Choir).
  Of all decorum swiftly I lost my sense;
  Enrapt I listened in—without a licence!
Eighth Citizen. Your deeds are fell; yet none as mine so
  dark,
  I wished to back a horse at Kempton Park.
  Instead of lawful message: "Quid each way,"
  I put a bob on in the street to-day!
Lord of Misrule. So this is mischief! Well, you never know
  What people will think wicked. Be it so.
  Your hour is short, my revellers! While it ticks
  On with the Dance and kick against the Jix.

IVOR BROWN.

A D. 1125.—In this year sent the King Henry, before Christmas, from Normandy to England, and bade that all the mint-men that were in England should be mutilated in their limbs. This was because the man that had a pound could not lay out a penny at a market. And the Bishop Roger of Salisbury sent all over England, and bade them all that they should come to Winchester at Christmas. When they came thither, then were they taken one by one, and deprived each of the right hand. All this was done within the Twelfth Night. And that was all in perfect justice, because that they had undone all the land with the great quantity of base coin that they all bought.

The Anglo-Saxon Chronicle.

A NOTE ON ALE ❦ ❦ ❦

Ld. Smart. Well, Sir *John,* how do you like it?

Sir John. Not as well as my own in *Derbyshire;* 'tis plaguy small.

Lady Smart. I never tast Malt Liquor; but they say, 'tis well hopp'd.

Sir John. Hopp'd! why, if it had hopp'd a little Further, it would have hopp'd into the River. O my Lord, my Ale is Meat, Drink, and Cloth; it will make a Cat speak, and a wise Man dumb.

Lady Smart. I was told, ours was very strong.

Sir John. Ay, Madam, strong of the Water; I believe the Brewer forgot the Malt, or the River was too near him: faith, it is mere whip-belly Vengeance; he that drinks most has the worst Share.

Col. I believe, Sir *John,* Ale is as plenty as Water at your House.

Sir John. Why, faith, at *Christmas* we have many Comers and Goers; and they must not be sent away without a Cup of *Christmas*-Ale, for fear they should —— behind the Door.

Lady Smart. I hear, Sir *John* has the nicest Garden in

England; they say, 'tis kept so clean, that you can't
find a place where to spit.

Sir John. O madam; you are pleased to say so.

Lady Smart. But, Sir *John*, your Ale is terrible strong and
heady in *Derbyshire*, and will soon make one drunk and
Sick; what do you then?

Sir John. Why, indeed, it is apt to fox one; but our
Way is, to take a Hair of the same Dog next Morning.
—I take a new-laid Egg for Breakfast; and faith, one
should drink as much after an Egg as after an Ox.

DEAN SWIFT.

NEWS FROM SALEM

1785. Dec. 25. Christmas. The service as follows: To
introduce the morning service. Two short anthems,
Hail, Hail, etc., and Methinks I see,—Boston. Before
Sermons, Shepherds rejoice, etc. After Sermon, Anthem,
Behold, etc. Preserved Elkins propounded to receive
Baptism for her child.

1792. 25 Dec. For the first time in this place the Clarionet,
and Violin introduced into Church Music—there is now
no ground of complaint against the Catholicks.

27 Dec. Curious proposals, as there are now fifteen
states in our Union, to represent them by Stars, pyramid-
wise.

1793. Dec. 25. Christmas. Rained all day. The inspector
of Police in Boston has forbidden "the Anticks," as they
are called, by which the resemblance of this Christian
feast to the Saturnalia has been so admirably maintained.

1799. Dec. 23. This evening the News reached this town
of the DEATH OF GENERAL WASHINGTON. 24. Notice was
taken of this great event by the tolling of bells at Sunrise,
by hoisting the flags at half-mast, and by discharge of
Cannon and by ceasing from business.

1816. Dec. 25. The Episcopalians and Foreign Com-
munions are not left to observe this day without Com-

petition. H. Ballon called his flock together in the afternoon to celebrate, just as it used to be on our 5th November. The great boys had their large Pope, but the little boys wanted him upon a shingle . . . These holydays are a reproach even in America to the name of religion. 1818. Dec. 25. Mr. Quady collected a small group of Catholics but without a crowd, tho' it was the first time a public Mass had been said in Salem on this day.

From the Diary of Dr. WILLIAM
BENTLEY of East Salem, Mass.

THE BIRTH OF FRANCE

℃ Christmas Day, A.D. 496.

THEN the Queen [St. Clotilde] sent secretly to Rémy, Bishop of Reims, praying him to instil into her husband's heart the word of salvation. The Bishop came to the King, and little by little, and in private, brought him to acknowledge the true God, Maker of heaven and earth, and to renounce his idols, which could be of no avail to him or to anyone.

Then said Clovis to the Bishop: "Most holy Sir, I hear you willingly, but there is a difficulty: the people I rule have no desire to abandon their gods. Nevertheless I will speak to them according to the spirit of your words." He thereupon went into the midst of the people; but already the Divine grace had operated, and even before he opened his mouth to speak the assembly cried with one voice: "Pious King, we renounce our mortal gods, we are ready to serve the God whose immortality Rémy preaches." This news was brought to the Bishop, and overcome with joy he ordered the sacred fonts to be prepared. Rich hangings adorn the streets; the churches are hung with tapestries; the incense - clouds arise; fragrant tapers blaze on every hand; and all the baptistery is filled with a heavenly odour. Such grace did Almighty

God shower upon those present, that they thought themselves transported among the joys of Paradise. The King first of all demanded baptism of the Bishop. Like a new Constantine he advances to the bath which is to wash away his deep-rooted leprosy, to the new water which is to cleanse him of the stains of his past. As he came to the font the saint of God addressed him with holy eloquence: "Bow thy head in humility, O Sicamber! adore what thou hast burned, burn what thou hast adored."

Clovis, having confessed one God, all-powerful in the Sacred Trinity, was baptised in the name of the Father, and of the Son, and of the Holy Ghost, and anointed with the sign of the Cross with the holy chrism. More than three thousand men of his army were baptised after him, as also his sister Albfledis, who a little time after departed this life in the Lord.

ST. GREGORY OF TOURS (544–595).

ON SATURNALIA

TRUE Saturnalia, public Saturnalia, were healthy because they were corporate. Custom and religion had dug a sort of channel into which all that emotion could commonly run, and in midwinter, when it had long been very dark, the mischiefs, the comic spirits came out of the woods and for some days possessed the souls of men, and these, by that possession, were purged and freed. So it was for hundreds upon hundreds of years—until quite the modern time. Why have we lost it, and how long must we wait for it to return?

When the relations of slave and master seemed as obvious and necessary as seem to us (let us say) the reading of a daily paper or the taking of a train, yet the obvious and necessary routine was broken in midwinter, the slave was the master for a moment and the master a slave.

When the ritual of the Church was as much a commonplace as the ritual of social life is to us to-day, there was
a season (it was this season, between Christmas and the
Epiphany) when the deadweight of order was lifted and
a boy dressed as a bishop or a donkey was put to chaunt
the Office, and the people sang:

Plebs autem respondet:
> Hé, sire Ane, ho! Chantez!
> Vous aurez du foin assez
> Et de l'avoine à manger!

When the awful authority of civil and hereditary powers
was unquestioned they yet set up in English halls Lords
of Misrule who governed that season. The Inns of
Court, I believe, delighted in them, and certainly till
quite late in the seventeenth century the peasantry of
the villages.

It has gone. It will return. During its absence (and
may that absence not be much prolonged) perhaps one
can see its nature the more clearly because one sees it
from the outside and as a distant though a desired thing.
Perhaps we, living in a very unreasonable age, when
realities are forgotten and imaginaries preferred, when
we solemnly reiterate impossibilities, affirm our faith in
scientific guesswork and our doubts upon the plain rules
of arithmetic, can understand why our much more reasonable fathers thirsted for and obtained these Feasts of
Unreason. It seems to have been a little like the natural
craving for temporary oblivion (sleep—a chaos) once in
every day; a sort of bath in that muddle or nothingness
out of which the world was made. Equality, which lies
at the base of society, was brought to surface by a paradox
and shown at large. Intensity of conviction and of
organisation took refuge in the relief of a momentary—
and not meant—denial of that conviction and organisation, and the whole of society collectively expanded its
soul by one collective foolery at high pressure, as does

the healthy individual by one good farce or peal of laughter when occasion serves.

.   .   .   .

Anyway, one way or another, sooner or later, the Saturnalia will return; may it be sooner rather than later, and at the latest not later than 1938, when so many of us will be so very old.

For my part I shall look for the first signs in the provinces of rich and riotous blood, as on the Border (and especially just north of it) or in Flanders, or, better still, in Burgundy from Nuits and Beaune northward and eastward. I have especially great hopes of the town of Dijon.

HILAIRE BELLOC.

THUNDER FROM THE THRONE

For truly it is with shame and blushes that we contemplate this gallimaufry of unhallowed rites which its instigators call the *Feast of Fools*; a festival, without the least doubt, of diabolic inspiration, to which in many churches Our priests and clergy lend themselves in the venerable name of Our Lord and at this holy and joyous season of His Nativity, in which season they should rather be giving their minds to sacred things. For the participators in this festival assemble for ignoble play in the very time of Divine service, wearing grotesque and monstrous masks (*larvatos et monstruosos vultus*) and dressed in women's attire, or disguised in the frippery of debauched mummers and strolling players, leading their riotous dance into church and into the very choir itself, bawling villainous songs, devouring food at the very side of the altar while the priest is celebrating Mass, playing at dice in the holy place, censing the sanctuary with foul smoke from the burning leather of old shoes (*de fumo fetido et ex corio veterum sotularium thurificando*),

leaping and dancing throughout the whole sacred building. Nor without blushing can be contemplated the spectacle of the half-nude players, lacking the merest shred of decency, who at this season swarm in the town and in the booths, playing on carts and sorry vehicles to arouse the laughter of those who stand around, making lewd gestures, proferring obscene words and scurrilous jests (*verba impudicissima atque scurrilia proferendo*) and many other abominations which it is a shame to recall. Rightly is this infamous assembly (*hoc flagitiosum coagulum*) named the Feast of Fools! that is to say, an assembly of wicked fellows exulting in their sin.

Pastoral Letter of Louis, Archbishop
of Sens, Epiphany, 1445.

A LITTLE LITANY

WHEN God turned back eternity and was young,
    Ancient of Days, grown little for your mirth
(As under the low arch the land is bright)
    Peered through you, Gate of Heaven—and saw the
      earth.

Or shutting out his shining skies awhile
    Built you about him for a House of Gold
To see in pictured walls his storied world
    Return upon him as a tale is told.

Or found his Mirror there; the only glass
    That would not break with that unbearable Light;
Till in a corner of the high dark house
    God looked on God, as ghosts meet in the night.

Star of his Morning; that unfallen star
    In the strange starry overturn of space
When earth and sky changed places for an hour
    And Heaven looked upwards in a human face.

Or young on your strong knees and lifted up
    Wisdom cried out, whose voice is in the street,
And more than twilight of twiformed cherubim
    Made of his throne indeed a mercy-seat.

Or risen from play at your pale raiment's hem
    God, grown adventurous from all time's repose,
Of your tall body climbed the ivory Tower
    And kissed upon your mouth the mystic Rose.
                      G. K. CHESTERTON.

THE BOAR'S HEAD CAROL

i. Queen's Coll. Oxon.

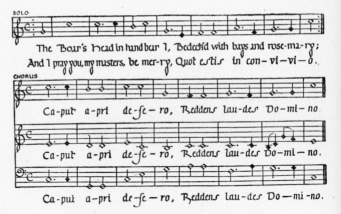

THE Boar's Head in hand bear I,
  Bedeck'd with bays and rosemary;
And I pray you, my masters, be merry,
    Quot estis in convivio.
    Caput apri defero,
    Reddens laudes Domino.

The Boar's Head, as I understand,
Is the rarest dish in all this land,
Which thus bedeck'd with a gay garland
  Let us *servire cantico.*
   Caput apri defero,
   Reddens laudes Domino.

Our steward hath provided this
In honour of the King of Bliss,
Which on this Day to be served is
  In Reginensi Atrio.
   Caput apri defero,
   Reddens laudes Domino.

ii. Balliol MS.

Caput apri refero
 Resonans laudes Domino.

The bores hede in hondes I bringe
With garlondes gay and birdes singinge,
I pray you all helpe me to singe,
  Qui estis in convivio.

The bores hede, I understande,
Is cheffe service in all this londe,
Where so ever it may be fonde,
  Servitur cum sinapio.

The bores hede, I dare well say,
Anon after the twelfthe day
He taketh his leve and goth away;
  Exivit tunc de patria.

OBVIOUSLY there should be a standard value for a certain type of Christmas present. One may give what one will to one's own family or particular friends; that is all right. But in a Christmas house-party there is a pleasant interchange of parcels, of which the string and the brown paper and the kindly thought are the really important ingredients, and the gift inside is nothing more than an excuse for these things. It is embarrassing for you if Jones has apologised for his brown paper with a hundred cigars and you have only excused yourself with twenty-five cigarettes; perhaps still more embarrassing if it is you who have lost so heavily on the exchange. An understanding that the contents were to be worth five shillings exactly would avoid this embarrassment.

And now I am reminded of the ingenuity of a friend of mine, William by name, who arrived at a large country house for Christmas without any present in his bag. He had expected neither to give nor to receive anything, but to his horror he discovered on the 24th that everybody was preparing a Christmas present for him, and that it was taken for granted that he would require a little privacy and brown paper on Christmas Eve for the purpose of addressing his own offerings to others. He had wild thoughts of telegraphing to London for something to be sent down, and spoke to other members of the house-party in order to discover what sort of presents would be suitable.

"What are you giving our host?" he asked one of them.

"Mary and I are giving him a book," said John, referring to his wife.

William then approached the youngest son of the house, and discovered that he and his next brother Dick were sharing in this, that, and the other. When he had heard this, William retired to his room and thought profoundly.

He was the first down to breakfast on Christmas morning. All the places at the table were piled high with presents. He looked at John's place. The top parcel said, "To John and Mary from Charles." William took out his fountain-pen and added a couple of words to the inscription. It then read, "To John and Mary from Charles and William," and in William's opinion looked just as effective as before. He moved on to the next place. "To Angela from Father," said the top parcel. "And William," wrote William. At his hostess' place he hesitated for a moment. The first present there was for "Darling Mother, from her loving children." It did not seem that an "and William" was quite suitable. But his hostess was not to be deprived of William's kindly thought; twenty seconds later the handkerchiefs "from John and Mary and William" expressed all the nice things which he was feeling for her. He passed on to the next place. . . .

It is of course impossible to thank every donor of a joint gift; one simply thanks the first person whose eye one happens to catch. Sometimes William's eye was caught, sometimes not. But he was spared all embarrassment; and I can recommend his solution of the problem with perfect confidence to those who may be in a similar predicament next Christmas.

A. A. MILNE.

THE POET EXPLAINS

BECAUSE in this month of December, when napkins fly about, and slim spoons, wax candles, and paper, and tapering jars of dried damsons, I have sent you nothing but my homely little books, I may perhaps seem stingy or discourteous. I hate the crafty and accursed arts of giving presents; gifts are like hooks—who does not know that the greedy sea-bream is deceived by the fly ? Every time a poor man gives nothing to a rich friend, Quintianus, he is generous.

MARTIAL.

THE THREE LOW MASSES

ℂ *Provençal Folk-Tale.*

I.

"Two truffled turkeys, Garrigou?"

"Yes, father. Two splendid turkeys stuffed with truffles. I know something about it, because I helped to stuff them. You'd say their skins would burst in the roasting, they were so tight!"

"Jésu-Maria! And I'm so fond of truffles! . . . Give me my alb, Garrigou, quickly. . . . And besides the turkeys, what else have you seen in the kitchen up to now?"

"Oh, all sorts of good things. Ever since midday we've been doing nothing else but plucking pheasants, lapwings, pullets, grouse; the air was thick with feathers. And then there are eels from the fishpond, and golden carp, and trout, and . . ."

"Trout? How big, Garrigou?"

"As big as that, father. . . . Huge!"

"I can almost see them. Have you put wine in the cruet?"

"Yes, father, I've put wine in the cruet. . . . But Lord! it isn't as good as the wine you'll be drinking pretty soon, at the end of Mass. If you could only see all the flasks and decanters in the Hall, full of wine of all colours . . . ! And the silver plate! And the epergnes, all chased! And the flowers, and the candelabra! There'll never have been such a Réveillon! His lordship has invited all the gentry round; you'll be at least forty at table, not counting the bailiff and the notary. Ah, father, you're lucky to be one of them! Just a sniff of those

lovely turkeys and the smell of truffles follows me
everywhere . . . Y'm!"

"Come, come, my child. Let us beware of the sin of
gluttony, and above all on this Eve of Christmas. Go now,
light the candles and ring the first chime. It is nearly midnight. We must not be late."

This was the conversation which passed, on Christmas
Eve of the year of grace 16—, between the reverend
Dom Balaguère, one time prior of Barnabites but now
chaplain to the Marquis de Trinquelage, and his young
acolyte Garrigou—or at any rate what he thought was
his acolyte Garrigou; for you are to know that the Devil
this night had assumed the round and simple features
of the young sacristan, the better to drag the good chaplain
into temptation and induce him to commit the deadly
sin of Gluttony. And while the seeming Garrigou (ha!
ha!) was ringing the bells of the Castle chapel with all
his might the priest finished vesting in the little sacristy;
and with his imagination already perturbed by all these
gastronomic rhapsodies, murmured absently to himself as
he did so:

"Roast turkeys! Golden carp! And trout . . . as big
as that!"

Outside the night wind whistled, scattering the music
of the bells. By degrees lights appeared in the darkness
of the slopes of Mont Ventoux, crowned by the ancient
towers of Trinquelage: the farmers and their families were
coming to get their midnight Mass at the castle. They
climbed the hill in groups of five or six, singing, the
father going first, lantern in hand, the women wrapped
in their ample brown cloaks, their children clinging and
sheltering. The late hour and the cold notwithstanding,
all these honest folk went gaily, sustained by the thought
that at the end of Mass there would be, as in every year,
tables spread for them below, in the kitchens. From time

to time on the rough hill road the windows of some
gentleman's coach, preceded by footmen carrying torches,
shimmered in the light of the moon. A trotting mule
shook its bells, and by the light of lanterns half blotted
out in the mist, the tenant farmers recognised their
bailiff, and saluted him as he went by.

"Good night, Master Arnoton!"

"Good night, my children. Good night!"

The night was clear, the stars crackled with the cold:
the winter blast blew shrewdly, and a fine sleet, slipping
off cloaks without wetting them, faithfully upheld the
tradition of a white Christmas. On the peak of the hill
the Castle stood like a target with its huge mass of towers
and gables, the spire of its chapel striking into the blue-
black sky, a multitude of little winking lights coming and
going and stirring at all the windows, glowing in the
sombre outline of the great pile like sparks darting to and
fro in the ash of burnt paper. Once over the drawbridge
and through the postern the way to the chapel led through
the outer courtyard, full of coaches, of servants, of sedan
chairs, lit by the flame of torches and the blaze from the
kitchens. One could hear the clinking of spits, the clang
of frying-pans, the chiming of glass and of silver being
set out for a banquet; and the warm mist, scented of
roasting meats and strong herbs for subtle sauces, which
hung over all inspired one reflection in the farmers, as
in the bailiff, the chaplain, and everybody:

"What a Réveillon we shall have after Mass!"

II.

Ting-a-ling-a-ling! Ting-a-ling-a-ling-a-ling!

Midnight Mass is beginning. In the Castle chapel, a
miniature cathedral with the interlaced vaulting of its
roof, and its oaken panelling, high as the walls, the tapestries are hung, all the candles lit. And what a crowd!

What costumes! Here, seated in the sculptured choir stalls, is the Marquis de Trinquelage in salmon-coloured silk, and with him his noble guests. Opposite, kneeling on their velvet prie-Dieu, are the old dowager Marquise in flame-coloured brocade and the young Marquise, wearing her high goffered tower of lace, in the last mode of the Court of France. Behind them, in black, with their huge pointed perukes and clean-shaven visages, appear the bailiff, Master Thomas Arnoton, and the notary, Master Ambroy; two notes of gravity among all these flaming silks and figured damasks. Then come the stout butlers, the pages, the grooms, the stewards, and Dame Barbe, with her keys jingling at her side on a ring of fine silver. At the end, on the benches, are the lower servants, male and female, and the tenants with their families; and finally, right against the door, which they open and close discreetly, behold our friends the turn-spits, slipping in between two sauces to hear a scrap of Mass, bringing with them a breath of Réveillon into the festal air of the chapel, warm with so many lighted candles.

Is it the sight of the flat white caps which distracts the celebrant? Or is it not rather Garrigou's sacring-bell, this feverish little bell which is tinkling at the altar foot with infernal precipitancy, seeming to say all the time:

"Hurry up! *Hurry* up! The sooner we've done, the sooner to table!"

The truth is that each time this diabolical little bell rings the chaplain forgets his Mass and remembers only his supper. He sees in his mind's eye the bustling cooks, the blazing forge-like fires, the mist rising from uncovered pans . . . and in this mist two turkeys, superb, bursting, straining, mottled with truffles. . . . He sees the file of pages go by, bearing dishes enveloped in tempting odours, and goes in with them to the great hall, already prepared for the feast. O delicious! There is the enormous table, laden and sparkling; the peacocks roasted in their feathers; the pheasants spreading their golden wings; the ruby flasks; the pyramids of glowing fruit among green branches, the miraculous fish of Garrigou's story (ha! ha! Yes, Garrigou!) on their bed of fennel, their scales as iridescent as if they were just out of water, with bunches of fragrant herbs stuck in their monster gills. So vivid is his vision that Dom Balaguère can almost see these mirific dishes spread before him on the embroidered cloth of the altar, and twice or thrice, instead of *Dominus vobiscum*, he is astonished to find himself beginning the *Benedicite*. But beyond these trifling slips the good man says his Office most conscientiously, without skipping one line or omitting one genuflexion: and all is well to the end of the first Mass: for as you know, on Christmas Day the same celebrant must celebrate three consecutive Masses.

"That's one!" says the chaplain to himself with a sigh of relief: and then, without losing a moment, he signs to his clerk—or the One he thinks is his clerk, and:

Ting-a-ling-a-ling-a-ling-ling!

The second Mass begins, and with it the sin of Dom Balaguère.

"Quick! Quick! Hurry!" screams Garrigou's little bell in its shrill little voice. And this time the unhappy priest, giving himself over to the Demon of Gluttony, flings himself on his missal and devours its pages with all the avidity of his raging appetite. Furiously he bows, stands erect, makes sketchy signs of the Cross, genuflects, shortening every gesture in order to get through sooner. He hardly touches his breast at the *Confiteor*; at the Gospel he barely extends his arms. It becomes a race between him and his clerk, which shall mumble through the quicker. Verses and responses hurry along, bustling one another: words half-pronounced without opening the mouth (which would take too much time) olur and melt away in incomprehensible murmurs.

" Oremus ps . . . ps . . . ps . . ."
" Mea culpa . . . pa . . . pa . . ."

They wallow in the Latin of the Mass like vintagers treading the grape at harvest, splashing on every side.

"Dom . . . scum!" says Balaguère.

" . . . Stutuo!" Garrigou answers him: and the whole time the devilish little bell is clamouring in their ears like the bells on post-horses galloping at top speed. You may imagine that at this rate a low Mass is soon finished.

" . . . And that's the second," says the chaplain, completely out of breath; and without waiting to recover, red in the face, sweating, he descends the altar steps again and—

Ting-a-ling-a-ling-a-ling-a-ling-a-ling!

The third Mass begins. It is now but a few steps to the Hall; but alas! as Réveillon comes nearer the miserable Balaguère feels himself in the grip of a fury of impatience and greed. His vision becomes sharper. The golden carp, the roasted turkeys are there. . . . He is touching them. . . . He—— O Heaven! the dishes smoke, the scent of the wines is in his nostrils . . . and the little bell cries to him furiously:

"Faster! Faster! Much faster!"

But how can he go any faster? His lips are now scarcely moving. He is not pronouncing any more words at all. He is within an ace of tricking the good God and filching His Mass from Him altogether. . . . And this is what he actually does, the unhappy sinner! Leaping from temptation to temptation he begins by jumping first one verse, then two; the Epistle is too long, he leaves it unfinished, skims through the Gospel, passes by the Creed, gives the Preface a distant salute, skips the *Pater*, and by hops, leaps, and bounds hurls himself thus into eternal damnation, at his heels the devilish Garrigou (*vade retro, Satanas!*) egging him on with cordiality, holding up the chasuble, turning the pages two at a time,

175

jostling the lectern, upsetting the cruet, incessantly ringing and ringing his little bell, louder and louder, faster and faster. You should see the aghast faces of the congregation! In their endeavour to follow the priest's movements in this Mass, of which they cannot distinguish one single word, some stand when the rest are kneeling, some sit when the others stand: all the succeeding phases of this singular Office jostle one another among the congregation in a dozen different attitudes. The Star of Bethlehem, marching across the skies on its journey to the Stable far away, turns pale with fear on seeing such confusion. . . .

"Really, the abbé is going too fast! It is impossible to follow him," murmurs the old dowager Marquise, shaking her coif in bewilderment.

Master Arnoton, his great steel spectacles on his nose, tries in vain to discover where the deuce he is in his missal. . . . But at heart all these honest folk are fixed equally on Réveillon, and are not too seriously perturbed at the post-haste speed of Mass. And when Dom Balaguère with shining face turns him at last and intones with all the force of his lungs *"Ite, missa est!"* his flock with one voice answers with a *"Deo gratias!"* so joyous and so overpowering that one would think oneself already at table, drinking the first toast.

III.

Five minutes afterwards the assembled gentry took their seats in the great hall, the chaplain in their midst. The castle, illuminated from top to bottom, resounded with songs, with shouts, and laughter, and merriment; and the venerable Dom Balaguère planted his fork in a wing of pullet, washing away the remorse for his sin in a flood of Clos du Pape and rich gravy. He ate and drank so heartily, the poor worthy man, that he died that

night of a terrible apoplexy, without time to repent, and in the morning arrived in Heaven still flushed from the night's feasting: and I leave you to imagine what sort of a reception he got.

"Out of My sight, bad Christian!" ejaculated the Sovereign Judge, Master of all mankind. "Your sin is great enough to efface a whole lifetime of goodness. You have robbed Me of a midnight Mass. Very well! You shall repay Me three hundred in its place, and you shall not enter My Paradise until you have celebrated, in your own chapel, these three hundred Christmas Masses in the presence of all those who have sinned with you and through your example."

And this is the true legend of Dom Balaguère, as they tell it in the olive country. To-day the castle of Trinquelage is no more; but the chapel still stands on the peak of Mont Ventoux, in a clump of green oaks. The wind shakes its ruined door; grass grows on the threshold; birds have built their nests at the angles of the altar and in the embrasures of the high windows, whence the coloured glass disappeared ages ago. But it seems that every year at Christmas a supernatural light glints among the ruins, and the country people going to Mass and Réveillon see this spectre of a chapel lighted up with invisible candles burning in the open air, even in snow and wind. Laugh if you like, but a vine-grower of the neighbourhood, one Garrigue (doubtless a descendant of Garrigou) has sworn to me that one Christmas Eve, having a little drink taken, he lost himself in the mountain near Trinquelage; and this is what he saw. Before eleven o'clock, nothing. All was silent and dead. Then suddenly, near midnight, a peal rang high above in the steeple, an old, old peal which sounded as if it were ten leagues away; and very soon, on the hill road, Garrigue saw lights trembling and vague moving

shadows. Under the chapel porch there was movement. There were whispers.

"Good night, Master Arnoton!"

"Good night, my children. Good night."

When all had entered my vine-grower, a courageous fellow, crept up gently and, peeping through the broken door, saw a singular sight. The people he had seen were all grouped around the choir and in the ruined nave, as if the old benches were still there: fair ladies in brocade with lace head-dresses, seigneurs bedizened from head to foot, peasants in flowered jackets, such as our ancestors wore, all appearing strangely old, faded, dusty, and weary. From time to time the night-birds who inhabit the chapel, awakened by so many lights, flew round the candles, whose flame stood up straight and dim, as if they burned behind a veil: and what highly amused Garrigue was the spectacle of a personage with huge steel glasses who incessantly shook at intervals his tall peruke, on which one of these birds was perched, its feet entangled, silently flapping its wings.

And at the east end a little old man with the figure of a child, kneeling in the centre of the choir, desperately rang a little silent bell, while a priest vested in ancient gold moved to and fro at the altar, reciting prayers in a soundless voice. . . .

Without doubt it was Dom Balaguère saying his third Low Mass.

ALPHONSE DAUDET (1840–1897).

CRADLE SONG

JOSEPH, lieber Joseph mein,
hilff mir wiegen mein Kindelein,
Gott der wil dein lohner seyn
im Himmelreich
der Jungfrau Sohn Maria

178

Es ist erfüllt,
was uns weissgesagt hat Gabriel
Eia, Eia!
die Jungfrau Gott geboren hat,
als die Göttliche weissheit werwilliget hat.

Es ist erschienen an diesem tag
in Israel
den verkündiget hat der Engel Gabriel.

XVIIth Century.

A DESSERT

i. *To Scorch Chesnutts*

TAKE yᵒʳ Chesnutts and put them in a close oven to take off the Husks, then take a little loafe suger in powder and a little water, and boyle to a Candy, take care it does not burn, then put in yᵒʳ chesnutts and stir it about in the Sugar till it stick on yᵒʳ Chesnutts, and put them on a stone.

Almonds is done the same way only put a little Carmine in yᵉ sugar.

ii. *To make Harts Horn Flummery.*

Take half a pound of Harts horn and an ounce of Isinglass steeped in rose-water all night, and boyle them till you make a strong Jelly will not make a quart, then straine it and put a little lemon juice and Cinamon and blade of Mace to it, boyle well together and put it in a China cup. When you use it turne it out and set it with Cream or white Wine or as you like.

XVIIth Century.

THE FEAST OF THE ASS

(Beauvais)

IN order that Our Lady might be represented fleeing into Egypt with the Child Jesus, there was chosen a most beautiful maiden, who, bearing in her arms an image of the Child, was placed upon an ass adorned gloriously for the occasion; and with great pomp she was led from the Cathedral to the parish church of St. Stephen, accompanied by clergy and people; and when this joyous procession arrived at St. Stephen's the maiden was led into the sanctuary and stationed, seated on the ass, at the Gospel side of the high altar. And then was begun a solemn Mass, of which the Introit, *Kyrie*, *Gloria*, and *Credo* each ended with a melodious *Hee-haw*: and what is more strange, there is a manuscript rubric for this festival which says: "At the end of Mass the priest, turning himself to the people, instead of intoning *Ite, missa est*, shall hee-haw thrice; and the people, instead of replying *Deo gratias*, shall respond thrice, "*Hee-haw, hee-haw, hee-haw*." This we record with pain, since such ceremonies were more suited to the theatre than to the service of Holy Church; but since it is not foreign to our plan, we may subjoin the Prose which was sung in the midst of Mass: a codex five hundred years old supplies us with this, from which may be judged the venerable antiquity of this festival.

THE PROSE OF THE ASS

Orientis partibus
Adventavit Asinus,
Pulcher et fortissimus,
Sarcinis aptissimus.

180

Hez, Sire Asnes, car chantez,
Belle bouche rechignez,
Vous aurez du foin assez,
Et de l'avoine à manger.

Lentus erat pedibus,
Nisi foret baculus,
Et eum in clunibus
Pungeret aculeus.
 Hez, Sire Asnes, etc.
Hic in collibus Sichem
Jam nutritus sub Ruben,
Transiit per Jordanem,
Saliit in Bethlehem.
 Hez, Sire Asnes, etc.
Ecce magnis auribus
Subjugalis filius
Asinus egregius
Asinorum dominus!
 Hez, Sire Asnes, etc.
Saltu vincit hinnulos,
Damas et capreolos
Super dromedarios
Velox Madianeos.
 Hez, Sire Asnes, etc.
Aurum de Arabia,
Thus et myrrham de Saba,
Tulit in Ecclesia
Virtus asinaria.
 Hez, Sire Asnes, etc.
Dum trahit vehicula
Multa cum sarcinula,
Illius mandibula
Dura terit pabula.
 Hez, Sire Asnes, etc.
Cum aristis hordeum
Comedit et carduum;
Triticum a palea
Segregat in area.
 Hez, Sire Asnes, etc.
Amen, dicas, Asine, *[Hic genuflectebatur.*
Jam satur de gramine;

Amen, amen itera,
Aspernare vetera.
> *Hez va! Hez va! Hez va! hez!*
> *Bialx Sire Asnes car allez!*
> *Belle bouche car chantez!*

Many times and often did the Bishops attempt to abolish this festival with canonical censures, but in vain, for it was too deeply rooted in tradition; nevertheless at last the authority of Parliament succeeded in suppressing it.

DU CANGE, *Glossarium*, 1678.

EHEU FUGACES!

DEAR old Friend and Absentee,—This is Christmas Day 1815 with us; what it may be with you I don't know, the 12th of June next year perhaps; and if it should be the consecrated season with you, I don't see how you can keep it. You have no turkeys; you would not desecrate the festival by offering up a withered Chinese Bantam, instead of the savoury grand Norfolcian Holocaust, that smokes all around my nostrils at this moment from a thousand firesides. Then what Puddings have you? Where will you get holly to stick in your churches, or churches to stick your dried Tea-Leaves (that must be the substitute) in? What memorials you can have of the holy time, I see not. A chopped missionary or two may keep up the thin idea of Lent and the wilderness; but what standing evidence have you of the Nativity? 'Tis our rosy-cheeked, homestalled divines, whose faces shine to the tune of "Unto us a child is born," faces fragrant with the mince-pies of half a century, that alone can authenticate the cheerful Mystery. I feel my bowels refreshed with the holy tide; my zeal is great against the unedified heathen. Down with the Pagodas—down with the idols—Ching-chong-fo—and his foolish priesthood! Come out of Babylon, O my Friend! for her time is

come; and the child that is native, and the Proselyte of her gates, shall kindle and smoke together! And in sober sense what makes you so long from among us, Manning? You must not expect to see the same England again which you have left.

Empires have been overturned, crowns trodden into dust, the face of the western World quite changed. Your friends have all got old—those you left blooming; myself (who am one of the few that remember you), those golden hairs which you recollect my taking a pride in, turned to silvery and grey. Mary has been dead and buried many years: she desired to be buried in the silk gown you sent her. Rickman, that you remember active and strong, now walks out supported by a servant maid and a stick. Martin Burney is a very old man. The other day an aged woman knocked at my door, and pretended to my acquaintance. It was long before I had the most distant cognition of her; but at last, together, we made her out to be Louisa, the daughter of Mrs. Topham, formerly Mrs. Kenney, whose first husband was Holcroft, the dramatic writer of the last century. St. Paul's church is a heap of ruins; the Monument isn't half so high as you knew it, divers parts being taken down which the ravages of Time had rendered dangerous; the horse at Charing Cross is gone, no one knows whither; and all this has taken place while you have been settling whether Ho-hing-tong should be spelt with a — or a —. For aught I see you might almost as well remain where you are, and not come like a Struldbug into a world where few were born when you went away. Scarce here and there one will be able to make out your face. All your opinions will be out of date, your jokes obsolete, your puns rejected with fastidiousness as wit of the last Age. . . .

You see what mutations the busy hand of Time has produced while you have consumed in foolish voluntary Exile that time which might have gladdened your Friends

—benefited your country; but reproaches are useless. Gather up the wretched reliques, my Friend, as fast as you can, and come to your old home. I will rub my eyes and try to recognise you. We will shake withered hands together, and talk of old things—of St. Mary's church and the barber's opposite, where the young students in Mathematics used to assemble. Poor Crips, that kept it afterwards, set up a fruiterer's shop in Trumpington Street, and for aught I know resides there still, for I saw the name up in the last journey I took there with my sister just before she died. I suppose you heard that I had left the India House, and gone into the Fishmongers' Almshouses over the bridge. I have a little cabin there, small and homely, but you shall be welcome to it. You like Oysters, and to open them yourself; I'll get you some if you come in oyster time. Marshall, Godwin's old friend, is still alive, and talks of the faces you used to make.

Come as soon as you can.

CHARLES LAMB to Thomas Manning.

CHRISTMAS LEAVE

℆ The Wheadles of the *Wapping-Hostess* to Gull the *Sea-Calves*.

WHILE we were busying our Brains with Thoughts relating to the Condition of a Seaman, in steps another of the *Tarpauling Fraternity*, with his Hat under his Arm, half full of Money, which he hug'd as close as a School-Boy does a *Bird's-Nest*. As soon as ever he came into the Entry, he sets up his Throat, like a *Country Bridegroom*, half drunk, so over-joy'd at his Prize, as if he was as little able to contain himself under the Blessing of so much Money, as a Bumpkin is under a Foresight of the Pleasures he expects to find in the Embraces of his

New Married *Hug - Booby. Ounds, Mother,* says our Marine *Cræssus, where are you?* She hearing his Tongue, thought, by his lively Expressing himself, he had brought good News; came running with all Speed to meet him, crying, *Here I am, Son* Bartholomew; *you're Welcome Ashore. I hope your Captain and Ships Crew are all well. By Fire and Gun-powder, I don't care if they be all Sick. Why, we are paid off in the* Downs, *and I am just come up in a Hoy. I hope I can have a Lodging with you, Mother? Ah, ah, Child! Do'st think I won't find a Lodging for one of my best Children?* In answer to which, he Innocently returns this Compliment, *Sure never any Sea-faring Son of a W——e had never such a good Mother upon Shore as I have. Ounds, Mother, let me have a Bucket full of Punch, that we may swim and Toss in an Ocean of good Liquor, like a couple of little Pinks in the Bay of* Biscay. *I always said* (said she) *thou wert my best Boy: Well, I'll go and prepare thee such a Bowl, that every Cup thou Drink'st on't shall make thee wish for a loving Sweet-Heart. Now, you talk of that, Mother, how does Sister* Betty? *She's very well* (says old *Suck-Pocket*); *poor Girl, she'll be at Home presently; I expect her every Minute. I believe she has ask'd for you above a Thousand times since you have been on Board. I dare swear She would be as glad to see you, as if you were her Husband.*

In this Interim, whilst she was mixing up a *Sea-Cordial* for her adopted *Sea-Calf, John* happens to return from his Enquiry after a Voyage. *Lack-a-day* John, says his Landlady with a seeming Sorrowful Countenance, *Here's the saddest Accident fallen out since you went Abroad, that has put me to such a puzzle, I know not how to order my Affairs, unless you will let me beg one Kindness of you. What a P——,* (says *John*) *I'll warrant you now 'tis to lie upon that Lousie Flock-bed that lies upon the Boards in the Garret. Why, truly,* John, *I must needs tell thee I have one of the best Friends I have in the World,*

just come on Shore; and if you don't Oblige me, I shall be put to a sad Non-plus. Here, John, says the old Wheedling Hypocrite, *here's to thee; come Drink, 'tis a cup of the best Brandy, I'll assure you; here,* John, *fill a long Pipe of Tobacco; well, son* John, *you say you'll let your Mother's Friend have your Room, Child, won't you? I don't care not I,* says the foolish Lubber, *he may ha't and he wool: I think I han't long to stay with you; I know now I have spent my Fifty Pound with you, you want to be rid of me.*

By this time the Bowl was just begun between *Mother* and *Son*; and who should step in, in the lucky Minute, but Sister *Betty*; and there was such a wonderful Mess of *Slip-Slop* lick'd up between *Brother Bat* and *Sister Bet*, that no two Friends, met by Accident in a Foreign *Plantation,* could have exprest more Joy in their Greeting: But as soon as the *White-Chapple Salutation* was over, Mrs. *Betty* I found began to exact some further Arguments of his Kindness, than just barely Kissing; and ask'd him, what, had he brought his Sister *Betty* no Present from *Sea* with him? *Yes, yes,* says he, *I have, sure, I can as soon forget the Points of the Compass, as forget my Sister* Betty, *as good a Girl as ever was Kist in a Cabbin. I told thee if ever I came Home again, I would present you with a Ring, and there's Money to buy it. How, now, Hussie,* crys the Mother, *how dare you put your Brother to this Charge, you forward Baggage you? Pray give it him again, you'd best, or I'll Ring you, marry will I, Minks.* The Daughter well acquainted with her Mothers Hypocrisie, replies, *I did not ask him for't, that I did not, I won't give it him, that I won't; as long as he gave it me, I will keep it, that I will, why shou'dn't I?*

By this time our Punch was Exhausted, and remembering we had heard of a famous Amphibious House of Entertainment, compounded of one half *Tavern* and t'other *Musick-House,* made us willing to Dedicate half an Hour to what Diversion we might there meet with.

Accordingly we left the old Subtile *Beldam*, and her Young Jilting *Fricatrix*, to empty the *Fools-Cap* of his Nine Months Earnings, and send his *Hat* and his *Pockets* to Sea again, as empty as his Noddle.

The London Spy, 1700.

MORE OF THE TURKEY

THE best way to roast a Turkey is to loosen the skin on the Breast of the Turkey, and fill it with Force-Meat, made thus: Take a Quarter of a Pound of Beef Sewet, as many Crumbs of Bread, a little Lemon peel, an Anchovy, some Nutmeg, Pepper, Parsley and a little Thyme. Chop and beat them all well together, mix them with the Yolk of an Egg, and stuff up the Breast; when you have no Sewet, Butter will do; or you may make your Force Meat thus: Spread Bread and Butter thin, and grate some Nutmeg over it; when you have enough roll it up, and stuff the Breast of the Turkey; then roast it of a fine Brown, but be sure to pin some white Paper [i.e. grease-proof] on the Breast till it is near enough. You must have a good gravy in the Dish, and Bread-Sauce, made thus: Take a good piece of Crumb, put it into a pint of Water, with a blade or two of Mace, two or three Cloves, and some Whole Pepper. Boil it up five or six times, then with a spoon take out the Spice you had before put in, and then you must pour off the Water (you may boil an Onion in it if you please) then beat up the Bread with a good Piece of Butter and a little Salt.

MRS. GLASSE, *The Art of Cookery made Plain and Easy*, 1755.

FOOTNOTE TO THE ABOVE

THE Turkey is surely one of the prettiest presents which the Old World has received from the New. Superlatively knowing persons maintain that the Romans

were addicted to the Turkey, that it was served at Charlemagne's wedding-feast, and that therefore it is false to praise the Jesuits for this most savoury of imports. Let us silence such dealers in paradox with a twofold refutation:

1°. The French name of the bird, which being *coq d'Inde* clearly betrays its origin: for at first America was always known as the Western Indies;

2°. The appearance of the bird, which is clearly outlandish.

A scholar could make no mistake about it. Nevertheless, convinced already as I was, I have been at some pains to investigate the subject, and here are my conclusions:

1°. That the Turkey appeared in Europe towards the end of the seventeenth century;

2°. That it was imported by the Jesuits, who bred it in large numbers, particularly on one of their farms in the neighbourhood of Bourges;

3°. That from there it gradually spread over the whole of France; and hence it was that in many dialects the word for Turkey became and still is *jésuite*;

4°. That America is the only place where the Turkey has been found wild and in a state of nature (there are none in Africa);

5°. That in North America, where it is very common, they rear it either from eggs found in the forest and hatched in captivity, or from young birds caught wild; so reared, it is nearer to its natural state, and retains its primitive plumage.

The case is proved to my complete satisfaction, and I here give thanks to the good Fathers for their enterprise in this matter as well as in another, namely the importation of quinine, which is called in English, Jesuit's-bark.

J. A. BRILLAT-SAVARIN (1755-1826).

LULLABY, Jesus Child, Pearl mine, be sleeping.
Lullaby, Most Belov'd, watch I am keeping.
Lullaby, Jesus Child.

Lullaby, Jesus Child, sleep, Babe, most sweetly,
And thou His Mother dear, comfort him meetly.
Lullaby, etc.

I'll give thee, Jesus mine, sweet berries growing—
Into Thy Mother's heart's garden I'm going.
Lullaby, etc.

Bread white and butter sweet I'll give thee lowly,
Laying them humbly in Thy cradle holy.
Lullaby, etc.

Hush, hush, the Babe doth rest—stilled is His weeping.
Like a small bird by His Mother He's sleeping.
Lullaby, etc.

Traditional, trans. H. E. Kennedy
and S. Uminska.

YOU have sent me at the Saturnalia, Umber, all the presents you have collected in five days; twelve three-leaved tablets and seven toothpicks, accompanied by a sponge, a napkin, a cup, half a peck of beans, a wicker crate of Picenian olives, and a black flagon of Laletanian must: and with these some small Syrian figs, dried prunes, and a jar heavy with the weight of Libyan figs. I scarcely think the whole lot worth thirty sesterces, yet eight hulking Syrians carried it. How much more conveniently, and with no labour, might a boy have brought five pounds of silver plate!

MARTIAL.

CHECK BY THE KING

WE, CHARLES, by the grace of God, etc.
It has been brought to our notice by Our beloved and loyal counsellor the Lord Bishop of Troyes, in a complaint made by him, that notwithstanding the decree [of the Council of Basle, 1436] by which servants and ministers of Holy Church are expressly debarred from celebrating certain derisive and scandalous ceremonies which they call the *Feast of Fools*, which it has been the custom to hold in several cathedrals and collegiate churches during the Feast of Christmas, in which ceremonies the aforesaid servants of Holy Church have been accustomed to commit irreverence and disloyalty towards Almighty God our Creator and His divine and holy service, to the great shame and scandal of the whole ecclesiastical state, making the churches like public places and performing even during the celebration of Holy Mass divers insolent and derisive mockeries and spectacles, disguising their bodies and wearing habits indecent and not pertaining to their state and profession, as the habits of fools, of men-at-arms, and of women, with the wearing of masks, etc., all of which abuses, and others customary at this season, have been forbidden on pain of penalties, nevertheless

in this present year at the said feast of Holy Innocents and the Circumcision these ceremonies have been carried out at Troyes with such excess of mockery, disguisings, farces, rhyming, and other follies as has not been known within the memory of man.

All these things having been made known to the Faculty of Theology of Our University of Paris, the Masters of the said Faculty, after ripe deliberation, have composed a certain notable letter to be despatched to all the prelates and chapters of Our Realm, detesting and condemning the said damnable Feast of Fools as superstitious and heathen, and declaring its introduction to be the work of pagans and unbelieving idolaters, as Monsieur Saint *Augustine* expressly sheweth. But since certain persons are determined to carry out and continue the celebration of the said feast, declaring in their foolish obstinacy and presumption that whatever Our Counsellors may decide, and notwithstanding the aforesaid conclusions and theological verities, they will still continue, Our said Counsellor the Bishop of Troyes humbly prays Us to grant him by Our offices aid and support, as he may have need.

For which purpose We, considering, etc., etc., do grant, etc., etc.,

Letter of Charles VII., April 1445.

CHRISTMAS WITH THE FORCE—1927

THE members of the "Silver Slipper" Club continued their revels into Christmas morning. . . . No regard to season is paid in police procedure. Christmas morning in the police is the same as any other morning. Therefore arrangements were made for inspecting the "Silver Slipper" on Christmas morning. The police were satisfied to take the names and addresses of those present together with bottled samples.

A London Newspaper, Dec. 27.

THE DISCOURSE OF THE DRINKERS

THEN did they fall upon the chat of Victuals and some belly-furniture to be snatched at in the very same Place, which purpose was no sooner mentioned, but forthwith began Flaggons to go, Gammons to trot, Goblets to fly, great Bowles to ting, glasses to ring, draw, reach, fill, mixe, give it me without water, so my Friend, so whip me off this Glasse neatly, bring me hither some Claret, a full weeping Glasse till it run over, a cessation and truce with Thirst. Ha, thou false Fever, wilt thou not be gone? by my figgins, Godmother, I cannot as yet enter in the humour of being Merry, nor drink so currantly as I would. You have catch'd a cold, gamer, yea forsooth, Sir; by the belly of Sanct Buf, let us talk of our Drink, I never drink but at my hours, like the Pope's Mule, and I never drink but in my breviary, like a faire father Gardien. Which was first, thirst or drinking? Thirst, for who in the time of Innocence would have drunk without being athirst? nay, Sir, it was drinking; for *privatio præsupponit habitum.* I am learned, you see: *Fecundi calices quem non fecere disertum?* we poor Innocents drink but too much without thirst: not I truly, who am a sinner, for I never drink without Thirst, either present or future, to prevent it, as you know, I drink for the thirst to come; I drink eternally, this is to me an Eternity of drinking, and drinking of eternity; let us sing, let us drink, and tune up our Round-lays; where is my funnel? What, it seems I do not drink but by an Attourney? do you wet yourselves to dry, or do you dry to wet you? pish, I understand not the rhethorick (Theorick,

I should say) but I help my self somewhat by the Practice. Baste, enough, I sup, I wet, I humect, I moisten my Gullet, I drink, and all for fear of dying; drink alwayes and you shall never die; if I drink not, I am a ground dry, gravelled and spent, I am stark dead without drink, and my Soul ready to flie into some marish among Frogs; the soul never dwells in a dry place, Drouth kills it. O you butlers, creators of new formes, make me of no drinker a Drinker, a perennity and Everlastingnesse of sprinkling, and bedewing me through these my parched and sinewy Bowels; he drinks in vaine, that feels not the Pleasure of it. I would willingly wash the Tripes of the calf, which I apparrelled this morning. I have pretty well now balasted my Stomack and stuft my Paunch.

•   •   •   •   •

I have a remedy against Thirst, quite contrary to that which is good against the Biting of a mad dog. Keep running after a Dog, and he will never bite you, drink alwayes before the Thirst, and it will never come upon you. There I catch you, I awake you. *Argus* had a hundred eyes for his Sight, a butler should have (like *Briareus*) a hundred Hands wherewith to fill us Wine indefatigably. Hey now lads, let us moisten our selves, it will be time to dry hereafter. White wine here, wine boyes, poure out all in the name of *Lucifer*, fill here you, fill and fill (pescods on you all) till it be full. My tongue peels. Lanstrinque, to thee, Countreyman, I drink to thee good Fellow, camarade to thee, lustie, lively, Ha, la, la, that was drunk to some Purpose, and bravely gulped over. *O lachryma Christi*, it is of the best Grape; i' faith, pure Greek, Greek, O the fine white Wine, upon my conscience it is a kinde of taffatas wine, hin, hin, it is of one eare, well wrought, and of good Wooll; courage, camarade, up thy heart, billy we will not be beasted at this Bout, for I have got one Trick, *ex hoç in hoc*, there is no

Inchantment, nor charme there, every one of you hath
seene it, my Prentiship is out, I am a free man at this
Trade. I am prester mast, (Prish)—Brum I should say
master past. O the Drinkers, those that are a dry, O
poore thirsty Souls, good Page my friend, fill me here
some and crowne the Wine, I pray thee, like a Cardinal,
Natura abhorret vacuum. Would you say that a flie could
drink in this, this is after the Fashion of *Swisserland,*
clear off, neat, supernaculum, come, therefore Blades
to this divine Liquor, and celestial juyce, swill it over
Heartily, and spare not, it is a decoction of Nectar and
Ambrosia.

FRANÇOIS RABELAIS (? 1483–? 1553);
tr. Urquhart.

A HIGH COMPANY

THE next day we departed and rode to dinner to
Montgarbel and so on to Arthez, and there we drank,
and by sun-setting came to Orthez. The knight alighted
at his own lodging and I alighted at the sign of the
Moon, where dwelt a squire of the Earl's, Ernaulton du
Puy, who well received me, because I was of France. Sir
Espang de Lyon went to the castle to the earl and
found him in his gallery, for he had but dined a little
before; for the earl's usage was always that it was high
noon or he arose out of his bed, and supped ever at
midnight. When the earl saw me he made me good cheer
and retained me as of his house, where I was more than
twelve weeks, and my horse, well entreated. The acquaintance of him and of me was because I had brought with
me a book, which I made at the contemplation of Wenceslas of Boeme, duke of Luxembourg and of Brabant,
which book was called the *Meliador,* containing all the
songs, ballades, rondeaux, and virelays, which the gentle
duke had made in his time.

Of the estate and order of the earl of Foix cannot be too much spoken or praised; for the season that I was at Orthez I found him such and much more than I can speak of; but while I was there, I saw and heard many things that turned me to great pleasure. I saw on Christmas Day sitting at his board four bishops of his country, two Clementines and two Urbanists; the bishop of Pamiers and the bishop of Lescar, Clementines, they sat highest, then the bishop of Aire and the bishop of Roy, on the frontiers of Bourdelois and Bayonne, Urbanists; then sat the earl of Foix, and then the viscount of Roquebertin of Gascoyne and the viscount of Bruniquel, the viscount of Gousserant and a knight of England of the duke of Lancaster's, who as then lay at Lisbon: the duke had sent him thither, the knight was called Sir William Willoughby. And at another table sat five abbots and two knights of Aragon called sir Ramón de Montflorentin and sir Martin de Roanès. And at another table sat knights and squires of Gascoyne and of Bigorre, and at other tables knights of Béarn a great number; and the chief stewards of the hall were sir Espang of Lyon, sir Chiquart de Bois-Verdun, sir Monaut de Navailles and sir Peter of Baulx of Béarn, and the Earl's two bastard brethren served at the table sir Ernaulton Guillaume and sir Peter of Béarn, and the Earl's two sons sir Yvain of l'Echelle was sewer and sir Gracien bare his cup.

There were many minstrels as well of his own as of strangers, and each of them did their devoir in their faculties. The same day the earl of Foix gave to the heralds and minstrels the sum of five hundred franks, and to the duke of Touraine's minstrels gowns of cloth of gold furred with ermines, valued at two hundred franks. This dinner endured four hours.

Sir John Froissart of Chimay.

INCIDENT IN SAXONY

THEY will be singing amorous Songs and Ditties (if yong especially), and cannot abstain though it be when they go to, or should be at Church. We have a pretty Story to this purpose in *Westmonasteriensis*, an old Writer of ours (if you will believe it). An. Dom. 1012, at *Colewiz* in *Saxony*, on *Christmass*-eve a company of yong Men and Maids, whilst the Priest was at Mass in the Church, were singing Catches and love songs in the Church-yard, he sent to them to make less noise, but they sung on still, and if you will, you shall have the very Song it self.

> Equitabat homo per sylvam frondosam,
> Ducebatque secum Meswinden formosam,
> Quid stamus, cur non imus?

> A fellow rid by the green-wood side,
> And fair Meswinde was his bride,
> Why stand we so, and do not go?

This they sung, he chaft, till at length, impatient as he was, he prayed to S. *Magnus*, patron of the Church, they might all there sing and dance 'till that time Twelve-month, and so they did, without Meat and Drink, wearisomness or giving over, till at Year's end they ceased singing, and were absolved by *Herebertus* Archbishop of *Colen*.

ROBERT BURTON (1577-1640).

FOND REPETITIONS

EXTRACT from an ordinance of Epiphany 1198 by Eudes de Sully, Bishop of Paris, concerning the too-frequent loud repetition of the seventh verse of the Magnificat, *Deposuit potentes de sede*—"He hath put down the mighty from their seat"—at the relinquishing of office by the Bishop of Fools:

"*We likewise command and ordain that the Master of Revels shall be conveyed with procession or singing neither*

196

to church, nor from church to his abode. . . . The Deposuit
*also shall be sung, in its appointed place, no more than
five times."*

AND SO TO BED

To the *Spectator*.

I HOPE you will oblige the World with some Reflections
upon Yawning, as I have seen it practised on a Twelfth
night among other *Christmas* Gambols at the House of
a very worthy Gentleman, who always entertains his
Tenants at this time of the Year. They yawn for a
Cheshire-Cheese, and begin about Midnight, when the
whole Company is disposed to be drowsy. He that
yawns widest, and at the same Time so naturally as to
produce the most Yawns among the Spectators, carries
home the Cheese. If you handle this Subject as you ought,
I question not but your Paper will set half the Kingdom
a yawning, though I dare promise you it will never make
any Body fall asleep.

RICHARD STEELE.

NEW YEAR DINNER

℃. Served on January 1, 1707, to thirteen guests of
Squire Timothy Burrell of Cuckfield, Sussex.

Plumm Pottage.	Plumm Pottage.
Calve's Head and Bacon.	Boil'd Beef, a clod.
Goose.	Two bak'd Puddings.
Pig.	Three Dishes of Minced Pyes.
Plumm Pottage.	Two Capons.
Roast Beef, sirloin.	Two Dishes of Tarts.
Veale, a sirloin.	Two Pullets.
Goose.	

To make Plumm Pottage:

Take of Beef-soup made of Legs of Beef, 12 Quarts;

if you wish it to be particularly good, add a couple of Tongues to be boil'd therein. Put fine Bread, slic'd, soak'd, and crumbled; Raisins of the Sun, Currants and Pruants two Lbs. of each; Lemons, Nutmegs, Mace and Cloaves are to be boil'd with it in a muslin Bag; add a Quart of Red Wine and let this be follow'd, after half an Hour's boyling, by a Pint of Sack. Put it into a cool Place and it will keep through Christmas.

Sussex Archæological Society's
Transactions.

MY LORD'S EXPENSES

ITEM, for two cloths of scarlet for the Earl against Christ-mass, one cloth of russet for the Bishop of Angew, seventy cloths of blue for the knights, fifteen cloths of medley for the lords' clerks, twenty-eight cloths for the esquires, fifteen cloths for officers, nineteen cloths for grooms, five cloths for archers, four cloths for minstrels and carpenters, with the sharing and carriage for the Earl's liveries at Christ-mass, £460 15s.

Item, for seven furs of variable miniver [powdered ermine], seven hoods of purple, three hundred and ninety-five furs of budge for the liveries of barons, knights, and clerks, one hundred and twenty-three furs of lamb for esquires, bought for Christ-mass, £147 17s. 8d.

Item, twenty-four silver dishes, so many saucers and so many cups for the buttery, one pair of pater-nosters, and one silver coffin [piedish], £103 5s. 6d.

Item, for one thousand seven hundred and fourteen pounds of waxe, with vermelion and turpentine to make red waxe, £314 7s. 4¼d.

Item, for two thousand three hundred and nineteen pounds of tallow candles for the household, and one thousand eight hundred and seventy of lights for Paris candles, called perchers, £31 14s. 3d.

In wine, wax, spices, cloths, furs, and other things for the Countess' wardrobe, £154 7s. 4½d.

> *From an Account of Expenses in the house of Thomas, Earl of Lancaster, Michaelmas 1314–Michaelmas 1315.*

AN AVENGING ANGEL

CHARLES CLAPP, Benjamin Jackson, Denis Jelks, and Robert Prinset, were brought to Bow Street Office by O. Bond, the constable, charged with performing on several musical instruments in St. Martin's Lane, at half-past twelve o'clock on Christmas morning, by Mr. Munroe, the authorised principal Wait, appointed by the Court of Burgesses for the City and Liberty of Westminster, who alone considers himself entitled, by his appointment, to apply for Christmas Boxes. He also urged that the prisoners, acting as minstrels, came under the meaning of the Vagrant Act, alluded to in 17th Geo. II.; however, on reference to the last Vagrant Act of the present King, the word "minstrels" is omitted; consequently they are no longer cognizable under that Act of Parliament; and in addition to that, Mr. Charles Clapp, one of the prisoners, produced his indenture of having served seven years as an apprentice to the profession of a musician to Mr. Clay, who held the same appointment as Mr. Munroe does under the Court of Burgesses. The prisoners were discharged, after receiving an admonition from Mr. Hall, the sitting magistrate, not to collect Christmas Boxes.

> *The Gentleman's Magazine,* 1822.

THE MELLSTOCK ROUNDS

BY this time they were crossing to a wicket in the direction of the school, which, standing on a slight eminence on the opposite side of a cross lane, now rose

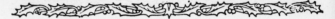

in unvarying and dark flatness against the sky. The instruments were re-tuned, and all the band entered the enclosure, enjoined by old William to keep upon the grass.

"Number seventy-eight," he softly gave out as they formed round in a semicircle, the boys opening the lanterns to get a clearer light, and directing their rays on the books. Then passed forth into the quiet night an ancient and well-worn hymn, embodying Christianity in words peculiarly befitting the simple and honest hearts of the quaint characters who sang them so earnestly.

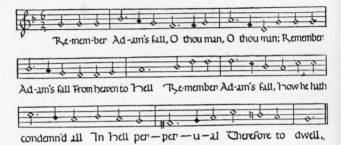

Remember Adam's fall,
O thou man;
Remember Adam's fall
From Heaven to Hell.
Remember Adam's fall;
How he hath condemn'd all
In Hell perpetual
Therefore to dwell.

Remember God's goodness,
O thou man:
Remember God's goodness,
His promise made.
Remember God's goodness;
He sent His Son sinless
Our ails for to redress,
Our hearts to aid.

In Bethlehem He was born,
O thou man:
In Bethlehem He was born,
For mankind's sake.
In Bethlehem He was born,
Christmas Day i' the morn:
Our Saviour did not scorn
Our faults to take.

Give thanks to God alway,
O thou man:
Give thanks to God alway
With heart-felt joy.
Give thanks to God alway
On this our joyful day:
Let all men sing and say,
Holy, Holy!

Having concluded the last note, they listened for a
minute or two, but found that no sound issued from the
school-house.

"Forty breaths, and then 'O, what unbounded goodness!' number fifty-nine," said William.

This was duly gone through, and no notice whatever
seemed to be taken of the performance.

"Surely 'tisn't an empty house, as befell us in the
year thirty-nine and forty-three!" said old Dewy with
much disappointment.

"Perhaps she's jist come from some noble city, and
sneers at our doings," the tranter whispered.

"'Od rabbit her!" said Mr. Penny, with an annihilating
look at a corner of the school chimney. "I don't quite
stomach her, if this is it. Your plain music well done
is as worthy as your other sort done bad, 'a b'lieve,
souls; so say I."

"Forty breaths, and then the last," said the leader
authoritatively. " 'Rejoice, ye tenants of the earth,'
number sixty-four."

At the close, waiting yet another minute, he said in

a clear loud voice, as he had said in the village at that
hour and season for the previous forty years:

"A merry Christmas to ye!"

THOMAS HARDY.

THE HAPPY HOWL

IT is characteristic of Dickens that his atmospheres are
more important than his stories. As with his backgrounds of gloom, so with his backgrounds of good will,
in such tales as *A Christmas Carol*. The incidents change
wildly; the story scarcely changes at all. *A Christmas
Carol* is a kind of philanthropic dream, an enjoyable
nightmare, in which the scenes shift bewilderingly and
seem as miscellaneous as the pictures in a scrap-book,
but in which there is one constant state of the soul, a
state of rowdy benediction and a hunger for human
faces. The beginning is about a winter day and a miser;
yet the beginning is in no way bleak. The author starts
with a kind of happy howl; he bangs on our door like
a drunken carol singer; his style is festive and popular;
he compares the snow and hail to philanthropists who
"come down handsomely"; he compares the fog to
unlimited beer. Scrooge is not really inhuman at the
beginning any more than he is at the end. There is a
heartiness in his inhospitable sentiments that is akin to
humour and therefore to humanity; he is only a crusty
old bachelor, and had (I strongly suspect) given away
turkeys secretly all his life. The beauty and the real
blessing of the story do not lie in the mechanical plot
of it, the repentance of Scrooge, probable or improb-
able; they lie in the great furnace of real happiness that
glows through Scrooge and everything around him;
that great furnace, the heart of Dickens. Whether the
Christmas visions would or would not convert Scrooge,
they convert us. Whether or no the visions were evoked

by real Spirits of the Past, Present, and Future, they were evoked by that truly exalted order of angels who are correctly called High Spirits. They are impelled and sustained by a quality which our contemporary artists ignore or almost deny, but which in a life decently lived is as normal and attainable as sleep, positive, passionate, conscious joy. The story sings from end to end like a happy man going home, and, like a happy and good man, when it cannot sing it yells. It is lyric and exclamatory, from the first exclamatory words of it. It is strictly a Christmas carol.

G. K. Chesterton.

A LOVABLE FISH

A D. 1392.—King Richard with Queene Anne his wife, foure bishops, as many Earles, the Duke of Yorke, many Lords, and fifteene Ladies held a royall Christmas at Langley neere to St. Albans. The same Christmas Day a Dolphin came foorth of the Sea and played himselfe in ye Thames at London to the bridge, foreshewing happily the tempests that were to follow within a week after, the which Dolphin being seene of the Citizens, and followed, was with much difficulty intercepted, and brought againe to London, shewing a spectacle to many, of the height of his body, for hee was ten foote in length. These Dolphins are fishes of the Sea that follow the voices of men, and rejoice in the playing of instruments & are wont to gather themselves at musicke. These when they play in rivers, with hasty

springings or leapings doe signifie Tempest to follow.
The Seas containe nothing more swift nor nimble, for
sometimes with their skips, they mount over the sailes
of ships.

Annales of JOHN STOW.

TO A COUNTRY AIR

Quand Ga-bri-el prit la vo-lé—e Sur les plaines de Ga-li-
lé—e Pour di-re que Dieu é-tait né L'air bruyait tel-le mé-lo-di—e Que
ja-mais pareille harmo-ni—e Sur fla-geo-let ne fut son-née.

QUAND Gabriel prit la volée
Sur les plaines de Galilée
Pour dire que Dieu était né,
L'air bruyait telle mélodie
Que jamais pareille harmonie
Sur flageolet ne fut sonnée.

Mille et mille légions d'Anges
Nous sonnaient dix mille mélanges,
Jamais je n'ouïs chants si beaux;
Mon cœur était rempli de joie
Si fort, que plus je ne songeais
A mener paître mes troupeaux.

De joie je pris donc ma musette,
Pensant dire une chansonette
Mais j'y étais tout nouvelet;

204

Je faisais un pauvre mélange
Avecque la chanson de l'Ange
Comme un petit rossignolet.

En décrivant mille gambades
Je n'en vins donner des aubades
Au logis de mes compagnons;
Sus! l'œil au guet! qu'on se réveille!
Il n'est plus temps que l'on sommeille:
Dormez-vous encore, garçons?

Venez donc tous, je vous appelle
Pour vous raconter la nouvelle,
La meilleure qu'on puisse ouïr;
C'est que le désiré Messie
Vient de naître en Béthanie:
Venez tous vous en réjouir.

                              XVIIth Century.

THE END OF THE ROAD

ELBING (West Prussia), January 1, 1813.—Telling
my two soldiers to wait till roll-call to be re-entered
in the company and receive a billet, I returned to my own
lodging. On the way I bought a large sugar-cake, which I
presented to my hostess, with the ring, begging her to
keep it as a souvenir from Moscow. She asked me how
I had bought it. I told her I had paid for it very dearly,
and that not for a million would I go on a similar search
for another.

At eleven o'clock I returned to the square in front of
the Palace. There were already a good many men there;
in three days our numbers were almost doubled. One
would have said all those one believed dead had come
to life again to wish each other a happy New Year. But

it was a melancholy sight, for a great number were without nose or fingers or toes; some had suffered all three misfortunes combined. The rumour that the Russians were advancing was confirmed. The order was given that we should hold ourselves in readiness, as if on the eve of a battle, and sleep with one eye open, in case of a surprise; to keep our arms primed and ready, to supply ourselves with new cartridges, and to attend the roll-call with all our weapons and accoutrements.

I was a little in front of my two comrades. A few steps before me I saw a man I fancied I recognised, who had stopped. I went up and found I was not mistaken; it was the oldest man in the regiment, who had sword, musket, and cross of honour, and who had disappeared since December 24th—Père Elliot, who had been through the Egyptian campaign. He was in a pitiable condition: both his feet were frozen and wrapped in bits of sheep-skin; his ears, also frozen, were covered with the same; his beard and moustache were bristling with icicles. I looked at him, so surprised I was unable to speak.

At last I said, "Well, Père Elliot, and here you are! And where the devil have you come from? And how you are dressed! You seem to be in terrible suffering."

"Ah, my good friend," said he, "I have been a soldier now for twenty years, and I have never wept; but I am shedding tears today more from rage than misfortune, for I shall be taken by these brutes of Cossacks without being able to strike a blow. For nearly four weeks I have been going about alone, ever since the passage of the Niemen, all across the snow in a savage country, and unable to get any news about the army. I had two companions; one died a week ago, and the second is very likely dead, too. Four days ago I had to leave them in the house of some poor Poles, where we had been sleeping. I have travelled more than four hundred leagues in the snow since leaving Moscow, unable to rest, my feet and my hands frozen, and even my nose."

I saw great tears flowing from the old soldier's eyes. Picart and Grangier just then joined me. Grangier recognised Père Elliot instantly; they belonged to the same company; but Picart, although he had known him for seventeen years, since the Italian campaigns, could not remember him. We entered the nearest house and were made very welcome: it belonged to an old sailor, and these people are generally kind. Picart made his old comrade in arms take a seat by the fire; then, drawing one of the two bottles of wine from the pocket of his overcoat, he filled a big bumper.

"Come, my old comrade of the 23rd Brigade, swallow this! Good! And now this! Very good! And now a morsel of bread, and you will feel better."

Since leaving Moscow he had not tasted wine, nor eaten such good bread, and he seemed to forget his miseries at once. The sailor's wife bathed his face with a linen cloth soaked in warm water; this melted the icicles on his beard and moustache.

"And now," said Picart, "we'll have a little chat. Do you remember when we embarked at Toulon on our way to Egypt . . ."

Grangier, meanwhile, had been out to see if the march had begun again, and now came in to tell us that a conveyance laden with heavy baggage belonging to Murat had stopped before the door. A fine chance for Père Elliot. He must get into it at once.

"Forward!" cried Picart; and with the help of the sailor we soon had the old sergeant perched on the vehicle. Picart put the other bottle of wine between his knees, and the white mantle over his back to keep him from the cold. Shortly afterwards we began to march, and half an hour later we were outside Elbing.

The same day we crossed the Vistula on the ice and

marched on, without any accident, till four o'clock,
when we halted at a large town where Marshal Mortier,
who was in command, decided we should spend the night.

Memoirs of Sergeant Bourgogne, 1812–1813.

ET VERBUM CARO FACTUM EST

i.

O MOODER mayde! O Maydë mooder fre!
O bussh unbrent, brennynge in Moyses sighte!
That ravysedest doun fro the Deitee,
Thurgh thyn humblesse, the Ghoost that in thalighte;
Of whos vertu, whan He thyn hertë lighte,
Conceyvëd was the Fadrës sapience,
Helpe me to telle it in thy reverence!

Prologe, the Prioresses Tale.

ii.

Withinne the cloistre blisful of thy sydis
Took mannës shape the Eterneel Love and Pees,
That of the trynë compas Lord and gyde is,
Whom erthe, and see, and hevens, out of relees,
Ay heryen; and thou Virgine wemmëlees
Bare of thy body, and dweltest mayden pure,
The Creatour of every creature.

Prologe, the Seconde Nonnes Tale.
GEOFFREY CHAUCER.

NEWS FROM COURT

The St. James's Evening Post.

MONDAY being Twelfth Day, his Majesty, according to annual custom, offered myrrh, frankincense,
and a small bit of gold; and at night, in commemoration
of the *three kings* or *wise men*, the King and Royal Family
played at hazard, for the benefit of a prince of the Blood.
There were above eleven thousand Pounds upon the

table: his most Sacred Majesty won three Guineas, and his R.H. the Duke three thousand four hundred Pounds.

There is lately arrived at the Lord Carpenter's a male Chimparozee, which has had the honour of being shown before the ugliest Princes in Europe, who all expressed their approbation; and we hear that he intends to offer himself a Candidate to represent the City of Westminster at the next general Election. Note: he wears breeches, and there is a gentlewoman to attend the Ladies.

The Hon. and Rev. Mr. James Brudenel was admitted a Doctor of Opium in the ancient University of White's, being received *ad eundem* by his Grace the Rev. Father in Chess, the Duke of Devonshire, president, and the rest of the senior Fellows.

The operation of shaving was happily performed on the upper lip of her Grace the Duchess of N—— by a celebrated Artist from Paris, sent over on purpose by the Duke of Albemarle. The performance lasted but one minute and three seconds, to the great joy of that noble Family.

At the Theatre Royal in the House of Lords, the Royal Slave, with Lethe.

At the theatre in St. Stephen's chapel, the Fool in Fashion.

The Jews are desired to meet on the 20th inst. at the sign of the Fort L'Evêque in Pharaoh-street, to commemorate the noble struggle made by one of their brethren in support of his Property.

Deserted—miss Ashe.

Lost—an Opposition.

To be let—an Embassador's masquerade, the Gentleman going abroad.

To be sold—the whole Nation.

Given gratis at the *Turn-stile*, the corner of Lincoln's-inn-fields, anodyne Stars and Garters.

HORACE WALPOLE to George Montagu.

"AH my dear, ah my dear son,"
   Said Mary, "ah my dear,
Kiss thy mother, Jesu,
   With a laughing cheer."

This enders night
I saw a sight
   All in my sleep;
Mary, that may,
She sang *Lullay*
And sore did weep.

To keep she sought
Full fast about
   Her son fro cold.
Joseph said "Wife,
My joy, my life,
   Say what ye wold."

"No thing, my spouse,
Is in this house
   Unto my pay;
My son, a king
That made alle thing,
   Lieth in hay."

"My mother dear,
Amend your cheer,
   And now be still;
Thus for to lie
It is soothly
   My Father's will.

"Derision,
Great passion,
   Infinitely,

210

THE NATIVITY : *Geertgen*

As it is found,
Many a wound
  Suffer shall I.

"On Calvary
That is so high
  There shall I be,
Man to restore,
Nailed full sore
  Upon a tree."
                    B.M. Addl. MS., XVth Century.

IN OLD QUEBEC

1645, December 25. The first bell was rung at eleven o'clock, the second a little before the half-hour, and immediately after we began to sing two carols, *Venez, mon Dieu*, and *Chantons Noé*, Monsieur de la Ferté playing the bass viol, Saint-Martin [Martin Boutet, sieur de Saint-Martin, professor of mathematics and clerk of the parish church of Quebec] the violin. We also had a German flute, but when it got to church we found it could not be played in tune.

We finished carols a little before midnight, and proceeded without delay to the *Te Deum*; and a little after this was done we fired off a cannon for the midnight signal, and Mass began.

                    Journal of JÉRÔME LALEMANT, S.J.

ON CHRISTMAS CARDS

I DO not receive many Christmas cards. This is not surprising, as I never remember to send any out. The most I have ever done, when feeling most strenuous, was to scramble out a few New Year's cards to people who

had sent me Christmas cards, and whose remembrance of me stirred my gratitude. But I do always get some, and I got a few this year.

I have just been looking at them all before cremating them. Those which come from the more intellectual of my friends have no longer anything peculiarly Christmas-cardy about them. They are in good taste, designed by or for the senders, admirably printed, and in point of language ready for the scrutiny of the most fastidious critic of style. Nothing could be more refined. There are no sprigs of holly on these, no claspings of amputated hands, no squat village towers amid snowy landscapes. They have brown collotype pictures of the owners' houses, choice etchings after Rembrandt, or exquisite coloured reproductions of St. Vincent and a Donor by Melozzo da Forli in the Palazzo Doria Pamphili at Rome. Each card of them is a silent protest against the old kind of card. As I look at them I hear them saying, "What an improvement we are! How clearly we demonstrate that Christmas greetings can be conveyed without vulgarity! What careful consideration we betray! The men and women who chose *us* really wished to send their friends something worth having." There is a beautiful woodcut on yellowish hand-made paper, with "A Happy Christmas" as the only inscription. There is a page from an illuminated manuscript. There is a card specially written out by an expert calligrapher. There is another displaying specimens of seventeenth-century typographical ornament. All very chaste, and not one of them (I need scarcely say) bearing a line of verse, even of good verse.

Yet from the more old-fashioned and less aspiring remnant of my acquaintance there still come a few tokens of the old Victorian sorts, freely powdered with Robin Redbreasts and mistletoe, and carrying quatrains to a card. It was one of these quatrains that checked me in

the middle of my campaign of destruction and made me begin these reflections. It runs as follows:

> Glad Christmas to you on this day,
> Good Fortune ever find you,
> Life's Sunlight be before you aye,
> Its shadows all behind you.

Well, you will say, there is nothing very odd about that; it is precisely like thousands of others. Wait a moment. The odd thing is that under those verses is printed the name "Browning."

I stand open to correction. I have, I admit, not searched Robert Browning's works for this sequence of elegant sentiments. But I really cannot suppose that he wrote it. Nor can I believe that his wife wrote it. Nor can I even believe that Mr. Oscar Browning wrote it, and with him is exhausted the catalogue of Brownings known to Fame or me. There have been, no doubt, other Brownings. John Browning or Nicodemus Browning may have been the author of this composition; or George Bernard Browning, or J. Pierpont Browning, or some inglorious but not altogether mute Ella Wheeler Browning. But if Robert Browning was really the author he must certainly have had a bad off-day, on which his style was indistinguishable from that of any other Christmas card poet. And the common style of the Christmas card poets reaches the lowest known or conceivable level of banality in conception and tameness in execution.

I look through some of the other missives which have been sent to me in the hope (I must presume) of cheering me up, of inducing merriment and an optimistic outlook. Here are some of the verses on them—if I am committing breaches of copyright I must apologise:

(1)

> To you and those within your home
> This Christmas Day may blessings come,
> And may good luck, good health, good cheer
> Be guests of yours for all the year.

As on Life's tide the seasons come and go
May sorrow ebb and gladness ever flow.

(3)

Milestones of olden memories
    Along sweet friendship's way;
Oh! how they brighten up the past,
    And cheer the coming day.

(4)

Greeting just to say we all unite,
In wishing you and yours a Christmas bright.

(5)

Deck out the walls with garlands gay,
And let the kindly laughter play.
List! the chimes are sweetly sounding,
Xmas happiness abounding;
All that's good and true be thine
At this merry festive time.

(6)

This is the time for sweet remembrance,
    For thoughts of friends both old and new;
The words will not express the wishes
    Sent within this card for you.

If Browning wrote one of them why not the lot? There is, I admit, a touch of *Mrs.* Browning about the rhyme of "time" and "thine" in Number Five, and the elaborate maritime image in Number Two has perhaps a touch of Swinburne. But except for these very slight local differences the whole of these, not to mention thousands of others, all that you have ever seen and all that your Aunt Maria has ever seen, might have come from one pen. It is amazing that every publisher of Christmas cards should have "on tap" a bard so skilful that he can turn out hundreds of these poems without ever introducing a touch of individuality or novelty. For somebody must write them, even if it be only the chairman of the

manufacturing company or the compositor who does the type-setting. Who are these mysterious people? Are they scattered amateurs everywhere? Or is it here that we find the explanation of how our professional and justly celebrated poets earn their living? Or is this one of those industries which are the hereditary monopoly of a few families, like flint-knapping, violin-making, and gold-beating? Does Mr. Jones of Putney, whose neighbours know him for one who "goes up to the City" every morning on some vague but presumably respectable business, really immure himself for eight hours per diem in an office in Chancery Lane and compose those verses which he never mentions at home, his father having left him a very valuable connection with the makers? Or—this is another solution—is it really that nobody has written any new ones for years?

J. C. SQUIRE.

NIGHT-PIECE

WHEN it was midnight, I walked out, and strolled in the woods. . . . I was suddenly roused from a delicious reverie, by observing a dark object moving slowly and cautiously among the trees. At first, I fancied it was a bear, but a nearer inspection discovered an Indian on all fours. For a moment I felt unwilling to throw myself in his way, lest he should be meditating some sinister design against me; however, on his waving his hand, and putting his finger on his lips, I approached him, and notwithstanding his injunction to silence, inquired what he did there. 'Me watch to see the deer kneel,' replied he; 'This is Christmas night, and all the deer fall upon their knees to the Great Spirit, and look up.' The solemnity of the scene, and the grandeur of the idea, alike contributed to fill me with awe.

JOHN HOWISON, Sketches of Upper
Canada (1821).

A REMAINING CHRISTMAS

THE world is changing very fast, and neither exactly for the better or the worse, but for division. Our civilisation is splitting more and more into two camps, and what was common to the whole of it is becoming restricted to the Christian, and soon will be restricted to the Catholic half.

That is why I have called this article "A Remaining Christmas." People ask themselves how much remains of this observance and of the feast and its customs. Now a concrete instance is more vivid and, in its own way, of more value than a general appreciation. So I will set down here exactly what Christmas still is in a certain house in England, how it is observed, and all the domestic rites accompanying it in their detail and warmth.

This house stands low down upon clay near a little river. It is quite cut off from the towns; no one has built near it. Every cottage for a mile and more is old, with here and there a modern addition. The church of the parish (which was lost of course three and a half centuries ago, under Elizabeth) is as old as the Crusades. It is of the twelfth century. The house of which I speak is in its oldest parts of the fourteenth century at least, and perhaps earlier, but there are modern additions. One wing of it was built seventy years ago at the south end of the house, another at the north end, twenty years ago. Yet the tradition is so strong that you would not tell from the outside, and hardly from the inside, which part is old and which part is new. For, indeed, the old part itself grew up gradually, and the eleven gables of the house show up against the sky as though they were of one age, though in truth they are of every age down along all these five hundred years and more.

The central upper room of the house is the chapel where Mass is said, and there one sees, uncovered by any wall of plaster or brick, the original structure of the house which is of vast oaken beams, the main supports and transverse pieces half a yard across, mortised strongly into each other centuries ago, and smoothed roughly with the adze. They are black with the years. The roof soars up like a high-pitched tent, and is supported by a whole fan of lesser curved oaken beams. There is but one window behind the altar. Indeed, the whole house is thus in its structure of the local and native oak, and the brick walls of it are only curtains built in between the wooden framework of that most ancient habitation.

Beneath the chapel is the dining-room, where there is a very large open hearth which can take huge logs and which is as old as anything in the place. Here wood only is burnt, and that wood oak.

Down this room there runs a very long oaken table as dark with age almost as the beams above it, and this table has a history. It came out of one of the Oxford colleges when the Puritans looted them three hundred years ago. It never got back to its original home. It passed from one family to another until at last it was purchased (in his youth and upon his marriage) by the man who now owns this house. Those who know about such things give its date as the beginning of the seventeenth century. It was made, then, while Shakespeare was still living, and while the faith of England still hung in the balance; for one cannot say that England was certain to lose her Catholicism finally till the first quarter of that century was passed. This table, roughly carved at the side, has been polished with wax since first it began to bear food for men, and now the surface shines like a slightly, very slightly, undulating sea in a calm. At night the brass candlesticks (for this house is lit with candles, as the proper light for men's eyes) are reflected in it as in still brown water; so are the vessels of glass and of silver and of pewter, and the flagons of wine. No cloth is ever spread to hide this venerable splendour, nor, let us hope, ever will be.

At one end of the house, where the largest of its many outer doors (there are several such) swings massively upon huge forged iron hinges, there is a hall, not very wide; its length is as great as the width of the house and its height very great for its width. Like the chapel, its roof soars up, steep and dark, so that from its floor (which is made of very great and heavy slabs of the local stone) one looks up to the roof-tree itself. This hall has another great wide hearth in it for the burning of oak, and there is an oaken staircase, very wide and of an easy slope, with an oaken balustrade and leading up to an open gallery above, whence you look down upon the piece. Above this gallery is a statue of Our Lady, carved in wood, uncoloured, and holding the Holy Child, and beneath her many shelves of books. This room is panelled, as are so many of the rooms of the house, but it has older panels than any of the others, and the great door of it opens on to the high road.

Now the way Christmas is kept in this house is this:

On Christmas Eve a great quantity of holly and of laurel is brought in from the garden and from the farm (for this house has a farm of a hundred acres attached to it and an oak wood of ten acres). This greenery is put up all over the house in every room just before it becomes dark on that day. Then there is brought into the hall a young pine tree, about twice the height of a man, to serve for a

Christmas tree, and on this innumerable little candles are fixed, and presents for all the household and the guests and the children of the village.

It is at about five o'clock that these last come into the house, and at that hour in England, at that date, it has long been quite dark; so they come into a house all illuminated with the Christmas tree shining like a cluster of many stars seen through a glass.

The first thing done after the entry of these people from the village and their children (the children are in number about fifty—for this remote place keeps a good level through the generations and does not shrink or grow, but remains itself) is a common meal, where all eat and drink their fill in the offices. Then the children come in to the Christmas tree. They are each given a silver piece one by one, and one by one, their presents. After that they dance in the hall and sing songs, which have been handed down to them for I do not know how long. These songs are game-songs, and are sung to keep time with the various parts in each game, and the men and things and animals which you hear mentioned in these songs are all of that countryside. Indeed, the tradition of Christmas here is what it should be everywhere, knit into the very stuff of the place; so that I fancy the little children, when they think of Bethlehem, see it in their minds as though it were in the winter depth of England, which is as it should be.

These games and songs continue for as long as they will, and then they file out past the great fire in the hearth to a small piece adjoining where a crib has been set up with images of Our Lady and St. Joseph and the Holy Child, the Shepherds, and what I will call, by your leave, the Holy Animals. And here, again, tradition is so strong in this house that these figures are never new-bought, but are as old as the oldest of the children of the family, now with children of their own. On this account, the donkey has lost one of its plaster ears, and the old ox which used to be all brown is now piebald, and of the shepherds, one actually has no head. But all that is lacking is imagined. There hangs from the roof of the crib over the Holy Child a tinsel star grown rather obscure after all these years, and much too large for the place. Before this crib the children (some of them Catholic and some Protestant, for the village is mixed) sing their carols; the one they know best is the one which begins: "The First Good Joy that Mary had, it was the joy of One." There are a half a dozen or so of these carols which the children here sing; and mixed with their voices is the voice of the miller (for this house has a great windmill attached to it). The miller is famous in these parts for his singing, having a very deep and loud voice which is his pride. When these carols are over, all disperse, except those who are living in the house, but the older ones are not allowed to go without more good drink for their viaticum, a sustenance for Christian men.

Then the people of the house, when they have dined, and their guests, with the priest who is to say Mass for them, sit up till near midnight. There is brought in a very large log of oak (you must be getting tired of oak by this time! But everything here is oaken, for the house is of the Weald). This log of oak is the Christmas or Yule log and the rule is that it must be too heavy for one man to lift; so two men come, bringing it in from outside, the master of the house and his servant. They cast it down upon the fire in the great hearth of the dining-room, and the superstition is that, if it burns all night and is found still smouldering in the morning, the home will be prosperous for the coming year.

With that they all go up to the chapel and there the three night Masses are said, one after the other, and those of the household take their Communion.

Next morning they sleep late, and the great Christmas dinner is at midday. It is a turkey; and a plum pudding.

with holly in it and everything conventional, and therefore satisfactory, is done. Crackers are pulled, the brandy is lit and poured over the pudding till the holly crackles in the flame and the curtains are drawn a moment that the flames may be seen. This Christmas feast, so great that it may be said almost to fill the day, they may reprove who will; but for my part I applaud.

Now, you must not think that Christmas being over, the season and its glories are at an end, for in this house there is kept up the full custom of the Twelve Days, so that "Twelfth Day," the Epiphany, still has, to its inhabitants, its full and ancient meaning as it had when Shakespeare wrote. The green is kept in its place in every room, and not a leaf of it must be moved until Epiphany morning, but on the other hand not a leaf of it must remain in the house, nor the Christmas tree either, by Epiphany evening. It is all taken out and burnt in a special little coppice reserved for these good trees which have done their Christmas duty; and now, after so many years, you might almost call it a little forest, for each tree has lived, bearing witness to the holy vitality of unbroken ritual and inherited things.

In the midst of this season between Christmas and Twelfth Day comes the ceremony of the New Year, and this is how it is observed:

On New Year's Eve, at about a quarter to twelve o'clock at night, the master of the house and all that are with him go about from room to room opening every door and window, however cold the weather be, for thus, they say, the old year and its burdens can go out and leave everything new for hope and for the youth of the coming time.

This also is a superstition, and of the best. Those who observe it trust that it is as old as Europe, and with roots stretching back into forgotten times.

While this is going on the bells in the church hard by

are ringing out the old year, and when all the windows and doors have thus been opened and left wide, all those in the house go outside, listening for the cessation of the chimes, which comes just before the turn of the year. There is an odd silence of a few minutes, and watches are consulted to make certain of the time (for this house detests wireless and has not even a telephone), and the way they know the moment of midnight is by the boom of a gun, which is fired at a town far off, but can always be heard.

At that sound the bells of the church clash out suddenly in new chords, the master of the house goes back into it with a piece of stone or earth from outside, all doors are shut, and the household, all of them, rich and poor, drink a glass of wine together to salute the New Year.

This, which I have just described, is not in a novel or in a play. It is real, and goes on as the ordinary habit of living men and women. I fear that set down thus in our terribly changing time it must sound very strange and, perhaps in places, grotesque, but to those who practise it, it is not only sacred, but normal, having in the whole of the complicated affair a sacramental quality and an effect of benediction: not to be despised.

Indeed, modern men, who lack such things, lack sustenance, and our fathers who founded all those ritual observances were very wise.

.   .   .   .   .   .

Man has a body as well as a soul, and the whole of man, soul and body, is nourished sanely by a multiplicity of observed traditional things. Moreover, there is this great quality in the unchanging practice of Holy Seasons, that it makes explicable, tolerable, and normal what is otherwise a shocking and intolerable and even in the fullest sense, abnormal thing. I mean, the mortality of immortal man.

Not only death (which shakes and rends all that is human in us, creating a monstrous separation and threatening the soul with isolation which destroys)—not only death, but that accompaniment of mortality which is a perpetual series of lesser deaths and is called change, are challenged, chained, and put in their place by unaltered and successive acts of seasonable regard for loss and dereliction and mutability. The threats of despair, remorse, necessary expiation, weariness almost beyond bearing, dull repetition of things apparently fruitless, unnecessary and without meaning, estrangement, the misunderstanding of mind by mind, forgetfulness, which is a false alarm, grief and repentance, which are true ones, but of a sad company, young men perished in battle before their parents had lost vigour in age, the perils of sickness in the body and even in the mind, anxiety, honour harassed, all the bitterness of living—become part of a large business which may lead to Beatitude. For they are all connected in the memory with holy day after holy day, year by year, binding the generations together; carrying on even in this world, as it were, the life of the dead and giving corporate substance, permanence and stability, without the symbol of which (at least) the vast increasing burden of life might at last conquer us and be no longer borne.

．　　　．　　　．　　　．　　　．　　　．

This house where such good things are done year by year has suffered all the things that every age has suffered. It has known the sudden separation of wife and husband, the sudden fall of young men under arms who will never more come home, the scattering of the living and their precarious return, the increase and the loss of fortune, all those terrors and all those lessenings and haltings and failures of hope which make up the life of man. But its Christmas binds it to its own past and promises its future; making the house an undying thing of which those subject to mortality within it are members, sharing in its continuous survival.

It is not wonderful that of such a house verse should be written. Many verses have been so written commemorating and praising this house. The last verse written of it I may quote here by way of ending:

> Stand thou for ever among human Houses,
>   House of the Resurrection, House of Birth;
> House of the rooted hearts and long carouses,
>   Stand, and be famous over all the Earth.

HILAIRE BELLOC.

BURGUNDIAN CAROL

LOR qu'an lai saison qu'ai jaule
  Au monde Jésu-Chri vin,
  L'áne et le beu l'échaufin
  De lo sôfle dans l'étaule;
  Que d'áne et de beu je sai
  Dan ce Royaume de Gaule,
  Que d'áne et de beu je sai
  Qui n'an airein pa tan fai!

On di que cé pôvre béte
  N'ure pa vu le Pôpon
  Qu'elle se mire ai genon
  Humbleman boissan lai téte.
  Que d'áne et de beu je sai
  Qui po tô se fon dé féte,
  Que d'áne et de beu je sai
  Qui n'an airein pa tan fai!

Ma le pu béa de l'histoire,
  Ce fu que l'áne et le beu
224

Ansin passire tô deu
Lai neù san maingé ni boire.
Que d'áne et de beu je sai,
Couvar de pane et de moire,
Que d'áne et de beu je sai
Qui n'an airein pa tan fai!

GUY BAROZAI (La Monnoye: 1641–1728).

SERMON OF THE BOY-BISHOP, 1493

Prologe.

IN the begynnynge thenne of this simple exhortacyon, that I a chylde, wantynge the habyte of connynge, maye be dyrected by hym that gave to that childe Danyell *Sermonem rectum et Spiritum Deorum,* somwhat to say to his laude and praysynge, and to alle pure chylderne that bene here present edifyenge, we shall atte this tyme devoutly make our prayers.

In the whiche prayers I recommende unto your devocyons the welfare of all Chrysts chirche; our holy fader the Pope with alle the Clergye, my Lorde of Caunterbury, and the ryghte reverende fader and worshipfull lorde my broder Bysshopp of London your dyocesan, also for my worshypfull broder [the] Deane of this cathedrall chirche, wyth all resydensaryes and prebendaryes of the same. And moost intyerly I praye you to have myself in your specyal devocyon, so that I may contynue in this degree that I now stande. . . .

In the seconde partye ye shall praye for the wele and peas of all Crysten reames, specyally for the reame of Englande, Our soverayne lorde the Kyng, Our Soverayne lady the Quene, My lorde the Prynce, My lady the Kynges Moder, My lorde her Husbande, with all the Lordes of the Realme; the welfare of this Cyte, for my ryght worshypful broder and lover the Mayer, with all the Aldermen and Shyrefs.

In the thyrde partye, all the soules lyenge in the paynes of Purgatory; specyally for the soule of the reverende fader my lorde Thomas Kempe late Bysshop, and for the soules of all Benefactours of thys chirche of Poules, with all Crysten soules, for the whiche and for the entent primysed I praye you devoutly saye a Pater Noster and an Ave.

Laudate Pueri Dominum.

In as moche Cryste sayth in the Gospell, *Sinite parvulos venire ad me, quia talium est regnum Celorum* (Mathei xix°.), "Suffre ye childerne to come to me, for of suche the Kyngdom of heven is fulfylled," by whom, after saynt Austyn, it is not oonly understoude those that bene chylderne of age, but those that bene chylderne pure in clennesse from synne and malyce. As the holy apostle saynt Poule sayth, *Nolite effici pueri sensibus, malicia autem parvuli estote* (prima ad Corintheos xiiij°) "Be ye not chylderne in your wyttes; but from all synne and malyce be ye chylderne in clennesse." And in this fourme alle maner of people and al manner of ages in clennesse of lyf ought to be pure as childerne, to whom generally may I saye *Laudate, pueri, Dominum: Laudate.*

Sequitur.

SNOW

> FADING slow
> And furred is the snow
> As the almond's sweet husk,
> And smelling like musk.
> The snow amygdaline
> Under the eglantine
> Where bristling stars shine
> Like a gilt porcupine—
> The snow confesses
> The little Princesses

226

On their small chioppines
Dance under the orpines.
See the casuistries
Of their slant flutt'ring eyes—
Gilt as the zodiac
(Dancing herodiac).
Only the snow slides
Like gilded myrrh
From the rose-branches—hides
Rose-roots that stir!

EDITH SITWELL.

A CALL FROM MASSACHUSETTS

Boston, December 28th , 1675.

'TIS verily believed with us, that all generous Minds
in both Englands, which concern themselves to
inquire after our Affairs in these parts of the World, and
wish us well, have a longing Desire the Indian Wars
might be ended; and we presumed ere this, that the
Powers of Perswasion or Force would have made a
happy Change, by altering the Minds, or restraining the
Malice, of our Heathen Foes.

But so it is, the rod of God's Anger is still upon us;
for the Pocanaket Sachem Metacom, *alias* Philip, still
lives! he lives to be a Vexation to us in all Places where
he comes. Yea, he lives, and by his Subtlety proves a
more forcible and perilous Enemy to us than ever we could
have imagined. He hath drawn into his Confederacie all
the Indians, from Cape Sables eastward to the Mohawks,
which is about three-hundred Miles, or upwards: and our
Fears are (which would to God they were but Fears!)
that some Traders of Europe, for love of Gain, have
from Time to Time supplied them with Ammunition.
At the eastward, the Indians have ruined Falmouth,
Black Point, and Saco, and slain in those Towns thirty

Persons. Some they took alive, and sat them upright in the Ground, using this Sarcasm: *You English, since you came into this Country, have grown exceedingly above Ground; let us now see how you will grow when planted into the Ground.* At Ketterey, they have slain fourteen Persons, and burnt sundry Houses: at Dover they have also killed some, and fired two or three Houses. . . .

Our People, since the Loss of Captain Lathrop of Beverly, (with about sixty Men, by Surprize) and the burning of Springfield, are grown not less valorous, but more cautious. Experience is the mother of Prudence, and little Good comes of despising an Enemy. Yet let not the World censure too much Captain Lathrop. He, in the Pequot Wars, had done Exploits; nor in this would have been behind-hand, if the narrow Passage or Causey, where his unexpected Enemies set on him, would have given him Leave to have drawn up his Men. But, however, this may be said, to use the Words of a wise Man: "There was never Censor that judged, Council that executed, General that commanded, Orator that persuaded, nor any other mortal Man, but sometimes he committed Errours." Let such, as are too apt to censure the Conduct of some Affairs here, remember this.

[A Manifesto of the Council of Massachusetts follows].

By the Council, EDWARD RAWSON, Sec.
From a Tract of 1676, published at London.

THE POET IS INDIFFERENT

A FLASK, enclosed in light wicker-work, containing boiled water iced, shall be your present for this Saturnalia. If you complain that I have sent you a summer gift in December, you may send me a thin smooth toga.

MARTIAL.

1403. A little before Christmass the Frenchmen came into the Ile of Wight, boasting that they would keep their Christmass there and when a thousand of the Frenchmen were entred into the Ilande, and driving flockes of Cattell towarde the Sea, sodainely there came upon them a companie of the Ilande menne, that forced them to leave their praye behinde them, and to gette them gone (with shame ynough) to their shippes with no small losse of their men.

Annales of JOHN STOW.

THE RESPITE

ℂ *Advent*. Act V. sc. ii.

A valley basin surrounded with steep black rocks. At the back stands a large pair of scales, where newcomers are weighed.

The Deemster and his Wife sitting at a table.

The Witch comes in with a large basket.

The Deemster. What's that?

The Witch. Christmas presents for the righteous. They are peep-shows. [*Gives him one.*] There you are. It costs nothing.

The Deemster. See, there is one kind human being at least! A little attention at my years and to a man of my standing honours your good taste and your kind heart.

The Witch. You are altogether too courteous, Deemster; but don't take it amiss if I have thought of the others a little, too.

The Deemster. [*Piqued.*] Infernal old woman, are you chaffing me?

The Witch. [*Spitting in his face.*] Shame on you! Pettifogger!

The Deemster. Think what company one can run into!

229

The Witch. Isn't it good enough for you, you old perjurer, bribe-taker, forger, inheritance-thief, corrupter? Look into the peep-show and you'll see the great tableau, *From the Cradle to the Grave.* There you'll find the whole biography and all the victims—just look! There!

> [*The Deemster looks into the peep-show, and rises in fear.*

The Witch. I hope the little remembrance will help toward your Christmas joy!

> [*She gives the Wife a peep-show and continues to distribute them among the others.*

The Deemster. What do you see?

The Wife. Everything is there; everything! And have you noticed everything is black? The long bright life is dark, the moments I thought innocent joy stand forth loathsome, fœtid, criminal, almost! It is as if one's memories, even the most beautiful, had become rotten—

The Deemster. Yes, you are right; not one memory can light up this darkness. When I see her, my youth's first love, I see a corpse; when I bring to mind the good Amalia there appears—a harlot; the little children make faces at me like so many street urchins; my house is a pigsty, the vineyard a dump-heap with thistles; when I think of the green forest it turns into snuff-brown leafage, and the trunks are white as masts; the blue river flows onward as from a barnyard, and the blue sky above is like a smoky ceiling. Even the sun I remember only as a name, and that which is called the moon and shone like a lamp over inlets and groves in the evenings of youth and love, I remember only as—No, I can't recall them any more. Only words remain with me, though they are but sounds without meaning. . . . Love, wine, song! Flowers, children, happiness!—Do not the words sound beautiful? And that is all that is left!—Love! What was love?

The Wife. What was it? Two cats on the roof of a back-house.

The Deemster. [*Idiotically.*] That's so! And three dogs on a street corner. It's delightful to recall.

The Wife. [*Pressing his hand.*] It is delightful.

The Deemster. [*Looking at his watch.*] My watch has stopped. I am so hungry; but I am thirsty too, and I long for tobacco. But I am tired too and would like to sleep. All my habits are awake; they scratch and urge me, and I cannot gratify one of them. Unfortunate we are! Unfortunate!

The Wife. And I long for a cup of tea so much that I cannot describe it.

The Deemster. Hot green tea. That is just what I would like now; and with a little, just a little rum.

The Wife. No, not rum: I should prefer cake—

The Prince. [*Coming forward.*] With frosting on top? Yes, if you will sing for it.

The Wife. This rude talk tortures me more than anything else.

The Prince. That's because you don't know how what is coming will torture you.

The Deemster. What is that?

The Wife. No! Silence! We don't want to know! Silence!

The Prince. Yes! I want you to know. It begins with——

The Wife. [*Holding hands over ears and shouting.*] Have pity! Keep quiet, keep quiet; keep quiet!

The Prince. No, indeed, I won't keep quiet. Brother-in-law is curious, and he shall be told. The second letter is H.

The Deemster. This uncertainty tortures me more than anything—Speak out, devil, or kill me!

The Prince. Kill? Ha, ha! Here we are all deathless, soul and body, what little is left. However . . . the third letter is—Now you'll know more!

The Gray-Clad One enters, a small emaciated man with gray clothes, gray face, black lips, gray beard and hands. He speaks in an undertone.

The Gray-Clad One. May I have a little talk with you, lady?

The Wife. [*Rising frightened.*] What about?

The Gray-Clad One. [*Smiles maliciously.*] I will tell you . . . out there.

The Wife. [*Weeping.*] No, no, I don't want to!

The Gray-Clad One. [*Laughing.*] It is not dangerous. Come along! I only want to talk to you a little. Come!
[*They go out, back.*

The Prince. A little whipping for a Christmas present does one good.

The Deemster. Do you mean to maltreat a woman?

The Prince. Here every injustice is effaced, and woman is on a level with man.

The Deemster. Devil!

The Other. [*Coming forward.*] Well, how about animal magnetism? It can work wonders with brutes.

The Deemster. I understand nothing of all this!

The Other. That is just what is intended. It is a beautiful confession from you that there are things you do not understand.

The Deemster. Assuming that I am in Hades—

The Other. Say Hell. That's what it's called.

The Deemster. [*Stammering.*] Then . . . then I would point out that He who came down here once to redeem the damned——
[*The Prince, at a wink from the Other, strikes the Deemster on the mouth.*

The Prince. Don't reason!

The Deemster. They will not hear me! This is utter despair! Without mercy, without hope, without end!

The Other. True. Only justice and retribution exist here, justice above everything; an eye for an eye, a tooth for a tooth. Just as you wished to have it.

232

The Deemster. But among humankind there is pardon that does not exist here.

The Other. Only the rules can pardon. And as a jurist you ought to know that a petition for pardon must be filed in order to receive consideration.

The Deemster. For me there is no mercy!

The Other. [*Signing to the Prince, who goes aside.*] You consider your guilt too great, then?

The Deemster. Yes.

The Other. Then I will speak to you with kindness. You see, there is always an end if only there is a beginning; and you have made a beginning. But the continuation is long and difficult.

The Deemster. Oh! God is good!

The Other. You have said it.

The Deemster. But . . . there is one thing that cannot be undone—there is one!

The Other. You mean the Monstrance that should have been gold, but became silver? Very well. Don't you believe that He who changed water into wine can transform silver into gold?

The Deemster. [*On his knees.*] But my misdeed is greater, greater than can ever be forgiven.

The Other. Now you are overrating yourself again! But rise now, for we are to celebrate Christmas in our way.—The sun never reaches us down here, as you know, nor the moon either, but tonight, tonight only, a star rises so high over the mountains that it is seen from here below. It is that star that lights the shepherd's way in the desert. It is the Morning Star.

> [*He claps his hands. The Wife comes in, quiet and peacefully happy; she goes to the Deemster and gives him her hand comfortingly. The scene is filled with shadows that all gaze up towards the mountain at the back. Voices are heard singing, accompanied only by violins and harps.*

Voices.	Puer natus est nobis;
	Et Filius datus est nobis;
	Cujus imperium super humerum Ejus;
	Et vocabitur nomen Ejus
	Magni consilii Angelus.
Chorus.	Cantate Domino canticum novum,
	Quia mirabilia fecit.

[*Now the Star appears over the mountain. All fall on their knees. Part of the rock is pushed to one side. Tableau: the Manger, with the Mother and Child. The Shepherds are praying at left, the three Kings at right.*

Chorus.	Gloria in excelsis Deo
	Et in terra pax
	Hominibus bonæ voluntatis!

AUGUST STRINDBERG (1849–1912).

THE BOON

WHAT persone beynge in clene lyfe desyre on thys daye a boone of God: as ferre as it is ryghtfull and good for hym, our Lorde at reverence of thys blessid and hye feste of his nativite wol graunt it to hym.

From *The Golden Legend.*

EPIPHANIE

DONC, Balthazar, Melchior et Gaspar, les Rois Mages,
Chargés de nefs d'argent, de vermeil et d'émaux
Et suivis d'un très long cortège de chameaux,
S'avancent, tels qu'ils sont dans les vieilles images.

De l'Orient lointain, ils portent leurs hommages
Aux pieds du Fils de Dieu, né pour guérir les maux
Que souffrent ici-bas les hommes et les animaux;
Un page noir soutient leurs robes à ramages.

234

Sur le seuil de l'étable où veille saint Joseph,
Ils ôtent humblement la couronne du chef
Pour saluer l'Enfant qui rit et les admire.

C'est ainsi qu'autrefois, sous Augustus Cæsar,
Sont venus, présentant l'or, l'encens et la myrrhe,
Les Rois Mages Gaspar, Melchior et Balthazar.

JOSÉ-MARIA DE HEREDIA (1842–1905).

THE COVENTRY CAROL

℃ *Coventry Nativity Play*

Joseph.   Arise up, Mary, hastily and soon!
      Our Lord's will needs must be done,
      Like as the angel bade.
Mary Moder. Meekly, Joseph, mine own spouse,
      Toward that country let us repair,
      In Egypt, some token of house,
      God grant us grace safe to come there.
*[There the women come in with their children, singing
them, and Mary and Joseph goeth clean away.*

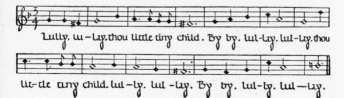

Lully, lu-lay, thou little tiny child. By by, lul-lay, lul-lay, thou
lit-tle tiny child. lul-ly, lul-lay. By by, lul-ly, lul-lay.

Lully, lulla, thou little tiny child;
By, by, lullay, lullay, thou little tiny child;
By, by, lully, lullay.

O sisters too! how may we do
For to preserve this day

235

This poor youngling, for whom we do sing
By, by, lully, lullay.

Herod the King in his raging,
Charged he hath this day
His men of might, in his own sight,
All young children to slay.

That woe is me, poor child for thee!
And ever morn and day,
For thy parting neither say nor sing,
By, by, lully lullay.

XVth Century.

FRANCISCAN SONG

VEGGIAMO il suo Bambino
Gammetare nel fieno
E le braccia scoperte
Porgere ad ella in seno,
Ed essa lo ricopre
Ed meglio che può almeno
Mettendoli la poppa
Entro la sua bocchina.

A la sua man manca,
Cullava lo Bambino,
E con sante carole
Nenciava il suo amor fino . . .
Gli Angioletti d'intorno
Se ne gian danzando
Facendo dolci versi
E d'amor favellando.

JACOPONE DA TODI (1228–1306).

[*Translation*]

Come and look upon her Child
Nestling in the hay!
See his fair arms open wide,
On her lap to play!

236

And she tucks him by her side,
Cloaks him as she may
Gives her paps unto his mouth
Where his lips are laid.

She with left hand cradling
Rocked and hushed her Boy,
And with holy lullabies
Quieted her toy . . .
Little angels all around
Danced, and carols flung;
Making verselets sweet and true,
Still of love they sung.

JOHN ADDINGTON SYMONDS.

THE HIGHER CRITICISM

THE tall, old, quaint, irregular town!
  It may be . . . though *which*, I can't affirm . . . any
Of the famous middle-age towns of Germany;
And this flight of stairs where I sit down,
Is it Halle, Weimar, Cassel, or Frankfort,
Or Göttingen, that I have to thank for 't?
It may be Göttingen—most likely.
Through the open door I catch obliquely
Glimpses of a lecture-hall;
And not a bad assembly neither—
Ranged decent and symmetrical
On benches, waiting what's to see there;
Which, holding still by the Vesture's hem,
I also resolve to see with them. . . .

But hist—a buzzing and emotion!
All settle themselves, the while ascends
By the creaking rail to the lecture-desk,
Step by step, deliberate
Because of his cranium's over-freight,
Three parts sublime to one grotesque,
If I have proved an accurate guesser,
The hawk-nosed, high-cheek-boned Professor. . . .

Over he bowed, and arranged his notes,
Till the auditory's clearing of throats
Was done with, died into a silence;
And when each glance was upward sent,
Each bearded mouth composed intent,
And a pin might be heard drop half a mile hence—
He pushed back higher his spectacles,
Let the eyes stream out like lamps from cells,
And giving his head of hair—a hake
Of undressed tow for colour and quantity—
One rapid and impatient shake . . .
The Professor's grave voice, sweet though hoarse,
Broke into his Christmas Eve's discourse.

And he began it by observing
How reason dictated that men
Should rectify the natural swerving
By a reversion, now and then,
To the well-heads of knowledge, few
And far away, whence rolling grew
The Life-Stream wide whereat we drink,
Commingled, as we needs must think,
With waters alien to the source. . . .

So he proposed inquiring first
Into the various sources whence
This Myth of Christ is derivable;
Demanding from the evidence
(Since plainly no such life was liveable)
How these phenomena should class:
Whether 'twere best opine Christ was,
Or never was at all, or whether
He was and was not, both together. . . .
     (etc.).

     ROBERT BROWNING (1812–1889).
238

i.

Friday, December 28, 1711.

M R. *SPECTATOR,*

I am a Footman in a great Family, and am in Love with the House-maid. We were all at Hot Cockles last Night in the Hall these Holidays; when I lay down and was blinded, she pulled off her Shoe, and hit me with the Heel such a Rap, as almost broke my Head to Pieces. Pray, Sir, was this Love or Spite?

ii.

Monday, January 7, 1712.

Mr. *Spectator,*

I desire to know in your Next, if the merry Game of *the Parson has lost his Cloke,* is not mightily in Vogue amongst the fine Ladies this Christmas; because I see they wear Hoods of all Colours, which I suppose is for that Purpose; if it is, and you think it proper, I will carry some of those Hoods with me to our Ladies in *Yorkshire;* because they injoined me to bring them something from London that was very new. If you can tell any Thing in which I can obey their Commands more agreeably, be pleas'd to inform me, and you will extreamly oblige,

Your humble Servant

RICHARD STEELE.

HOW TO MAKE A TANSY

T AKE half a handful of Tansey, of the yongest ye can get, and a handful of young borage, Strawberry leaves, Lettice and Violet leaves, and wash them cleane, and beat them very small in a morter: then put to them eight Egges, whites and all, and six yolkes besides, and straine them together through a strainer & then season it with a good handful of sugar, and a Nutmeg beaten small. Then take a frying pan, and halfe a disk of sweet butter and melt it: then put your Egs to it, set it on the fire,

and with a sawcer, or with a ladle, stir them till they be
half baked: then put them into a Platter, and all, to beat
them still till they be very small: then take your frying
pan made cleane, and put a disk of sweet Butter in it,
and melt it: then put your stuffe into your pan by a spoone-
ful at once, and when the one side is fried, turn them and
fry them together: then take them out, lay them in a
platter, and scrape Sugar on them.

From A Booke of Cookerie (1597).

ROBIN HOOD'S EPITAPH

HEAR undernead dis laith stean
Laiz Robert Earl of Huntington
Nea arcir ver az hie sa geude:
An piple kaud im Robin Heud.
Sic utlawz as hi an iz men,
Wil England never sigh agen.
Obiit 24 kal. Decembris, 1247.

From a gravestone in Kirklees Church-
yard, Yorkshire.

A TWELFTH-DAY PROPHECY

❧ *On the death of King Richard II. of England.*

NOW consider well, ye great lords, kings, dukes, earls,
barons and prelates, and all men of great lineage
and puissance; see and behold how the fortunes of this
world are marvellous and turn diversely. This king
Richard reigned king of England twenty-two year in
great prosperity, holding great estate and seignory.
There was never before any king of England that spent
so much in his house as he did, by a hundred thousand
florins every year; for I, sir John Froissart, canon and
treasurer of Chimay, knew it well, for I was in his court

more than a quarter of a year together, and he made me good cheer, because that in my youth I was clerk and servant to the noble king Edward the third, his grandfather, and with my lady Philippa of Hainault, queen of England, his granddam; and when I departed from him, it was at Windsor, and at my departing the king sent me by a knight of his called sir John Golofre a goblet of silver and gilt weighing two mark of silver, and within it a hundred nobles, by the which I am as yet the better, and shall be as long as I live: wherefore I am bound to pray God for his soul, and with much sorrow I write of his death.

I was in the city of Bordeaux and sitting at the table when king Richard was born, the which was on a Tuesday about ten of the clock. The same time there came thereas I was, sir Richard Pontchardon, marshal as then of Acquitaine, and he said to me: "Froissart, write and put in memory that as now my lady princess is brought abed with a fair son this Twelfth Day, that is the day of the three kings, and he is son to a king and shall be a king." This gentle knight said truth, for he was king of England twenty-two year; but when this knight said these words, he knew full little what should be his conclusion. And the same time that king Richard was born, his father the prince was in Galice, the which king Don Peter had given him, and he was there to conquer the realm.

Thus when king Richard had lain two hour in the chare [funeral car] in Cheapside, then they drave the chare forward; and when the four knights that followed the chare afoot were without London, they leapt then on their horses, which were there ready for them, and so they rode till they came to a village called Langley, a thirty mile from London, and there this king Richard was buried. God have mercy on his soul.

FROISSART.

TAKE a faire panne, and set hit under the goose whill sche rostes, and kepe clene the grese that droppes therof, and put thereto a godele [good deal] of wyn and a litel vynegur, and verjus, and onyons mynced or garlek; then take the gottes of the goose, and slitte hom and scrape hom clene in watur and salt, and so wassh hom, and sethe hom, and hak hom smal; then do all this togedur in a postenet, and do thereto raisinges of corance [Corinth] and pouder of pepur, and of gynger, and of canell, and hole clowes, and maces, and let hit boyle, and serve hit forthe.

XIVth–XVth Century: Arundel Collection.

A CUSTOM OF THE ENGLISH

Rome, New Year's Day, 1700.

AFTER 8 days diligent Search, we have at last found 2 or 3 chambers to our Satisfaction, where I hope we shall be able to avoid splitting on the Rock which I observe few of our English can keep clear of: that is, the herding with one another in Ordinarys and Coffee-houses, where they engage in Play, and scarce hear a word of Italian from morning to Night.

The principal entertainments these Holydays have afforded us, have been the Musick, and the Reliques exposed in the churches: wherein, as to the former, none have exceeded that at the English Colledge on St. Thomas Becket's day, [December 29], where Bishop Ellis officiated, 19 Cardinals assisted, and so many English gentlemen were present as occasioned particular Notice to be taken of it.

JOHN JACKSON to Samuel Pepys.
The Pepys Correspondence.

I SAW the curl'd drops, soft and slow,
    Come hovering o'er the place's head;
Offering their whitest sheets of snow,
    To furnish the fair Infant's bed.
Forbear, said I, be not too bold;
Your fleece is white, but 'tis too cold.

I saw th' obsequious Seraphim
    Their rosy fleece of fire bestow,
For well they now can spare their wing,
    Since Heaven itself lies here below.
Well done, said I; but are you sure
Your down, so warm, will pass for pure?

No, no! your King's not yet to seek
    Where to repose His royal head;
See, see, how soon His new-bloom'd cheek
    'Twixt mother's breasts is gone to bed!
Sweet choice, said we! no way but so,
Not to lie cold, yet sleep in snow.

She sings Thy tears asleep, and dips
    Her kisses in Thy weeping eye;
She spreads the red leaves of Thy lips,
    That in their buds yet blushing lie.
She 'gainst those mother-diamonds tries
The points of her young Eagle's eyes.

.   .   .   .   .

Welcome, tho' not to those gay flies
    Gilded i' the beams of earthly kings;
Slippery souls in shining eyes,
    But to poor shepherds, homespun things,
Whose wealth's their flocks, whose wit's to be
Well-read in their simplicity.

Yet, when young April's husband-showers
   Shall bless the fruitful Maia's bed,
We'll bring the first-born of her flowers
   To kiss Thy feet, and crown Thy head;
To Thee, dread Lamb! whose love must keep
The shepherds more than they keep sheep.

RICHARD CRASHAW, Canon of Loretto
(1613–1649).

THE CROMWELL MANNER

25 Dec. I went to London with my wife, to celebrate Christmas-day, Mr. Gunning preaching in Exeter-Chapell, on 7 Micah 2. Sermon ended, as he was giving us the holy sacrament, the chapell was surrounded with souldiers, and all the communicants and assembly surpriz'd and kept prisoners by them, some in the house, others carried away. It fell to my share to be confin'd to a room in the house, where yet I was permitted to dine with the master of it, the Countess of Dorset, Lady Hatton, and some others of quality who invited me. In the afternoone came Col. Whaly, Goffe, and others, from White-hall, to examine us one by one; some they committed to the Marshall, some to prison. When I came before them they took my name and abode, examin'd me why, contrarie to an ordinance made that none should any longer observe the superstitious time of the Nativity (so esteem'd by them) I durst offend, and particularly be at Common Prayers, which they told me was but the Masse in English, and particularly pray for Charles Steuart, for which we had no Scripture. I told them we did not pray for Cha. Stewart, but for all Christian Kings, Princes, and Governours. They replied, in so doing we praid for the K. of Spaine too, who was their enemie and a papist, with other frivolous and insnaring

questions and much threatning; and finding no colour
to detaine me, they dismiss'd me with much pitty of
my ignorance. These were men of high flight and above
ordinances, and spake spiteful things of our Lord's
Nativity. As we went up to receive the sacrament the
miscreants held their musketts against us as if they would
have shot us at the the altar, but yet suffering us to finish
the office of Communion, as perhaps not having instruc-
tions what to do in case they found us in that action.
So I got home late the next day, blessed be God.

EVELYN'S *Diary*, 1657.

THE POET IS JUDICIOUS

SO may December be kind to you, Paulus, and may
you receive no worthless three-leaved tablets and
measly napkins, nor light half-pounds of frankincense;
but may either some hulking defendant or rich friend
bring you dishes and antique goblets; or—what pleases
and gratifies you more—may you beat Novius and
Publius hemmed in by your pawns and glass robbers
[in the game of *latrunculi*]: so may the ring of well-oiled
athletes looking on give you the palm and award you
victory over the half-naked ball players, nor praise at
your expense the left-handers of Polybus. And if some
malignant fellow assert poems steeped in black venom to
be mine, do you lend me a patron's voice and shout
at the top of your voice, without stopping: "My Martial
did not write that!"

MARTIAL.

IT is snowing. Doubtless the great world is dead.
It is December.
And how good it is, dear God, in the little room!
The grate full of glowing coals
Colours the ceiling with a drowsy reflection,
And nothing is heard but water gently simmering.
Up there, on the cabinet-shelf, above the two beds,
Under a glass globe, with a crown on His head,
One hand holding the world, the other ready
To cover these little ones who trust it,
All-lovable in His great ceremonial robe,
And magnificent under that huge yellow hat,
The Infant Jesus of Prague reigns and rules.
Alone before the hearth which lights Him,
Like the Host hidden in the heart of the sanctuary,
Till day the Child-God guards His little brothers.
Unheard, like the exhaling of a breath,
Eternal existence fills the room, shared
By all these humble, innocent, and simple things!
When He is with us no harm can come near,
We can sleep: Jesus our Brother is here.
He is ours, like all these other good things; the wonderful
doll, and the wooden horse,
And the lamb are there, all three in the corner,
And we are asleep, but all these good things are ours!
The curtains are closed. . . . Far away, somewhere or
other
In the snow and the night, an hour of some kind strikes.
The child in his warm bed knows happily
That he is asleep, and that Someone who loves him well
is there;
He moves a little, murmurs vaguely, puts out an arm,
Tries to wake, and cannot.

PAUL CLAUDEL, *L'Enfant Jésus de Prague* (*Corona
Benignitatis Anni Dei*).

℄ The Carol of the Deanery of Sainte-Ménehould.

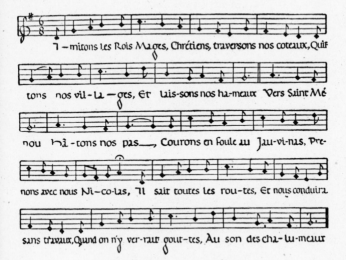

IMITONS les Rois Mages, Chrétiens, traversons nos coteaux, Quit-tons nos vil-la—ges, Et lais-sons nos ha-meaux Vers Saint Mé-nou hâ-tons nos pas_, Courons en foule au Jau-vi-nas, Pre-nons avec nous Ni-co-las, Il sait toutes les rou-tes, Et nous conduira sans travaux, Quand on n'y ver-rait gout-tes, Au son des cha-lu-meaux

*I*MITONS *les Rois Mages,*
  Chrétiens, traversons nos coteaux,
Quittons tous nos villages
Et laissons nos hameaux.

Vers Saint'-Ménou hâtons nos pas,
Courons en foule au Jauvinas;
Prenons avec nous Nicolas,
  Il sait toutes les routes
Et nous conduira sans travaux
  Quand on n'y verrait gouttes,
  Au son des chalumeaux.

Les Anges qui l'ont annoncé
Ont parcouru le doyenné
247

Pas un village n'ont oublié :
   Les bergers de nos plaines
Plus d'un concert ont entendu,
   Et droit à Chaud'fontaines
   Courent tout éperdus.

Quand Bigniport vit la clarté
Incontinent s'est apprêté
Tout le premier est arrivé ;
   Sur d'la paille sans toies
Trouvent ce Prodige nouveau
   Des plumes de ses oies
   Garnit tout son berceau.

Saint' Ménehould devient Ephrem,
N'imite pas Jérusalem,
Soudain court à ce Bethléem
   Et les peuples convie,
Par son exemple et ses présents,
   Malgré son incendie,
   Offre or, myrrhe, et encens.

Les nonnes de Saint-Augustin
Entre elles députent un capucin
Barbe touffue, visage plein,
   Pour présenter des langes
Et bijoux de dévotion
   A ce grand Roi des Anges
   Par vénération.

Les jolies filles de Florent,
Que l'on disait depuis longtemps
Belles dehors, laides dedans,
   Sont dignes de louanges ;
De leur sexe faisant l'honneur,
   Ayant (selon les Anges)
   L'estime du Sauveur.

Pour toi, perfide Grange-aux-Bois,
Qui, jurant, jadis protestais
Qu'aucun Dieu ne reconnaissais,
    Viens ici reconnaître,
Convaincu de cette clarté,
    Un seul Souverain être,
    Et sa divinité.

Les Passavantains bien crottés,
Passant aux Frutilles sont volés,
Et par Verrières sont bien raillés:
    Chose désagréable.
Aucun d'eux ne peut dire deux mots,
    Paraissant dans l'étable,
    On les prit pour des sots.

Les Villerois, peur d'accident,
Se joignent à Châtrice en passant,
Prennent avec eux un moine blanc,
    Qui présente l'offrande,
Au nom de deux communautés:
    Une tarte friande,
    Avec deux gros pâtés.

De Verrières les railleurs,
Fils de Nemrod, fameux chasseurs,
Battent les bois avec clameurs,
    Font des présents bien riches,
Dont on charge plusieurs mulets;
    Trois sangliers, deux biches,
    Une ânée de poulets.

Daucourt, Elize, Braux-Saint-Rémy,
Puis Plagnicourt et Maujouy,
Tous ensemble avec Maupertuy
    Présentent vingt halottes,
Douze canards et cent vanneaux,
    Un panier d'échalottes,
    Avec trois fins gâteaux.

De Valmy les fendants bourgeois,
Généreux gascons-champenois,
Marchent tous sur le pied françois
    Comme à des épousailles;
Puis, après beaucoup de façons,
    Présentent au bœuf des pailles,
    A l'âne des chardons.

Ce que réjouit plus l'Enfant
Fut lorsque Marie doucement
Déploya pour lui le présent
    De la Maison des Planches;
C'était un bonnet très-mignon,
    De fines cottes blanches,
    Et des bas de coton.

Somme-Bionne et Hans, les plus dévots,
S'avançaient à pas d'escargots,
N'ayant aux pieds que des sabots,
    Lorsqu'une pluie subite
Tombant sur eux dans le chemin
    Les obligea bien vite
    De gagner Dommartin.

Les habitants de Dommartin,
Croyant que c'était Gros-Westein,
Courent à l'église, sonnent le tocsin,
    Tiraient d'humeur constante

Sur eux, les croyant partisans,
   Sans une voix perçante
   Qui crie: *J'étans de Hans!*

Les bons enfans de Courtémont
Réveillant les Mâcats du Pont
De là s'en vont droit à Moiremont;
   Leur chemin ils poursuivent
Et par la chaussée de Sougnas
   A la fin ils arrivent
   Auprès du Jauvinas.

Arrivés au pied du berceau
Ils présentent trois gros agneaux,
Les plus jolis de leurs troupeaux:
   Marie, douce et divine,
Les reçoit au nom de l'Enfant,
   Qui sitôt leur fait signe
   Qu'il en est très-content.

Ceux de Moiremont entrent soudain,
Ayant le chapeau à la main,
A leur tête un bénédictin,
   Qui pour eux complimente
Fort poliment ce nouveau Roi,
   Et chacun lui présente
   Son hommage et sa foi.

Or ceux du Pont, bien fatigués,
La hotte au dos, chapeaux troussés,
A la main des bâtons ferrés,
   Déchargent quelques bottes
D'échalas et de vieux sarment
   Qu'ils jettent dans la grotte
   Pour réchauffer l'Enfant.

Les Chaud'fontainois, désolés
D'avoir presque toujours passés
Pour des quoate-ventes affamés,
　　Les premiers donnent exemple
D'une exacte frugalité:
　　Une offrande bien ample
　　A jeun ont présenté.

Triaucourt apprend à son tour
Qu'un Enfant-Dieu fait son séjour
Sur terre, et sa céleste Cour;
　　Arrive en diligence,
D'un air poli et gracieux
　　Soulage l'indigence
　　De ce Maître des cieux.

XVIIth Century.

A NOTE ON FATHER CHRISTMAS

TO-MORROW — for you are reading this on the twenty-fourth of December, or at least all the good people that I write for are—to-morrow, I say, Father Christmas will be coming to this house. Indeed, he will be coming twice; he did last year and the year before, and we have every hope that he will not disappoint us this Christmas. We are specially favoured in this matter. The first time he comes, we don't see him, of course, because he arrives in the middle of the night and creeps round filling stockings. But we have a kind of arrangement with him—nothing formal, nothing in black-and-white—that brings him here again, just after tea. We are all hanging about in the hall—it is one of those square halls with a big fireplace, the sort of hall you can hang about in—and suddenly we hear a knock at the door. Who can it be? It is Father Christmas. You can tell at once by his white hair and beard and fine red hood and

252

cloak. Last year he looked rather like one of the children's uncles, who was indeed staying at the house but had gone out for a walk, but that is nothing, of course, for after all Father Christmas has got to look like somebody —and anyhow that uncle, who is quite young, could never have grown all that white hair and beard. Besides, he admits at once that he *is* Father Christmas. He has come to give out presents, not his own presents, the magical Lapland stuff, but all our own gifts to one another, which are heaped up on the hall table. You should see him standing there—a tremendous old fellow —picking up parcel after parcel, peering at the labels (he has left off his spectacles) and saying, "From So-and-So to Such-a-one." You don't notice even the Christmas Tree when he's there.

If you imagine that the children will be tremendously excited to-morrow afternoon, when Father Christmas himself appears in the hall, then you don't understand these matters. They will be excited enough in the morning, when—oh, wonderful moment—they grope in the dark and discover all those heavy bulging things at the bottom of their beds. But it doesn't astonish them that Father Christmas should arrive in person later in the day. Why should it? Their attitude towards him differs little from their attitude towards any other caller, a poet or an American editor or the lady who has the two big dogs or the man who pretends to put the electric bells in order. As usual, they are a little shy at first, but after a few minutes they walk up and talk to him quite coolly. Why shouldn't he come to our house and give out presents for us after tea? They live confidently in a world where an elderly fairy, with a long white beard and red cloak, might call any time. Why, just down the road there is a big white nanny-goat (you can see it—and sometimes smell it—for yourself) that has a large house of its own, and in this house it gives the most splendid

teas, no bread-and-butter but all jellies and chocolate cake, and invites little girls and boys and other nanny-goats and Tiny the pony and Fancy the brown cow and the speckledy hen and oh, lots of people. I know that white nanny-goat well because, like the children, I see it every time I walk down the road, but I had no idea that it was such a lavish hostess until they told me. And if a nanny-goat can give chocolate cake teas, why shouldn't Father Christmas call and talk to us?

No, it is not the children but the rest of us, the grown-ups, who get excited when Father Christmas arrives. We cannot take him for granted. Even though we may have arranged his beard and pinned up his cloak and hood, the sight of him, actually standing there, gives us thrill after thrill. You see, we go from one world to another, and there is nothing more exciting than making that journey. People write wise books about the plurality of worlds, but they never mention family life. Yet it is in family life that you discover the best plurality of worlds.

"Children sweeten labours; but they make misfortunes more bitter; they increase the cares of life, but they mitigate the remembrance of death": thus Bacon. Of the increase in the cares of life, the modern parent can speak at length; he knows he has indeed "given hostages to fortune." There is nothing that would make a parent's lot easier, from a good supply of comfortable houses and loyal domestics to light costs and taxes, that is not now at its worst. The world of to-day offers all its prizes to sterility. Outside its house of easy living is fixed the notice: "No children or dogs allowed." But it may be that the compensations have been correspondingly increased, that our labours require yet more sweetening, that there are more deaths whose remembrance may be mitigated. For we die more deaths than one.

And among these compensations, not the least, in my reckoning, is that acquaintance with a plurality of worlds.

You live so richly in your own house. A host of old friends are kept alive for you. Open the nursery door, and Jack Horner and Little Tom Tucker and Cinderella and Red Riding Hood spring out upon you. Quaint worlds, lit with magic, are spread before you again, and your own childhood, not dead but sleeping, quickens into life. The shades of the prison-house are lifted for us. Nothing has gone for ever. Something indeed has been added. You are both the fairy bringing gifts and the child happy with its magical treasures. You can have one foot in the world of knowledge and affection and the other in the world of wonder and fantasy.

But the clown with the pink nose has caught my eye again, and now I don't feel like saying anything more than " A Merry Christmas!"

J. B. PRIESTLEY.

A CHRISTMAS SONG FOR THREE GUILDS

℃ To be Sung a Long Time Ago—or Hence.

The Carpenters

ST. JOSEPH to the Carpenters said on a Christmas Day:
"The master shall have patience and the 'prentice shall obey;
And your word unto your women shall be nowise hard or wild:
For the sake of me, your master, who have worshipped Wife and Child.
But softly you shall frame the fence, and softly carve the door,
And softly plane the table—as to spread it for the poor,
And all your thoughts be soft and white as the wood of the white tree.
But if they tear the Charter, let the tocsin speak for me!

Let the wooden sign above your shop be prouder to be
scarred
Than the Lion-Shield of Lancelot that hung at Joyous
Garde."

The Shoemakers

St. Crispin to the Shoemakers said on a Christmastide:
  "Who fashions at another's feet will get no good of
pride.
They were bleeding on the Mountain, the feet that
brought good news,
The latchet of whose shoes we were not worthy to
unloose.
See that your feet offend not, nor lightly lift your head,
Tread softly on the sunlit roads the bright dust of the
dead.
Let your own feet be shod with peace; be lowly all your
lives,
But if they touch the Charter, ye shall nail it with your
knives.
And the bill-blades of the commons drive in all as dense
array
As once a crash of arrows came, upon St. Crispin's Day."

The Painters

St. Luke unto the Painters on Christmas Day he said:
  "See that the robes are white you dare to dip in gold
and red;
For only gold the kings can give, and only blood the saints,
And his high task grows perilous that mixes them in
paints.
Keep you the ancient order; follow the men that knew
The labyrinth of black and white, the maze of green
and blue;
Paint mighty things, paint paltry things, paint silly
things or sweet—

But if men break the Charter, you may slay them in the
    street.
And if you paint one post for them, then . . . but you
    know it well,
You paint a harlot's face to drag all heroes down to Hell.'

All Together

Almighty God to all mankind on Christmas Day said He:
  "I rent you from the old red hills and, rending, made
    you free.
There was charter, there was challenge; in a blast of
    breath I gave;
You can be all things other; you cannot be a slave.
You shall be tired and tolerant of fancies as they fade,
But if men doubt the Charter, ye shall call on the
    Crusade—
Trumpet and torch and catapult, cannon and bow and
    blade,
Because it was My challenge to all the things I made."

                        G. K. CHESTERTON.

A PRESENT OF NUTS

FROM my small garden, behold, eloquent Juvenal,
I send you Saturnalian nuts. The rest of the fruit
the rakish Garden God has bestowed on frolicking girls.

                           MARTIAL.

THEY have their part, in Brittany, in every domestic ceremony. When the tables are cleared and the guests have gone to bed their share is left, and it is then that the souls come back, released after the midnight Mass from their nightly vigil, and taste at these tables the illusion of a renewed earthly existence. One night in the year, at Christmas only, their sufferings cease; the purifying flames of Purgatory die out; a wave of happiness comes over all the world. And what miracles do not happen during this holy night! Tonight no animal sleeps, save the serpent. The cock crows at every hour, and certain animals—the ox and the ass—converse in human speech. That is why one must not enter a stable on Christmas Eve.

And this is so truly the Holy Night for the Bretons that they believe Our Lady and the Child, under the escort of St. Christopher or some other saint renowned for muscular vigour, walk the roads inquiring about the needs of their people; and in vain do they assume the dress of the peasants they visit, since the brilliance which streams from them soon betrays their incognito. . . .

Happy the sons of misty, shadowy Alklutha! They are not, like us, prisoners of the palpable: the supernatural surrounds them and bathes them in its enchanted waves.

CHARLES LE GOFFIC.

ARTICLES *made and appointed in the year 1635 by the Right Wo*ll *Richard Evelyn Esq. [father of the Diarist] High Sheriffe and Deputy Leavetenant to the King's Ma*tie *for the Counties of Surrey and Sussex:*

IMPRIMIS, I give free leave to Owen Flood, my trumpeter, gentleman, to be Lord of Misrule of all good orders during the Twelve Days. And also I give free leave to the said Owen Flood to command all and every person whatsoever, as well servants as others, to be at his command whensoever he shall sound his trumpet or music, and to do him good service, as though I were present myself, at their perills.

His LoPP commands every person or persons whatsoevr to appeare at the Hall at seaven of the clocke in the morning to be at prayers, and afterwards to be at his LoPPs commaunds, upon paine of punishment, accordinge as his LoPP shall thinke fitt.

· · · · ·

If any man shall bee drunke, or drinke more than is fitt, or offer to sleepe during the time abovesaid, or do not drinke up his bowle of beere but flings away his snuffe, (that is to say) the second draught, he shall drinke two, and afterwards be excluded.

If any person shall come into the kitchen whiles meate is a dressinge, to molest the Cookes, he shall suffer the rigor of his LoPPs law.

If any man shall kisse any maid, widdow or wife, except to bid welcome or farewell, whout his LoPPs consent, he shall have punishment as his LoPP shall thinke convenient.

I give full power and authority to his Lordship to break up all locks, bolts, bars, doors and latches, and to fling up all doors out of hinges, to come at those who disobey his Lordships commands.

GOD SAVE THE KING!

i. *To make Sillybubbs*

TAKE a quart of Creame, and half a pound of suger and a pint of sack and Renish together, and about half a pint of strong Beer, and when it up to a froth save some of the Froth on a sive to top y^m, then fill the glass half full with that which is not whipt much, and fill it up with the whipt, and top them with that on ye sive. Mem: No Whites of Eggs mentioned in ye sillybubb which I think ought to be in.

ii. *To make Buttered Oranges*

Take a pint of Creame, raspe the peels of two Oranges into half a pint of water of Orange juice, six eggs, two whites, as much suger as will sweeten it, so straine and set over a fire. When it is thick put in a piece of Butter as big as a Egg and keep it stirring till cold.

XVIIth Century.

A CARGO OF PORT

℃ Mr. Richard Estcourt, Comedian, to the *Spectator*.

Wednesday, January 2, 1712.

MR. SPECTATOR,
   Having observ'd in *Lilly's* Grammar how sweetly *Bacchus* and *Apollo* run in a verse: I have, to preserve that Amity between them, called in *Bacchus* to the aid of my profession of the Theatre. So that while some People of Quality are bespeaking Plays of me to be acted on such a Day, and others, Hogsheads for their Houses against such a Time, I am wholly employed in the agreeable Service of Wit and Wine. Sir, I have sent you Sir *Roger de Coverley's* letter to me, which pray comply with in favour of the *Bumper* Tavern. Be kind, for you know a Player's utmost Pride is the Approbation of the *Spectator*.

I am your Admirer,
though unknown,
Richard Estcourt.

¶ Sir Roger de Coverley to Mr. Estcourt, at his House in Covent-Garden.

Coverley, December the 18th, 1711.

Old Comical One,

        The Hogsheads of neat Port came safe, and have gotten thee good Reputation in these Parts; and I am glad to hear, that a Fellow who has been laying out his Money ever since he was born, for the mere Pleasure of Wine, has bethought himself of joining Profit and Pleasure together. Our Sexton (poor man) having receiv'd Strength from thy Wine since his fit of the Gout, is hugely taken with it: he says it is given by Nature for the use of Families, that no Steward's Table can be without it, that it strengthens Digestion, excludes Surfeits, Fevers, and Physick; which green Wines of any Kind cannot do. Pray get a pure snug Room, and I hope next Term to help fill your *Bumper* with our People of *the Club*; but you must have no Bells stirring when the *Spectator* comes; I forbore ringing to Dinner while he was down with me in the Country. Thank you for the little Hams and *Portugal* Onions; pray keep some always by you. You know my Supper is only good *Cheshire*-Cheese, best Mustard, a golden Pippin, attended with a Pipe of *John Sly's* best. Sir *Harry* has stolen all your Songs, and tells the Story of the 5th of November to Perfection.

        Your's, to serve you,

        Roger de Coverley.

We have lost old *John* since you were here.

        RICHARD STEELE.

NEW Year's Day.—Sich a crowd! Sich compliments of the season, and sich screws. Old Doleful grinnin' about on Fair Rosamond like Death on the Pale 'Oss. Found in the Cloud Quarries, but might as well have been in the clouds, the field surrounded it so and drove the fox into the mouth of the 'ounds. A young gentleman in nankeens and patent leather boots rode over old Barbara. "That's right!" exclaimed Pigg, "ride amang 'em!—ride amang 'em! Kill a hund or two; we've plenty mair at hyem! It mun be a poor concern that won't stand a hund today." Differ from Pigg there though. Howsomever, old Barbara ain't worth much. Declared she was the best in the pack notwithstandin'.

Staunton Snivey.—Batsay brought up shavin' water, saying Binjimin wished to be excused 'unting, havin' got the gout. All moonshine, I dare say! Boy has no passion for the chase. Have a good mind to stuff him full of Hunter's pills, and see if they will have any effect upon him. Wot business has a boy like him with the gout? Only for rear-admirals, town counsellors, and such like cocks. Caught Charley pinchin' Belinda under the table. Mounted him on Xerxes, as Ben couldn't go. Largish field. Captain Thompson (who never pays his £3) observed he never saw a pack of foxhounds without a whip before, and muttered somethin' about Master livin' out of the hounds. Shall set Fleecy at him.

Drew Longford Plantations; then on to Fawsley Wood. Found immediately, but Reynard inclined to hang in cover. No great scent either, but cover surrounded with foot people and little holiday boys. Bin useful in coaxin' them into crowds, to listen to his "hallegations," as he calls his lies. At length Reynard broke from the west end, and made straight for Iver Heath, runnin' a wide circuit by Staunton Snivey and over the hill up to Bybury Wood. Scent poor and pace bad. All the holiday hobble-dehoy boys treadin' on the 'ounds' tails. A short check at Farmer Hayband's, and thought all was over, when Priestess hit off in a grass field behind the barn, and away they went with the scent improvin' at every yard. Pace changed from an 'unting run to a reg'lar bust, and quite straight over the cream of the country. How the tail lengthened! A quarter of a mile, increasin' as they went. Young gen'lemen charged to bring home the brush, found their grass ponies beginnin' to gape. Captain Shortflat made Duncan Nevin's mare cry Capevi on Hutton Bank top, and many bein' anxious to give in, great was the assistance he received. Major Spanker would bleed her in the jugular, Mr. Wells thought the thigh vein, and another thought the toe, so that the mare stood a good chance of bein' bled to death, if Duncan's man who was cruising about hadn't fortinately cast up and saved her from her frinds.

On the hounds went for Crew, passing Limbury, leaving Argod Dingle to the right, over the Lily-white Sand Railway near the station at Stope, pointing for Gore Cross, the fox finally taking refuge in a pigsty behind the lodge of Button Park. Piggy at home and unfortunately killed, but who would grudge a pig after such a werry fine run? Pigg rode like a trump!—seven falls—knocked a rood of brick-wall down with his 'ead. What a nob that must be! Charley left one of his York-shire coat-laps in a hedge—Barnington lost his hat—Hudson his whip—Mr. Ramshay a stirrup, and Captain Martyn his cigar-case. Only seven up out of a field of sixty—day fine and bright—atmosphere clear, as if inclining for frost—hope not.

R. S. SURTEES (1803–1864).

CHRISTMASS Eve 1562. At the first course the Minstrells must sound their instruments, and go before: and the Steward and Marshall are next to follow together; and after them the Gentleman Sewer; and then cometh the meat. Those three Officers, are to make altogether three solemn Curtesies, at three several times, between the Skreen and the upper Table; beginning with the first, at the end of the Benchers table; the second at the midst; and the third at the other end; and then standing by, the Sewer performeth his Office.

When the first table is set and served, the Stewards Table is next to be served. After him, the Masters table of the Revells. Then that of the Master of the Game. The high Constable-Marshall: Then the Lieutenant of the Tower: then the Utter-barristers table; and lastly the Clerks table: All which time the Musick must stand right above the Harthside, with the noise of their Musick; their faces direct towards the highest Table: and that done, to return into the Buttry, with their Musick sounding.

Dinner ended, the Musicians prepare to sing a Song, at the highest Table: which ceremony accomplished, then the Officers are to address themselves every one in his office, to avoid [clear] the Tables in a fair and decent manner, they beginning at the Clerks Table; thence proceed to the next; and thence to all the others till the highest table be solemnly avoided.

Then after a little repose, the persons at the highest Table arise, and prepare to Revells: in which time the Butlers and other Servitors with them, are to dine in the Library.

At night, before Supper, are Revells and Dancing; and so also after Supper, during the twelve days of Christmas. The antientest Master of the Revells, is after Dinner and Supper to sing a Caroll, or Song; and command other Gentlemen then there present, to sing with him and the Company, and so it is very decently performed.

A Repast at Dinner is—viii d.

. . .

Christmass Day. Service in the Church ended, the Gentlemen presently repair into the Hall, to Breakfast, with Brawn, Mustard, and Malmsey.

At Dinner . . . the first Course is served in, a fair and large Bores-head, upon a Silver Platter, with Minstralsye.

A Repast at Dinner is xii d. which Strangers of worth are admitted to take in the Hall.

. . . . .

St. Stephans Day. This day the Sewer, Carver, and Cup-Bearer, are to serve as afore. After the first Course served in, the Constable Marshall cometh into the Hall, arrayed with a fair rich and compleat Harneys, white and bright, and gilt; with a Nest of Fethers of all Colours upon his Crest or Helm, and a gilt Pole-Axe in his hand: to whom is associate the Lieutenant of the Tower, armed with a fair White Armour, a Nest of Fethers in his Helm, and a like Pole-Axe in his hand; and with them sixteen Trumpetters; four Drums and Fifes, going in rank before them; and with them attendeth four men in white Harneys, from the middle upwards, and Halberds in their hands, bearing on their shoulders the Tower; which persons, with the Drums, Trumpets and Musick go three times about the Fire. Then the Constable-Marshall, after two or three Curtesies made kneeleth down before the Lord Chancellour; behind him the Lieutenant; and they kneeling, the Constable-Marshall pronounceth an Oration of a quarter of an hours length, thereby declaring the purpose of his coming; and that his purpose is to be admitted into his Lordships service.

The Lord Chancellour saith, He will take farther advice therein.

Then the Constable-Marshall standing up, in submissive manner delivereth his naked Sword to the

K

Steward; who giveth it to the Lord Chancellour: and thereupon the Lord Chancellour willeth the Marshall, to place the Constable-Marshall in his Seat: and so he doth, with the Lieutenant also in his Seat or place. During this Ceremony the Tower is placed beneath the Fire.

Then cometh the Master of the Game apparalled in green Velvet; and the Ranger of the Forest also, in a green suit of Satten bearing in his hand a green Bow, and divers Arrows, with either of them a Hunting Horn about their Necks; blowing together three blasts of Venery, they pace round about the Fire three times. Then the Master of the Game maketh three Curtesies, as aforesaid; then the Master of the Game standeth up.

This Ceremony also performed, a Huntsman cometh into the Hall, with a Fox and a Purse-net; with a Cat, both bound at the end of a Staff; and with them nine or ten Couple of Hounds, with the blowing of Hunting-Hornes. And the Fox and Cat are by the Hounds set upon, and killed beneath the Fire. This sport finished, the Marshall placeth them in their several appointed places.

Then proceedeth the second Course: which done and served out the Common Serjeant delivereth a plausible speech to the Lord Chancellour. . . .

St. John's Day. About seaven of the Clock in the Morning, the Lord of Misrule is abroad; and if he lack any Officer or attendant, he repaireth to their Chambers, and compelleth them to attend in person upon him after Service in the Church, to Breakfast, with Brawn Mustard & Malmsey. After Breakfast ended, his Lordships power is in suspence, untill his personall presence at night; and then his power is most potent.

If any offendor escape from the Lieutenant into the Buttry, and bring into the Hall a Manchet upon the point of a Knife, he is pardoned: For the Buttry in that Case is a Sanctuary.

From the *Accompts* of the Inner Temple, London.

ESTENNIALON de tson8e Ies8s ahatonnia!
Onna8ate8a d'oki n'on8andask8aentak
Ennonchien sk8atrihotat n'on8andilonrachatha
Ies8s ahatonnia!

Aloki onkinnhache eronhialeronnon
Iontonk ontatiande ndio sen tsatonnharonnion
8arie [1] onna8ak8eton ndio sen tsatonnharonnion
Ies8s ahatonnia!

Te ek8atatennonten ahek8achiendaen
Ti hek8annonronk8annion de son8entenrade
8toleti sk8annonh8e ichierhe akennonhonstha
Ies8s ahatonnia!

[*Translation*]

O mortal men, take courage! Jesus is born.
Now the reign of the Enemy is destroyed—
Hear ye no more what he whispers to your souls.
Jesus is born!

Listen to the angels in the skies!
Do not now reject what they proclaim to you,
Mary has borne the Great Spirit, as they foretell.
Jesus is born!

Now let us all come and pray to Him,
Adore Him! He hath granted our desire.
Hear Him! He wishes you to be good.
Jesus is born!

JEAN DE BRÉBEUF, S.J. (†1649).

MUSIC NOTE

PARIS, Jour de Noël, 1903.—9½, gd. messe, tout en feu; ce sont les pensionnaires qui chantent là-haut, aux gds. orgues—solo de violon—quelle musique! C'est tout de même malheureux aussi: quand on a l'Office canonial, de ne savoir même pas psalmodier! C'est a fuir.

From the Diary of J. K. HUYSMANS.

---

[1] The Hurons have no *M*. "8arie"="Ouarie"="Marie."

ON SNAPDRAGON

Memory. O I remember this dish well, it was first
invented by *Pluto,* to intertaine *Proserpina* withall.

Phantastes. I thinke not so, *Memory,* for when *Heracles*
had kild the flaming Dragon of *Hesperdia* with the
Apples of that Orchard he made this fiery meate; in
memory whereof hee named it Snap-dragon.

From the Play *Lingua,* 1607.

SIBERIA

A T an early hour, before it was light, the drum
sounded, and the under-officer whose duty it was to
count the convicts wished them a happy Christmas. The
prisoners answered him in an amiable tone, expressing a
like wish. Akim Akimitch and many others, who had
their geese and their sucking-pigs, went to the kitchen,
after saying their prayers, in a hurried manner to see
where their victuals were and how they were being
cooked. Through the little windows of our barracks,
half hidden by snow and ice, could be seen, flaring in
the darkness, the bright fire of the two kitchens where
six stoves had been lighted. In the courtyard, where
it was still dark, the convicts, each with a half-pelisse
round his shoulders, or perhaps fully dressed, were
hurrying towards the kitchen. Some of them meanwhile
—a very small number—had already visited the drink-
sellers.

I went out of barracks like the others. It was beginning
to get late. The stars were paling, a light, icy mist was
rising from the earth, and spirals of smoke ascended in
curls from the chimneys. Several convicts whom I met
wished me, with affability, a happy Christmas. I thanked
them and returned their wishes. Some of them had never
spoken to me before. Near the kitchen a convict from the
military barracks, with his sheepskin on his shoulder,
came up to me. Recognising me, he called out from the
middle of the courtyard, "Alexander Petrovitch!" He

ran towards me. I waited for him. He was a young fellow with a round face and soft eyes, not at all communicative as a rule. He had not spoken to me since my arrival, and seemed never to have noticed me. I did not know on my side what his name was. When he came up he remained planted before me, smiling a vacuous smile, but with a happy expression.

"What do you want?" I asked, not without astonishment.

He remained standing before me, still smiling and staring, without replying.

"Why, it is Christmas Day," he muttered.

He understood that he had nothing more to say, and hastened into the kitchen.

Round the flaming stoves in the kitchen the convicts were rubbing and pushing against one another, every one watching his own property. The cooks were preparing dinner, which was to take place a little earlier than usual. No one began to eat before the time, though many wished to do so; but it was necessary to be well behaved before the others. We were waiting for the priest, and the fast preceding Christmas would not be at an end till his arrival.

At last the priest arrived, with the cross and holy water. He prayed and chanted before the image, and then turned to the convicts, who one after the other came and kissed the cross. The priest then walked through all the barracks, sprinkling them with holy water. When he got to the kitchen he praised the bread of the convict-prison, which had a reputation in the town; the convicts at once expressed a desire to send him two loaves of new bread, still hot, which an old soldier was ordered to take to his house forthwith. Almost immediately afterwards the Major and the Commandant arrived. The Commandant was liked, and even respected; he made the tour of the barracks with the Major. wished the convicts a happy

Christmas, and went into the kitchen and tasted the cab-
bage-soup, which was excellent that day. Each convict
was entitled to nearly a pound of meat, with millet-seed,
and certainly the butter had not been spared. The Major
saw the Commandant to the door, and then ordered the
convicts to begin dinner.

•   •   •   •   •

Meanwhile it was getting dusk. Weariness and general
depression were making themselves felt through the
drunkenness and general debauchery. The prisoner who
an hour before was holding his sides with laughter now
sobbed in a corner, exceedingly drunk: others were
fighting, or wandering in a tottering manner through
the barracks, pale, very pale, seeking someone to quarrel
with. Petroff came up to me twice. As he had drunk very
little he was calm; but until the last moment he expected
something which he made sure would happen—something extraordinary, and highly diverting; although he
said nothing about it this could be seen from his looks.
He ran from barrack to barrack, without fatigue; but
nothing happened; nothing except general intoxication,
idiotic insults from drunkards, and general giddiness of
heated heads. . . .

But enough of this tumultous scene, which at last
came to an end. The convicts went heavily to sleep on
their camp-beds. They spoke and raged during their
sleep more than on other nights. Here and there they still
went on playing cards. The festival looked forward to
with such impatience was over; to-morrow the daily
work, the hard labour, would begin again.

FEDOR DOSTOIEVSKY (1821–1881).

CORDE natus ex parentis
Ante mundi exordium
Alpha et O cognominatus
Ipse fons et clausula
Omnium quæ sunt, fuerunt,
Quæque post futura sunt
Sæculorum sæculis.

PRUDENTIUS (348–413).

FANTASIA ON PORT

A CHIRRUP was in the Rev. Doctor's tone: "Hocks,
too, have compassed age. I have tasted senior Hocks.
Their flavours are as a brook of many voices; they have
depth also. Senatorial Port! we say. We cannot say
that of any other wine. Port is deep-sea deep. It is in its
flavour deep; mark the difference. It is like a classic
tragedy, organic in conception. An ancient Hermitage
has the light of the antique; the merit that it can grow
to an extreme old age; a merit. Neither of Hermitage
nor of Hock can you say that it is the blood of those long
years, retaining the strength of youth with the wisdom
of age. To Port for that! Port is our noblest legacy!
Observe, I do not compare the wines; I distinguish the
qualities. Let them live together for our enrichment;
they are not rivals like the Idæan Three. Were they
rivals, a fourth would challenge them. Burgundy has
great genius. It does wonders within its period; it does
all except to keep up in the race; it is short-lived. An aged
Burgundy runs with a beardless Port. I cherish the fancy
that Port speaks the sentences of wisdom, Burgundy
sings the inspired Ode. Or put it, that Port is the Homeric
hexameter, Burgundy the Pindaric dithyramb. What do
you say?"

"The comparison is excellent, sir."

GEORGE MEREDITH (1828–1909).

THE
ARRAIGNMENT,
CONVICTION, and IMPRISONING,
OF
CHRISTMAS:
On St. *Thomas* day laſt.

AND

How he broke out of Priſon in the Holidayes and got away, onely left his hoary hair, and gray beard, ſticking between two Iron Bars of a Window.

WITH,

An Hue and Cry after CHRISTMAS, and a Letter from Mr.
Woodcock a Fellow in Oxford, to a Malignant Lady in
LONDON

And divers paſſages between the Lady and the Cryer,
about Old Chriſtmas: And what ſhift he was fain to make
to ſave his life, and great ſtir to fetch him back
again.

With divers other Witty Paſſages.

~~Jan. ~~ *~~London~~*

Printed by *Simon Minc'd-Pye*, for *Ciſſely Plum-porridge*; And are to be
ſold by *Ralph Fidler* Chandler, at the ſigne of the *Pack of Cards*
in *Muſtard-Alley*, in *Brawn-ſtreet.*
164~~5~~. 1645

SONNET

*With the Compliments of the Season, to a Popular Leader much to
be Congratulated on the Avoidance of a Strike at Christmas.*

I KNOW you. You will hail the huge release,
  Saying the sheathing of a thousand swords
In silence and injustice, well accords
With Christmas bells. And you will gild with grease
The papers, the employers, the police,
  And vomit up the void your windy words
To your New Christ; who bears no whip of cords
For them that traffic in the doves of peace.

The feast of friends, the candle-fruited tree,
  I have not failed to honour. And I say
It would be better for such men as we,
And we be nearer Bethlehem, if we lay
Shot dead on scarlet snows for liberty,
  Dead in the daylight upon Christmas Day.

G. K. CHESTERTON.

PULVIS ET UMBRA

THE elders, with whom I was brought up, were of a
character not likely to let slip the sacred observance
of any old institution; and the ringing out of the Old
Year was kept by them with circumstances of peculiar
ceremony.—In those days the sound of those midnight
chimes, though it seemed to raise hilarity in all around
me, never failed to bring a train of pensive imagery into
my fancy. Yet I then scarce conceived what it meant, or
thought of it as a reckoning that concerned me. Not
childhood alone, but the young man till thirty, never
feels practically that he is mortal. He knows it indeed, and,
if need were, he could preach a homily on the fragility
of life; but he brings it not home to himself, any more
than in a hot June we can appropriate to our imagination
the freezing days of December. But now, shall I confess

a truth?—I feel these audits but too powerfully. I begin to count the probabilities of my duration, and to grudge at the expenditure of moments and shortest periods, like misers' farthings. In proportion as the years both lessen and shorten, I set more count upon their periods, and would fain lay my ineffectual finger upon the spoke of the great wheel. I am not content to pass away "like a weaver's shuttle." Those metaphors solace me not, nor sweeten the unpalatable draught of mortality. I care not to be carried with the tide, that smoothly bears human life to eternity; and reluct at the inevitable course of destiny. I am in love with this green earth; the face of town and country; the unspeakable rural solitudes, and the sweet security of streets. I would set up my tabernacle here. I am content to stand still at the age to which I am arrived; I, and my friends; to be no younger, no richer, no handsomer. I do not want to be weaned by age; or drop, like mellow fruit, as they say, into the grave.— Any alteration, on this earth of mine, in diet or in lodging, puzzles and discomposes me. My household gods plant a terrible fixed foot, and are not rooted up without blood. They do not willingly seek Lavinian shores. A new state of being staggers me.

Sun, and sky, and breeze, and solitary walks, and summer holidays, and the greenness of fields, and the delicious juices of meats and fishes, and society, and the cheerful glass, and candle-light, and fireside conversations, and innocent vanities, and jests, and *irony itself*— do these things go out with life?

Can a ghost laugh, or shake his gaunt sides, when you are pleasant with him?

And you, my midnight darlings, my Folios; must I part with the intense delight of having you (huge armfuls) in my embraces? Must knowledge come to me, if it come at all, by some awkward experiment of intuition, and no longer by this familiar process of reading?

Shall I enjoy friendships there, wanting the smiling indications which point me to them here,—the recognisable face—the "sweet assurance of a look"?—

In winter this intolerable disinclination to dying—to give it its mildest name—does more especially haunt and beset me. In a genial August noon, beneath a sweltering sky, death is almost problematic. At those times do such poor snakes as myself enjoy an immortality. Then we expand and burgeon. Then we are as strong again, as valiant again, as wise again, and a great deal taller. The blast that nips and shrinks me, puts me in thoughts of death. All things allied to the insubstantial, wait upon that master feeling; cold, numbness, dreams, perplexity; moonlight itself, with its shadowy and spectral appearances,—that cold ghost of the sun, or Phœbus' sickly sister, like that innutritious one denounced in the Canticles:—I am none of her minions—I hold with the Persian.

Whatsoever thwarts, or puts me out of my way, brings death into my mind. All partial evils, like humours, run into that capital plague-sore.—I have heard some profess an indifference to life. Such hail the end of their existence as a port of refuge; and speak of the grave as of some soft arms, in which they may slumber as on a pillow. Some have wooed death—but out upon thee, I say, thou foul, ugly phantom! I detest, abhor, execrate, and (with Friar John) give thee to six score thousand devils, as in no instance to be excused or tolerated, but shunned as an universal viper; to be branded, proscribed, and spoken evil of! In no way can I be brought to digest thee, thou thin, melancholy *Privation*, or more frightful and confounding *Positive*!

Those antidotes, prescribed against the fear of thee, are altogether frigid and insulting, like thyself. For what satisfaction hath a man, that he shall "lie down with kings and emperors in death," who in his lifetime never greatly coveted the society of such bed-fellows?—or, forsooth, that "so shall the fairest face appear"?—why, to comfort me, must Alice W—n be a goblin? More than all, I conceive disgust at those impertinent and mis-becoming familiarities, inscribed upon your ordinary tombstones. Every dead man must take upon himself to be lecturing me with his odious truism, that "Such as he now is I must shortly be." Not so shortly, friend, perhaps, as thou imaginest. In the meantime I am alive. I rove about. I am worth twenty of thee. Know thy betters! Thy New Years' days are past. I survive, a jolly candidate for 1821. Another cup of wine—and while that turncoat bell, that just now mournfully chanted the obsequies of 1820 departed, with changed notes lustily rings in a successor, let us attune to its peal the song made on a like occasion, by hearty, cheerful Mr. Cotton.

CHARLES LAMB.

"HAIL, SWEETEST FLOWERS"

NASCENTE Domino, luctus cœpit, non cælo sed mundo: indicitur matribus lamentatio, Angelis ex-sultatio, infantibus transmigratio. Deus est, qui natus est: Innocentes illi debentur victima, qui venit damnare mundi malitiam. Agnelli debent immolari, quia Agnus futurus est crucifigi, qui tollit peccata mundi. Sed oves ululant matres, quia agnos perdunt sine voce balantes.

Grande martyrium, crudele spectaculum! Eximitur machæra, et nulla intervenit causa: sola stridet invidia, cum qui natus est, nulli faciat violentiam. Sed oves cernimus matres, quæ super agnos lugent. Vox in Rama audita est, ploratus et ululatus magnus. Pignora sunt, non credita, sed creata; non deposita, sed exposita.

From a sermon of ST. AUGUSTINE, *Bishop,*
for Holy Innocents' Day.

IN fighting for Christmas Dickens was fighting for the old European festival, Pagan and Christian, for that trinity of eating, drinking, and praying which to moderns appears irreverent, for the holy day which is really a holiday. He had himself the most babyish ideas about the past. He supposed the Middle Ages to have consisted of tournaments and torture-chambers, he supposed himself to be a brisk man of the manufacturing age, almost a Utilitarian. But for all that he defended the medieval Feast which was going out against the Utilitarianism which was coming in. He could only see all that was bad in medievalism. But he fought for all that was good in it. And he was all the more really in sympathy with the old strength and simplicity because he only knew that it was good and did not know that it was old. He cared as little for medievalism as the medievals did. He cared as much as they did for lustiness and virile laughter and sad tales of good lovers and pleasant tales of good livers. He would have been very much bored by Ruskin and Walter Pater if they had explained to him the strange sunset tints of Lippi and Botticelli. He had no pleasure in looking on the dying Middle Ages. But he looked on the living Middle Ages, on a piece of the old uproarious superstition still unbroken; and he hailed it like a new religion. The Dickens character ate pudding to an extent at which the modern medievalists turned pale. They would do every kind of honour to an old observance, except observing it. They would pay to a Church feast every sort of compliment except feasting.

G. K. Chesterton.

A WELSH CAROL

O, GRISTNOGION, dyma 'r dydd
    Y mae i ni'n brudd lewnychu,
Y mae'n uchel drwy holl gred,
    Y dydd y ganed Iesu.

Dyw Nadolig, gwir iawn yw,
　Y ganed Duw o wyry,
Forwyn Fair, ond difai gwnaeth
　Roi un mab maeth i'n prynu?

O dra chariad ar ei ddyn
　Fe'i rhoes ei hun i'n prynu
Ar y groes a'i ais yn don,
　A gwaed ei fron yn tarddu.

A heb geisio tal na hur
　Am ei ddolur, Iesu,
Ond gwir galon pob rhyw ddyn,
　A'i gadw ei hun rhag pechu.

Ag o gwnawn ni felly'n brudd
　Pan ddêl dydd terfyu,
Ni gawn weled brenin nef
　A chydag ef wledychu.

Lle nad oes na chur na haint,
　Ond dawn a braint a gallu,
Na theyrnas i neb dan sêl
　Ond sawl a ddel i'w phrynu.

SIANKIN MORGAN (XVIth Century).

[*Translation*]

O! Christians! Hail the dawn,
　Your joyous tributes pay;
Its glory shines from shore to shore,
　For Christ was born this day.

O dawn of wondrous truth,—
　God of a Virgin born;
A Son who shall our souls redeem
　Is ours this Christmas morn.

278

Himself He sacrificed
　　To make us ever free;
Out of His riven side His blood
　　Flowed down on Calvary.

And for that cruel hurt,
　　For every bitter part,
He seeketh nor reward nor hire
　　Save to possess our heart.

Thus if His yoke we bear
　　Before we end our day,
We shall behold the King of Heaven
　　And reign with Him for aye.

No sorrow there abides,
　　But pow'r and love and light;
And they shall wear the victor's crown
　　Who triumph in His might.

　　　　　　　　　　　　DAVID EMRYS.

RETURN OF THE NATIVE

THE night of Christmas Eve, as we waited for midnight Mass, was always long; and gathered around the hearth we talked of our ancestors and praised their deeds. Then, little by little and not unwillingly, my good father would come to the topic of Spain and his memories of the siege of Figuières.

"What if I told you," he would begin, "that when I was over in Catalonia with the army I found a way, at the worst period of the Revolution, to get back from Spain, in spite of the war and everything, to spend Christmas with my own people? Well, on my solemn word, this is how the thing was arranged:

"At the foot of the Canigou, which is a high mountain between Perpignan and Figuières, we had been dodging about for some little time, fighting the Spaniards in

hand-to-hand battles. Aie! What deaths, what casualties, sufferings, and misery! It had to be seen to be believed. In addition, there was a shortage of everything in camp, and the month was December. Our mules and horses, for lack of fodder, used to gnaw at the wheels of the wagons and gun-carriages. Well, imagine that one day, as I was prowling round in a gorge on the side of the sea, I came across a tree full of oranges, red as gold!

"'Aha!' I said to the owner. 'You're going to sell me these, no matter what the price.' And having bought the lot I returned to camp, made straight for the tent of Captain Perrin (he came from Cabanes), took in my basket and said to him:

"'Captain, I've brought you a few oranges.'

"'Where did you get those?'

"'Oh, I found them, captain.'

"'You dog, you couldn't have given me greater pleasure. And now tell me what you want and you shall have it, if I have any say in it.'

"'I would very much like,' said I, 'before a cannon-ball cuts me in half, like so many others, to go home once more and bring in the Christmas Log with my family in Provence.'

"'Nothing simpler,' said he. 'Pass me the inkstand.' And Captain Perrin (may God have received him into Paradise, the good fellow!) scrawled on a sheet of paper (I have it still) these words:

Army of the Eastern Pyrenees.

WE, Perrin, Captain of Military Transport, grant leave to the Citizen François Mistral, a good Republican and soldier, aged 22, height five feet six, nose ordinary, mouth the same, chin round, forehead medium, face oval, to travel to his own country through the whole Republic, or to the Devil, if he likes.

"And so, my children, you see me arriving in Mail-

lane on the blessed eve of Christmas, and you may imagine the astonishment of everybody, the huggings, and the jollity. But next day the maire (I won't tell you the name of the swaggering ass—his children are still alive) ordered me to attend at the town-hall and questioned me.

"'In the name of the Law, citizen, how comes it that you are not with the army?'

"'The reason,' I told him, 'is that I took a fancy to get back this year to place the Log at Maillane.'

"'Really? In that case, citizen, you will explain your step to the district tribunal at Tarascon.'

And as I am telling you, I submitted to being taken by two of the National Guard before the district magistrates, three arrogant fellows in red bonnets and beards down to here.

"'Citizen,' they said to me, rolling ferocious eyes, 'how comes it that you are a deserter?'

I pulled my pass out of my pocket.

"'Here,' I said, 'read this.'

As soon as they had done so, my darlings, they got up and shook me by the hand.

"'Good, citizen! Good, citizen!' they cried. 'With papers like that you can send your maire of Maillane to the devil.'

"I could have stayed on after New Year's day, couldn't I? But I had my duty to do, and I went back to the line."

FRÉDÉRIC MISTRAL.

RURAL TIFF

ONE Christmas night
of snow,
Came father and son to words—such words! more cruel
because the blow
To crown each word was wanting, while taunt matched
gibe, and curse

Competed with oath in wager, like pastime in hell—nay,
          worse;
For pastime turned to earnest, as up there sprang at last
The son at the throat of the father, seized him and held
          him fast.

"Out of this house you go!—(there followed a hideous
          oath)—
This oven where now we bake, too hot to hold us both!
If there's snow outside, there's coolness; out with you,
          bide a spell
In the drift, and save the sexton the charge of a parish
          shell!"

ROBERT BROWNING.

TWO FESTAL QUATRAINS

THE COBBLER'S CATCH

COME sit we by the fire's side,
  And roundly drink we here;
Till that we see our cheeks ale-dy'd
  And noses tanned with beer.

A FROLIC

Bring me my rosebuds, drawer, come;
  So, while I thus sit crown'd,
I'll drink the aged Cæcubum,
  Until the roof turn round.

ROBERT HERRICK.

AT a prolonged drinking-bout one of the party remarked, "What gars the Laird of Garskadden luk sae gash?"

"Ou," says his neighbour, the Laird of Kilmardinny, "Garskadden's been wi' his Maker these twa hours; I saw him step awa', but I dinna like to disturb gude company."

DEAN RAMSAY.

THE FAIR UNHAPPY

MILORD CHESTERFIELD had no difficulty in following advice he already regarded as the only kind possible from a friend; but his wife, who had not yet realised the new discovery as to her conduct, imagined him to be jesting when he ordered her to prepare to go into the country in two days' time; all the more so because it was in the depth of an extremely bitter winter. But she soon perceived that he was in earnest. She saw from the air and expression of her husband that he believed himself to have good grounds for treating her with this hauteur, and finding all her relatives frigid and grave when she complained to them, she ceased, in the midst of her universal abandonment, to hope in anything but the tenderness of Hamilton. She confidently expected that he would enlighten her as to the reason for this un-pleasantness, of which she was quite ignorant, and that his passion would eventually find a way to release her from an exile at which, she flattered herself, that he would be even more exasperated than herself. But it was expecting pity from a crocodile.

At length arrived the eve of her departure, with all her preparations made for a long journey, with all the ceremonial visits bidding her good-bye, and still no news of Hamilton. She was at the end of her patience and her strength of mind in such a dreadful situation. Tears would have relieved her, but she preferred to restrain

them rather than to give her husband any pleasure thereby. Hamilton's conduct seemed to her inconceivable, and seeing that he made no appearance she found a means to send him this letter:

Can you be among those who, without condescending to explain to me the crime for which I am being treated like a slave, are willing to let me be carried off? What mean your silence and inaction in a position which should have awakened your tenderness all the more? I am on the eve of going away, and I am ashamed to feel that you allow me to face such a thing, which gives me horror, since I have reason to believe that you are less affected by it than anyone else. At least tell me where I am being taken, and what is going to happen to me in the wilds, and why, like all the rest of the world, you seem so changed towards one who would not change for the world, if your weakness or ingratitude did not make you unworthy of her tenderness.

The letter only made Hamilton harder and more proud of his revenge. The Court was full of the rumour of this happening. No one was ignorant of the reason for this sudden departure, but few approved the behaviour of Milord Chesterfield. People contemplated with astonishment the spectacle of an English husband who had the ill-breeding to be jealous of his wife. For the town it was up to now an unheard-of thing that a husband should have recourse to such violent methods of warding off the affliction which jealousy most fears and most merits. But many people excused the unfortunate Chesterfield—as far as they dared without drawing on themselves the general loathing—by blaming his defective education, and every mother made a devout promise to Providence that her son should never set foot in Italy during her lifetime, for fear of bringing back this brutal custom of wife-oppression.

Chesterfield himself had some trouble to make the best of the affair in the eyes of his patient compatriots, and by making a ridiculous display to cover up the

details of an adventure which might perhaps never been
known outside the Court, and which everyone would
have forgotten within a month. But as soon as he had
turned his back to convey away his fair prisoner and the
paraphernalia with which everyone declared that she
had equipped him, God only knows how they fell upon
his rearguard! The Rochesters, the Middlesexes, the
Sedleys, the Etheredges, the whole troop of wits evolved
a thousand quips which amused the town at his expense.

The Chevalier de Grammont found these witty and,
as they say, recreative; and in every place where the topic
cropped up he would say, willing to produce his own con-
tribution, *It is a singular thing that the country, which one
might call the Gibbet or the Galleys of youth and beauty,
should in England be reserved for the unfortunate, and not
the guilty. This poor little Chesterfield, simply for a few
imprudent glances, is packed away by her cross-grained
husband to spend the Christmas holidays in a country-
house fifty leagues from Town, whereas there are a thousand
more who are able to do what they please, and do it, and
whose behaviour deserves twenty strokes of the birch any
day. I name nobody—God forbid! but the Middleton, the
Denham, the Queen's Maids of Honour, the Duchess's,
and a hundred others hand out their favours right and
left, and nobody lifts an eyebrow. As for Lady Shrewsbury, it is a gift: I will wager she would have her man
killed every day and hold her head the higher for it. One
would say she had a plenary indulgence for the things she
does; there are three or four people going about wearing
a yard of her hair made into a bracelet, and nobody says a
word. Yet a surly fellow like Chesterfield is allowed to
exercise a tyranny unknown in this country before against
the prettiest woman in England, and for nothing at all!
But if he thinks he has brought off a good stroke, I am his
very humble servant! Faith, such precautions avail nothing!
Very often a woman who would think of nothing wrong if*
285

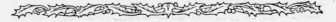

*you only left her alone will be drawn that way by a longing
for revenge, or reduced to it by necessity. This is gospel
truth. Listen to what it says in the Saraband of Francisco:*

> Jaloux, que sert tout votre effort ?
> L'Amour est trop fort;
> Et quelque peine,
> Que l'on prenne,
> Elle est vaine,
> Quand deux Cœurs une fois sont d'accord.
> Il faut devant vous
> Cacher ce qu'on fait de plus doux.
> On contraint ses plus chers désirs;
> On prend cent plaisirs.
> Mais, pour les soins
> De cent Témoins,
> En secret on n'aime pas moins.

Such are the words of which the Chevalier de Grammont passed as the author. Neither justice nor style lent
them any excessive brilliance, but as they contained
certain sentiments which flattered the genius of the
nation and the amateurs of the fair sex, all the ladies
wished to have a copy to teach their children.

HAMILTON, *Memoirs of Grammont*, 1713.

THIS AMERICAN BUSINESS

Arlington Street, December 26, 1774.

IT is supposed here, that the new proceedings of the
French parliament will produce great effects: I don't
suppose any such thing. What America will produce I
know still less; but certainly something very serious.
The merchants have summoned a meeting for the second
of next month, and the petition from the Congress to
the King is arrived. The heads have been shown to lord
D——; but I hear one of the agents is against presenting
it; yet it is thought it will be delivered, and then be ordered

286

to be laid before Parliament. The whole affair has already been talked of there on the Army and Navy days; and Burke, they say, has shone with amazing wit and ridicule on the late inactivity of Gage, and his losing his cannon and straw; on his being entrenched in a town with an army of observation; with that army being, as Sir William Meredith has said, an asylum for magistrates, and to secure the port. Burke said, he had heard of an asylum for debtors and ——, never for magistrates; and of ships, never armies, securing a port. This is all there has been in Parliament, but elections.

I have but two or three words more. Remember my parcel of letters from madame du D., and pray remember this injunction, not to ruin yourselves in bringing presents. A very slight fairing of a guinea or two obliges as much, is more fashionable, and not a moment sooner forgotten than a magnificent one.

January 5th.

An account is come of the Bostonians having voted an army of 16,000 men, who are to be called *minute-men*, as they are to be ready at a minute's warning. Two Directors or Commissioners, I don't know what they are called, are appointed. There has been too a kind of mutiny in the 5th Regiment. A soldier was found drunk on his post. Gage, in this time of *danger*, thought rigour necessary, and sent the fellow to a court-martial. They ordered 200 lashes. The general ordered them to improve their sentence. Next day it was published in the Boston Gazette. He called them before him, and required them on oath to abjure the communication: three officers refused. Poor G. is to be a scape-goat, not for this, but for what was a reason against employing him, incapacity. I wonder at the precedent! Howe is talked of for his successor. . . .

HORACE WALPOLE to the Hon. H. S. Conway.

January 3, 1712.

I AM engaged in this Speculation by a Sight which I lately met with at the Opera. As I was standing in the hinder Part of the Box, I took notice of a little Cluster of Women sitting together in the prettiest coloured Hoods I ever saw. One of them was blue, another yellow, and another philemot; the fourth was of a pink Colour, and the fifth of a pale Green. I looked with as much Pleasure upon this party-coloured Assembly, as upon a Bed of Tulips, and did not know at first whether it might not be an Embassy of *Indian* Queens; but upon my going about into the Pit, and taking them in Front, I was immediately undeceived, and saw so much Beauty in every Face, that I found them all to be *English*.

I am inform'd that this Fashion spreads daily, insomuch that the Whig and Tory Ladies begin already to hang out different Colours, and to shew their Principles in their Head-dress. Nay, if I may believe my Friend *Will Honeycomb*, there is a certain old Coquette of his Acquaintance who intends to appear in a Rainbow Hood, like the Iris in Dryden's *Virgil*, not questioning but that among such Variety of Colours she shall have a Charm for every Heart. My friend *Will*, who very much values himself upon his great Insight into Gallantry, tells me, that he can already guess at the Humour a Lady is in by her Hood, as the Courtiers of *Morocco* know the Disposition of their present Emperour by the Colour of the Dress which he puts on. When *Melesinda* wraps her Head in Flame-colour, her Heart is set upon Execution. When she covers it with purple, I would not, says he, advise her Lover to approach her; but if she appears in white, it is Peace, and he may hand her out of the Box with Safety.

Will informs me likewise, that these Hoods may be used as Signals. Why else, says he, does *Cornelia* always put on a Black Hood when her Husband is gone into the Country?

Such are my Friend *Honeycomb's* Dreams of Gallantry.

For my own Part, I impute this Diversity of Colours in the Hoods to the Diversity of Complexion in the Faces of my pretty Countrywomen.

JOSEPH ADDISON.

MORAL FANTASIA ON A DIARY

MINE is one of your No. 12 diaries, three shillings cloth boards; silk limp, gilt edges, three-and-six; French morocco, tuck ditto, four-and-six. It has two pages, ruled with faint lines for memoranda, for every week, and a ruled account at the end, for the twelve months from January to December, where you may set down your incomings and your expenses. I hope yours, my respected reader, are large; that there are many fine round sums of figures on each side of the page; liberal on the expenditure side, greater still on the receipt. I hope, Sir, you will be "a better man," as they say, in '62, than in this moribund '61, whose career of life is just coming to its terminus. A better man in purse? in body? in soul's health? Amen, good sir, in all. Who is there so good in mind, body, or estate, but bettering won't still be good for him? O unknown Fate presiding over next year, if you will give me better health, a better appetite, a better digestion, a better income, a better temper in '62 than you have bestowed in '61 I think your servant will be the better for the changes. For instance, I should be the better for a new coat. This one, I acknowledge, is very old. The family says so. My good friend, who amongst us would not be the better if he would give up some old habits? Yes, yes. You agree with me. You take the allegory? Alas! at our time of life we don't like to give up those old habits, do we? It is ill to change. There is the good old loose easy slovenly bedgown, laziness, for example. What man

of sense likes to fling it off and put on a tight *guindé* prim
dress-coat that pinches him? There is the cosy wrap-
rascal, self-indulgence — how easy it is! How warm!
How it always seems to fit! You can walk out in it, you
can go down to dinner in it. You can say of such what
Tully says of his books: *Pernoctat nobiscum, peregrinatur,
rusticatur.* It is a little slatternly—it is a good deal stained
—it isn't becoming—it smells of cigar-smoke; but *allons
donc!* let the world call me idle and sloven. I love my
ease better than my neighbour's opinion. I live to please
myself; not you, Mr. Dandy, with your supercilious airs.
I am a philosopher. Perhaps I live in my tub, and don't
make any other use of it——. We won't pursue further
this unsavoury metaphor.

A diary. *Dies. Hodie.* How queer to read are some of
the entries in the journal! Here are the records of dinners
eaten and gone the way of flesh. The lights burn blue
somehow, and we sit before the ghosts of victuals. Hark
at the dead jokes resurging! Memory greets them with
the ghost of a smile. Here are the lists of the individuals
who have dined at your own humble table. The agonies
endured before and during those entertainments are
renewed, and smart again. What a failure that special
grand dinner was! How those dreadful occasional waiters
did break the old china! What a dismal hash poor Mary
the cook made of the French dish which she *would* try
out of Francatelli: How angry Mrs. Pope was at not
going down to dinner before Mrs. Bishop! How Trimalchio sneered at your absurd attempt to give a feast; and
Harpagon cried out at your extravagance and ostenta-
tion! How Lady Almack bullied the other ladies in the
drawing-room (when no gentleman was present): never
asked you back to dinner again: left her card by her
footman: and took not the slightest notice of your wife
and daughters at Lady Hustleby's assembly! On the

other hand, how easy, cosy, merry, comfortable, those little dinners were; got up at one or two days' notice; when everybody was contented; the soup as clear as amber; the wine as good as Trimalchio's own; and the people kept their carriages waiting, and would not go away till midnight!

W. M. THACKERAY.

A DANCE AT WHITE HALL

1662. December 31st. Mr. Povy and I to White Hall, he taking me thither on purpose to carry me into the ball this night before the King. By and by, comes the King and Queen, the Duke and Duchess, and all the great ones: and after seating themselves, the King takes out the Duchess of York, and the Duke the Duchess of Buckingham; the D. of Monmouth my Lady Castlemaine; and so other lords other ladies; and they danced the Branle. After that, the King led a lady a single Coranto; and then the rest of the lords, one after another, other ladies; very noble it was, and great pleasure to see. Then to country-dances; the King leading the first, which he called for; which was, says he, *Cuckolds all awry*, the old dance of England:

The manner was, when the King dances, all the ladies in the room, and the Queen herself, stand up; and indeed he dances rarely, and much better than the Duke of York. Having staid here as long as I thought fit, to my infinite content, I went home, leaving them dancing.

SAMUEL PEPYS's Diary.

NOW the schoolboy, loath to desert his playthings, is recalled by his clamorous master; now the boozy gambler, foully betrayed by the sound of his fascinating dice-box and just dragged out of a secluded tavern, begs mercy of the Ædile. Saturnalia are all over, Galla, yet you have sent me no small presents—not even any smaller than usual. Well, let my December pass thus; I fancy you know your own Saturnalia are surely coming soon, the Kalends of March. Then, Galla, I will return you what you gave.

MARTIAL.

A GIFT FROM THE LEGION

WHEN I was a boy, which was a good many years ago, there was a very queer celebration on New Year's Day in the little Monmouthshire town where I was born, Caerleon-on-Usk. The town children—village children would be nearer the mark, since the population of the place amounted to a thousand souls or thereabouts —got the biggest and bravest and gayest apple they could find in the loft, deep in the dry bracken. They put bits of gold leaf upon it. They stuck raisins into it. They inserted into the apple little sprigs of box, and then they delicately slit the ends of hazel-nuts, and so worked that the nuts appeared to grow from the ends of the box leaves, to be the disproportionate fruit of these small trees. At last, three bits of stick were fixed into the base of the apple, tripod-wise, and so it was borne round from house to house; and the children got cakes and sweets, and—those were wild days, remember—small cups of ale. And nobody knew what it was all about.

And here is the strangeness of it. Caerleon means the Fort of the Legions, and for about three hundred years the Second Augustan Legion was quartered there and made a tiny Rome of the place, with amphitheatre, baths, temples, and everything necessary for the comfort of a Roman-Briton. And the Legion brought over the custom of the *strena* (French, *étrennes*), the New Year's Gift of good omen. The apple, with its gold leaf, raisins, and nuts, meant "good crops and wealth in the New Year." It is the poet Martial, I think, who alludes to the custom. He was an ungrateful fellow; somebody sent him a gold cup as a New Year's gift, and he said the gold of the cup was so thin that it would have done very well to put on the festive apple of the day.

Well, I suppose the Second Augustan was recalled somewhere about A.D. 400. The Saxon came to Caerleon, and after him the Dane, and then the Norman, and then the modern spirit, the worst enemy of all; and still, up to fifty years ago, the Caerleon children kept New Year's Day as if the Legionaries were yet in garrison.

ARTHUR MACHEN.

"I DON'T CARE WHERE THE WATER GOES . . ."

COME, boy, you who pour the Old Falernian, fill me stronger cups, as the law of Postumia, Mistress of the Revels, ordains—Postumia, tipsier than the tipsy grape. But you, water, begone, away with you, water, poisoner of wine, away to your killjoys! This is the true Thyonian god.

CATULLUS (B.C. 84-?47).

LONDON, Dec. 26, 1712. I was to wish th Duke of Ormond a happy Christmas, & give half a Crown to his Porter. It will cost me a dozen half Crowns among such Fellows; I din'd with Lord Treasurer, who chid me for being absent 3 days. Mighty kind, with a P—— less of Civility and more of his Interest.

27. I mett Mr. Addison and Pastorall Philips on te Mall to-day and took a Turn with them; But they both looked terribly dry and cold; A Curse of Party! And do y' know that I have taken more pains to recommend th' Whig Witts to te Favor & Mercy of te Ministers than any other People; yet I am worse used by that Faction than any man. Well, go to Cards, sollah Ppt, & dress te Wine and Orange, sollah MD, and I'll go seep. 'Tis late. Nite, MD.

28. My Cold is so bad that I could not go to Church to-day, nor to Court; but, I was engaged to Lord Orkney's, with Duke of Ormond, at dinner; and ventured, because I could cough & spitt there as I pleased. The Duke and Lord Arran left us, and I have been sitting ever since with Ld & Ldy Orkney till past 11; and my Cold is worse, & makes me giddy. I hope it is onely my Cold. Oh, says Ppt, every body is giddy with a Cold; I hope it is no more; but I'll go to bed, for te fellow has bawld past 12. Nite deels.

29. I got out early to-day, & scaped all my Duns. I went to see Lord Bolingbroke about some Business, & truly he was gone out too. I dined in te City upon te boild leg of a Goose and a bitt of Brawn with my Printer. . . . My Cold is very bad. Every [body] has one. Nite, two dee rogues.

31. My Cold is still so bad that I have not te least Smelling. I am just got home, & 'tis past 12; and I'll go to bed, and settle my head, heavy as lead. Nite MD.

January 1, 1713. A great many new years to dearest

little MD. Pray God Almighty bless you, and send you ever happy.

2. I cannot smell yet, tho my Cold begins to break; it continues cruell hard frosty weather. Go and be merry, little sirrahs.

5. Our Frost is broke, but it is bloody cold.

7. Very warm slabby weather, but I made a shift to get a walk; yet I lost half of it by shaking off Lord Rochester, who is a good, civil, Simple man. . . . I am plagued with bad Authors, Verse and Prose, who send me their Books and Poems, the vilest Trash I ever saw; but I have given their names to my man, never to let them see me. I have got new ink, and it is very white, & I don't see that it turns black at all. I'll go to sleep; 'tis past 12. Nite, MD.

SWIFT, *Journal to Stella.*

A HEBRIDEAN FROLIC

MR. MACLEAN informed us of an odd game, of which he did not tell the original, but which may perhaps be used in other places, where the reason of it is not yet forgot. At New-year's eve, in the hall or castle of the Laird, where, at festal seasons, there may be supposed a very numerous company, one man dresses himself in a cow's hide, upon which other men beat with sticks. He runs with all this noise round the house, which all the company quits in a counterfeited fright: the door is then shut. At New-year's eve there is no great pleasure to be had out of doors in the Hebrides. They are sure soon to recover from their terrour enough to solicit for re-admission; which, for the honour of poetry, is not to be obtained but by repeating a verse, with which those that are knowing and provident take care to be furnished.

DR. SAMUEL JOHNSON (1709–1784).

A. D. 1065.—About midwinter King Edward came to Westminster, and had the minster there consecrated, which he had himself built to the honour of God, and St. Peter, and all God's saints. This church-hallowing was on Childermas Day. He died on the eve of Twelfth Day; and he was buried on Twelfth Day in the same minster; as it is hereafter said:

Here Edward the King,
of Angles lord,
sent his stedfast
soul to Christ;
in the kingdom of God
a holy spirit.
He in the world here
abode awhile,
in the kingly throng
of council sage,
four and twenty
winters wielding
the sceptre freely,
wealth he dispensed.
In the tide of health
the youthful monarch,
offspring of Ethelred,
ruled well his subjects;
the Welsh and the Scots,
and the Britons also,
Angles and Saxons—
relations of old.
Blithe-minded aye
was the harmless king,
though he long ere,

of land bereft,
abode in exile
wide on the earth;
when Knut o'ercame
the kin of Ethelred
and Danes wielded
the dear kingdom
of Engle-land.
Eight and twenty
winters' rounds
they wealth dispensed.
Then came forth
free in his chambers,
in royal array,
good, pure, and mild,
Edward the noble;
by his country defended—
by land and people.
Until suddenly came
the bitter Death
and this dear king
snatched from the earth.
Angels carried
his soul sincere
into heaven light.

At this time also was Earl Harold hallowed to king; but he enjoyed little tranquillity therein the while he wielded the kingdom.

The Anglo-Saxon Chronicle.

Christmas, 1653.

. . . You would see me, you say? You may do so if you please, though I know not to what end. You deceive yourself if you think it would prevail upon me to alter my intention; besides, I can make no contrivances; it must be here, and I must endure the noise it will make, and undergo the censures of people that choose ever to give the worst interpretation that anything will bear.

Why should you make an impossibility where there is none? A thousand accidents might have taken me from you, and you must have borne it. Why would not your own resolution work as much upon you as necessity and time does infallibly upon people? Your father would take it very ill, I believe, if you should pretend to love me better than he did my Lady, yet she is dead and he lives, and perhaps may do to love again. There is a gentlewoman in this country that loved so passionately for six or seven years that her friends, who kept her from marrying, fearing her death, consented to it; and within half a year her husband died, which afflicted her so strongly nobody thought she would have lived. She saw no light but candles in three years, nor came abroad in five; and now that 'tis some nine years past she is passionately taken again with another, and how long she has been so nobody knows but herself. This is to let you see 'tis not impossible what I ask, nor unreasonable. Think on't, and attempt it at least; but do it sincerely, and do not help your passion to master you. As you have ever loved me do this.

I shall long to hear from you; but if you should deny the only hope that's left me, I must beg you will defer it till Christmas Day be past.

DOROTHY OSBORNE to Sir William Temple.

Nowel, nowel, nowel, nowel, nowel, nowel!

OUT of youre slepe arise and wake,
For God mankind now hath itake
All of a maide without any make;
    Of all women she berethe the belle.
      Nowel.

And throwe a maide faire and wis
Now man is made of full grete pris;
Now angeles knelen to manes servis;
    And at this time all this bifel.
      Nowel.

Now man is brighter than the sonne;
Now man in heven an hie shall (wonne);
Blessed be God this game is begonne
    And his moder emperesse of helle.
      Nowel.

That ever was thralle, now is he free;
That ever was smalle, now grete is she;
Now shall God deme bothe thee and me
    Unto his blisse, if we do well.
      Nowel.

Now man may to heven wende;
Now heven and erthe to him they bende;
He that was fo now is oure frende.
    This is no nay that I you telle.
      Nowel.

Now blessed brother, graunte us grace,
A domes day to see thy face,
And in thy court to have a place,
    That we mow there singe Nowel.
      Nowel.

      Bodleian (Selden) MS., XVth Century.

Paris, December 31st, 1870.

MASTER, I am sending you by balloon a great heap of kisses, and it gives me pleasure to send them in Provençal, since then I know that the Barbarians, if this balloon falls into their hands, won't be able to read my writing and publish this letter in the *Swabian Mercury*.

It is cold, it is dark, we are eating horse, cat, camel, and hippopotamus (oh for the good onions, the fish-ragout and the cheese-dish of our frolic at Trinquetaille!). Our guns burn our fingers. Wood is rare. The Armies of the Loire have not arrived. But never mind; the cockroaches from Berlin will have to be bored for some time yet in front of Paris ramparts. . . . And then if Paris falls I know one or two good patriots who can show M. de Bismarck the way round some of the little streets of our poor capital.

Good-bye, Master: three huge kisses—one from me, one from my wife, the third from my son. And with this a happy New Year, as ever, from to-day till a year hence.

ALPHONSE DAUDET to Frédéric Mistral.

CHRISTMAS WITH THE FANCY (1810)

NOTWITHSTANDING the rain came down in torrents and the distance from London the FANCY were not to be deterred from witnessing the MILL, and waded through a clayey road, nearly knee deep for five miles, as if it had been as smooth as a bowling-green, so great was the curiosity and interest manifested upon this battle. About twelve o'clock MR. JACKSON, with his usual consideration, had the ring formed at the foot of a hill (twenty-four feet roped) surrounded by the numerous carriages which had conveyed the spectators thither, to ward off the chilling breeze and rain which came keenly from the eastward. Immediately upon this being com-

pleted, *Molineaux* came forward, bowed, threw up his hat in defiance, and retired to strip; *Cribb* immediately followed, and they were soon brought forward by their seconds; GULLEY and JOE WARD for the *Champion*, and RICHMOND and JONES for *Molineaux*.

First Round:—The first appearance of the Young Roscius excited not greater attention than the SETTING-TO of the above pugilists; the eyes of the spectators were stretched to their utmost, waiting for the first blow, when, after a few seconds of scientific display, the MOOR put in a left-handed hit, but which did no execution. *Cribb* returned but his DISTANCE was incorrect; however, he made a good stop, and planted a blow with his left hand under the eye of his opponent. A rally now ensued, and Molineaux was thrown.

Second Round:—The *Moor* rallied with a left-handed blow, which did not tell, when *Cribb* planted a most tremendous one on his adversary's right eyebrow. . . . Desperation was now the order of the round in which Cribb showed the utmost Science, although he received a dreadful blow in the mouth that made his teeth chatter again, and exhibited the first signs of CLARET. Four to one on *Cribb*.

Third Round:—After a short space, occupied in sparring, Molineaux attempted a good blow on Cribb's NOB, but the Champion parried it, and returned a right-handed hit under the MOOR's lower rib, when he fell rapidly in the extreme. Still four to one.

Fifth Round:—This round was a display of such united SKILL and BOTTOM that both the combatants claimed peculiar notice for their extraordinary efforts. The *Moor* put in a tremendous hit on the left eye of the Champion and a desperate MILLING continued for half-a-minute, when *Molineaux* fell from a feeble blow. The knowing ones were lost for a moment, and no bets were offered.

Sixth Round:—The *Moor* planted a blow on the NOB

of the Champion who fell from the bad state of the ground.

Eighth Round:—Cribb showed himself off in good style but the *Moor* rallied in PRIME TWIG and stood up undismayed, proving that his courage was of no ordinary nature till he fell almost in a state of stupor from the MILLING his head had undergone.

Ninth Round:—Molineaux gave such proof of gluttony that four to one now made many tremble who had sported it. The FLASH SIDE were full of palpitations.

Tenth Round:—*Cribb* kept knocking *Molineaux* about the NOB but he seemed to disregard it and kept close to his man till they both went down.

Eleventh Round:—The *Moor* evinced strength enough to give *Cribb* a heavy fall.

Thirteenth Round:—*Molineaux* in boring in upon his adversary, received a severe FACER from him, but who went down from the force of his own blow. To show the uncertainty of betting, it is necessary to state that the odds had changed six to four on the *Moor* to the no small chagrin of those who had sported their money that *Molineaux* would not become the favourite during the fight.

Fourteenth Round:—The Champion was LEVELLED.

Fifteenth Round:—Those persons who were fond of viewing MILLING, might now witness it in perfection; no shifting but giving and taking were displayed on both sides.

Sixteenth Round:—Rallying still the most prominent feature. Odds changed about until they became even.

Seventeenth Round:—*Molineaux* not only gave *Cribb* a desperate fall, but fell upon him. Betting very shy, if any, it appearing to be anybody's battle.

Nineteenth Round:—To distinguish the Combatants by their features would have been utterly impossible—but their difference of *colour* supplied this sort of defect. . . .

Cribb, acting upon the defensive was got by *Molineaux* against the ropes. Molineaux held Cribb in such a manner that he could neither make a hit nor fall down. About 200 persons rushed from the outer to the interior ring and it is asserted that if one of the *Moor's* fingers was not broken it was much injured by some of them. All this time *Molineaux* was gaining his wind by laying his head on *Cribb's* breast, and refused to release his victim; the champion, by a desperate effort to extricate himself was at length run down to one corner of the ring, and *Molineaux* having got his head under his arm, *jibbed* away most unmercifully.

Twenty-first Round :—*Cribb* planted two blows upon the head and body of his opponent which *Molineaux* returned by a desperate blow in *Cribb's* face, when they closed and the Champion was thrown. The well-known BOTTOM of *Cribb* induced his friends to back him six to four.

Twenty-fourth Round :—*Molineaux* began this round with considerable spirit and some hits were exchanged, when *Cribb* was thrown. The betting tolerably even.

Twenty-sixth Round :—The Champion now endeavoured to hit the right eye of *Molineaux*, the left having been DARKENED for some time.

Twenty-seventh Round :—Weakness conspicuous on both sides and after some pulling and hauling both fell.

Twenty-ninth Round :—The *Moor* was running in with spirit, but the *Champion* stopped his Career by planting a hit upon his right eye, which materially damaged his peeper. The fate of the battle might be said to be decided by this round.

Thirtieth Round :—*Molineaux* with a courage and ferocity unequalled, rising superior to exhaustion and fatigue, rallied his adversary with as much resolution as at the commencement of the fight, his *nob* defying all the *milling* it had received and contending nobly with

302

Cribb right and left, knocking him away by his hits and gallantly concluding the round by closing and throwing the Champion. The *Moor* was now convinced that, if he did win, he must do it offhand as his sight was much impaired.

Thirty-second Round:—Strength was fast leaving both the combatants—they staggered against each other like inebriated men, and fell without exchanging a blow.

Thirty-third Round:—To the astonishment of every spectator, *Molineaux* rallied with strength enough to bore his man down, but both their *hits* were of more *show* then effect.

Thirty-fourth Round:—This was the last round that might be termed fighting, in which *Molineaux* had materially the worst of it; but the battle was continued to the 39th when *Cribb* evidently appeared the best man and at its conclusion, the *Moor, for the first time complained* that 'HE COULD FIGHT NO MORE!' but his seconds who viewed the NICETY OF THE POINT, persuaded him to try the *chance* of another round, to which request he acquiesced, when he fell from weakness, reflecting additional credit on the manhood of his brave CONQUEROR, *TOM CRIBB.*

PIERCE EGAN, *Boxiana.*

THE MAN IN BLACK

WEDNESDAY, January 5th, 1757.—This day has witnessed a most terrible affair. The King has been stabbed with a knife between the fourth and fifth rib of the right side, by a villain who was taken on the spot. Next morning, Twelfth Day, consternation spread all over Paris; the churches were full of people in tears. In the evening it was learned with relief that the blow was neither mortal nor dangerous; and in fact the King rose on Saturday and held a Council, and on the Sunday

the Forty Hours' prayers were concluded and the theatres re-opened.

The King had come from Trianon to Versailles at about four in the afternoon to see his daughters, Madame Adelaide having a cold. At a quarter to six he descended the smaller staircase to the Marble Court, to go to his coach and return to Trianon. There were few persons about and few torches, and M. le Duc d'Ayen, captain of the bodyguard, was not with the King. His Majesty stayed a moment on the staircase to chat with the Maréchal de Richelieu, having with him a brigadier of the Royal Guard. As he turned to go, a man in black, wearing a greatcoat and having a wig *en bourse*, with, they say, a hat on his head, shoved aside the brigadier, approached the King, placed one hand on his shoulder, and drove a poignard between his ribs. The King, feeling a blow, clapped his hand to the place, felt the blood flowing, and said, "I have been stabbed." At the same time he said, "It is that man there." And as the assassin was about to escape the King added, "Arrest him, but do him no harm." They say that he would have had about three seconds, after striking the blow, to get away under cover of the darkness; but a footman, a soldier of the Bodyguard, and one other threw themselves on him at once. The King went up to his apartments without being carried, though he was losing a great deal of blood, and it was a matter of getting him to bed at once and summoning a surgeon.

The weapon with which the villain was armed, according to the *Gazette de France*, was a two-bladed knife, one blade ordinary and the other like a penknife-blade, except that it was four inches long and fairly broad, making it an actual poignard. Although the King was fully dressed the blade entered some four fingers deep; but as the blow was directed from below it failed to penetrate the breast. The King was given an antidote for fear the blade had been poisoned; but fortunately it

was not, having been tried on a dog, the assassin himself assuring them that it was not.

The King wished to make his confession, and as his own confessor, Father Desmarets of the Company of Jesus, was not at Versailles, his Majesty was confessed by a priest attached to the Household. On the arrival of Father Desmarets from Paris, the King again made his confession. The assassin meanwhile had been taken to the guard-room in the Marble Court, where he was stripped and made to drink an antidote, his life and preservation being important. There were found on him the knife, about 30 louis d'or and some crowns of six livres, and an Old and New Testament, splendidly bound and gilt-edged. He gave his name as Pierre d'Amiens, a native of Arras, by profession a hawker on the Pont-Neuf, lodging on the Quai de l'Ecole. He is about five feet six in height and very strong, with a bold and determined expression. His hands were bound, and the King's Guard committed the imprudence of heating the pincers with which they secured his leg-irons, to make him talk, a procedure which might have thrown him into a fever, or even delirium. He was given his clothes again and passed the night in the guard-room.

He has since been seen by various officers of State in this room, and has been questioned on his enormous crime. They say that his only reply was that if it had to be done over again he would do it, and that he knew what to expect; but whatever punishments were inflicted, he would say no more. On the observation being made that he had plenty of money, he replied that he had been promised a great deal more.

The news having been carried to Paris by several couriers at nine o'clock on the night of the attempt, all the princes, nobles of the Court, ambassadors, and others set out at once, in a freezing night, and the road to Versailles was crowded with coaches. In Paris the consternation was general. The Archbishop ordered the Forty Hours' prayers to be said in Notre Dame and all the churches of Paris; and the officiating priests and monks could scarcely intone the *Salvum fac Regem* for emotion, which their congregations shared.

Journal of the Avocat Barbier.

THE NEW YEAR'S GIFT: OR CIRCUMCISION'S SONG

℃ Sung to the King in the Presence at Whitehall.

1. Prepare for songs; He's come, He's come;
   And be it sin here to be dumb,
   And not with lutes to fill the room.

2. Cast holy water all about,
   And have a care no fire goes out,
   But cense the porch and place throughout.

3. The altars all on fire be;
   The storax fries; and ye may see
   How heart and hand do all agree
To make things sweet. *Chor.* Yet all less sweet than He.

4. Bring Him along, most pious priest,
   And tell us then, whenas thou seest
   His gently-gliding, dove-like eyes,
   And hear'st His whimpering and His cries;
   How can'st thou this Babe circumcise?

5. Ye must not be more pitiful than wise;
   For now unless you see Him bleed,
   Which makes the bapti'm, 'tis decreed
The birth is fruitless. *Chor.* The work God speed.

306

6. Touch gently, gently touch; and here
Spring tulips up through all the year;
And from His sacred blood, here shed,
May roses grow to crown His own dear head.

Chor. Back, back again; each thing is done
With zeal alike, as 'twas begun;
Now singing, homeward let us carry
The Babe unto His mother Mary;
And when we have the Child commended
To warm her bosom, then our rites are ended.

ROBERT HERRICK.

THE STOCK EXCHANGE CAROL

SWIFT we be come on joyful feet,
Through wind and snow from Lombard Street,
To tell glad tidings far and wide
Of Patagonian Allied.

Noël, Noël, Noël, Noël!
Sing jolly men, who buy and sell,
For Trans. Rhd. Corp. (ex-bonus) Tea
Has risen again to 93.

Lo! Far and near we hear the call,
And Belgian Zinc's begun to fall,
Sing we and tell with joyous tongue
How badly old Sir George was stung.
Noël, Noël, etc.

Bright is the light, and wild, and strange,
That shines above the Stock Exchange;
Contentment crowns the happy scene—
There is a boom in Margarine.
Noël, Noël, etc.

High over all a Voice is heard—
"Lord Funck is buying Tin Preferred!"
Loud chaunts th'angelic syndicate,
"Sell out, sell out at 48!"
Noël, Noël, etc.

J. B. MORTON.

THE INNS THAT ARE DEAD

IN the evening we reached a village where I had deter-mined to pass the night. As we drove into the great gateway of the inn, I saw on one side the light of a rousing kitchen fire beaming through a window. I entered, and admired, for the hundredth time, that picture of convenience, neatness, and broad honest enjoyment, the kitchen of an English Inn. It was of spacious dimensions, hung round with copper and tin vessels highly polished, and decorated here and there with Christmas green. Hams, tongues, and flitches of bacon were suspended from the ceiling; a smoke-jack made its ceaseless clanking beside the fireplace, a clock ticked in one corner. A well-scoured deal table extended along one side of the kitchen, with a cold round of beef and other hearty viands upon it, over which two foaming tankards of ale seemed mounting guard. Travellers of inferior order were preparing to attack this stout repast, while others sat smoking and gossiping over their ale on two high-backed oaken settles beside the fire. Trim housemaids were hurrying backwards and forwards under the direction of a fresh bustling landlady; but still seizing an occasional moment to exchange a flippant word and have a rallying laugh with the group round the fire. The scene completely realised Poor Robin's humble idea of the comforts of mid-winter,

Now Trees their leafy Hats do bare
To reverence *Winter's* silver Hair;

A handsome Hostess, merry Host,
A pot of Ale now and a Tost,
Tobacco and a good coal Fire,
Are things this Season doth require.

WASHINGTON IRVING (1783–1859).

CAME THE DAWN . .

THIS is the true place to speak of the properties of chocolate flavoured with amber; properties which I have verified by many experiments, the result of which I am proud to lay before my readers. Listen, then:

Let any man who shall have drunk too deeply of the cup of pleasure, or given to work too many of the hours which should belong to sleep; who shall find the accustomed polish of his wit turned to dulness, feel damp oppression in the air and time hanging heavily, or be tortured by a fixed idea which robs him of all liberty of thought; let all such, we say, administer to themselves a good pint of Ambered Chocolate, allowing from sixty to seventy-two grains of amber to a pound, and they will see marvels.

In my own particular way of specifying things, I call ambered chocolate the *chocolate of the afflicted*.

J. A. BRILLAT-SAVARIN.

THE SPARKLING BOUGH

THE kindly Christmas tree, from which I trust every gentle reader has pulled a bonbon or two, is yet all aflame whilst I am writing, and sparkles with the sweet fruits of its season. You young ladies, may you have plucked pretty giftlings from it; and out of the cracker sugar-plum which you have split with the captain or the

309

sweet young curate may you have read one of those delicious conundrums which the confectioners introduce into the sweetmeats, and which apply to the cunning passion of Love. Those riddles are to be read at *your* age, when I dare say they are amusing. As for Dolly, Merry, and Bell, who are standing at the tree, they don't care about the love-riddle part, but understand the sweet-almond portion very well. They are four, five, six years old. Patience, little people! A dozen merry Christmasses more, and you will be reading those wonderful love-conundrums, too. As for us elderly folks, we watch the babies at their sport, and the young people pulling at the branches: and instead of finding bonbons or sweeties in the packets which *we* pluck off the boughs, we find Mr. Carnifex's review of the quarter's meat; Mr. Sartor's compliments, and little statement for self and the young gentlemen; and Madame de Sainte-Crinoline's respects to the young ladies, who encloses her account, and will send on Saturday, please; or we stretch out our hand to the educational branch of the Christmas tree, and there find a lively and amusing article from the Reverend Henry Holyshade, containing our dear Tommy's exceedingly moderate account for the last term's school expenses.

W. M. THACKERAY.

MAN of many Snipes,—I will sup with thee (Deo volente et diabolo nolente), on Monday night, the 5th of January, in the new year, and crush a cup to the infant Century.

A word or two of my progress: Embark at six o'clock in the morning, with a fresh gale, on a Cambridge one-decker; very cold till eight at night; land at St. Mary's light-house, muffins and coffee upon table (or any other curious production of Turkey, or both Indies), snipes exactly at nine, Punch to commence at ten, with *argument*; difference of Opinion is expected to take place about eleven; perfect Unanimity, with some haziness and dimness, before twelve.—N.B. My single affection is not so singly wedded to Snipes; but the curious and epicurean eye would also take a pleasure in beholding a delicate and well-chosen assortment of Teals, Ortolans, the unctuous and palate-soothing flesh of Geese, wild and tame, nightingales' brains, the sensorium of a young sucking-pig, or any other Christmas Dish, which I leave to the judgment of you and the cook of Gonville.

CHARLES LAMB to Thomas Manning.

THE NEW YEAR'S GIFT

LET others look for pearl and gold,
Tissues, or tabbies manifold:
One only lock of that sweet hay
Whereon the blessed baby lay,
Or one poor swaddling-clout, shall be
The richest New-Year's gift to me.

ROBERT HERRICK.

YA que llegado el tiempo
  En que de nacer había,
Asi como desposado
De su tálamo salía,

  Abrazado con su Esposa,
Que en sus brazos la traía,
Al cual la graciosa Madre
En un pesebre ponía,

  Entre unos animales
Que a la sazón allí había:
Los hombres decián cantares,
Los ángeles melodía,

  Festejando el desposorio
Que entre tales dos había;
Pero Dios en el pesebre
Allí loraba y gemía,

  Que eran joyas que la esposa
Al desposorio traía;
Y la Madre estaba en pasmo
De que tal trueque veía;

  El llanto del hombre en Dios,
Y en el hombre la alegría,
Lo cual del uno y del otro
Tan ajeno ser solía.

  ST. JOHN OF THE CROSS (1542-1605).

[*Translation by E. Allison Peers*]

  When the ancient dispensation
Its predestined course had run,
Straight from out His bridal chamber
Came the Bridegroom, God the Son.

  Once on earth, with arms extended
He embrac'd His heavenly Bride,
And his blessèd Mother laid Him
In the manger, at her side.

312

All around that helpless Baby
Animals were standing by;
Men sang songs of glad rejoicing,
Angels join'd their songs on high,

Celebrating the betrothal
'Twixt the Bridegroom and the Bride,
While the Almighty, in the manger,
As an infant wept and cried.

Gems these tears, which human nature
Brought to the betrothal-rite,
And the Maid was lost in wonder
As she witness'd such a sight.

Man was full of joy and gladness;
God was weeping, weak and lone.
Ne'er before throughout the ages
Had so strange a thing been known.

NATIVITY

STABAT Mater speciosa
Juxta fœnum gaudiosa
Dum jacebat parvulus,
Cujus Animam gaudentem
Lætabundam et ferventem
Pertransivit jubilus.

O quam læta et beata
Fuit illa immaculata
Mater unigeniti
Quæ gaudebat et ridebat
Exultabat, cum videbat
Nati partum inclyti.

Quisquam est, qui non gauderet
Christi matrem si videret
In tanto solatio?
Quis non potest collætari
Christi matrem contemplari
Ludentem cum filio?

Pro peccatis suæ gentis
Christum vidit cum jumentis
Et algori subditum;
Vidit suum dulcem natum
Vagientem, adoratum
Vili diversorio.

Nato Christo in præsepe
Cœli cives canunt læte
Cum immenso gaudio;
Stabat senex cum puella
Non cum verbo nec loquela
Stupescentes cordibus.

Eja, mater, fons amoris,
Me sentire vim ardoris
Fac, ut tecum sentiam,
Fac, ut ardeat cor meum
In amatum Christum Deum,
Ut sibi complaceam.

Sancta mater, istud agas,
Prone introducas plagas
Cordi fixas valide;
Tui nati cœlo lapsi,
Jam dignati fœno nasci
Pœnas mecum divide.

Fac me vere congaudere
Jesulino cohærere
Donec ego vixero;
In me sistat ardor tui,
Puerino fac me frui,
Dum sum in exsilio.

Virgo virginum præclara,
Mihi jam non sis amara,
Fac me parvum rapere;
Fac ut pulchrum infantem portem,
Qui nascendo vicit mortem,
Volens vitam tradere.

Fac me tecum satiari,
Nato me inebriari,
Stantem in tripudio;
Inflammatus et accensus
Obstupescit omnis sensus
Tali me commercio.

Fac me nato custodiri,
Verbo Dei præmuniri,
Conservari gratia;
Quando corpus morietur
Fac, ut animæ donetur
Tui nati gloria!

Omnes stabulum amantes,
Et pastores vigilantes,
Pernoctantes sociant
Per virtutem Nati tui,
Ora ut electi sui
Ad patriam veniant.   Amen.

JACOPONE DA TODI.

[*Translation by Denis MacCarthy*]

By the Crib wherein reposing,
With His eyes in slumber closing
Lay serene her Infant-boy,
Stood the beauteous mother feeling
Bliss that could not bear concealing,
So her face o'erflowed with joy.

O the rapture naught could smother
Of the most Immaculate Mother.
Of the sole begotten One;
When with laughing heart exulting,
She beheld her hopes resulting
In the great birth of her Son.

Who would not with jubilation
See the happy consolation
Of Christ's Mother undefiled?
Who would not be glad surveying
Christ's dear Mother bending, praying,
Playing with her heavenly Child? . . .

For a sinful world's salvation,
Christ her Son's humiliation
She beheld and brooded o'er;
Saw Him weak, a child, a stranger,
Yet before Him in the manger
Kings lie prostrate and adore.

O'er that lowly manger winging,
Joyful hosts from heaven were singing
Canticles of holy praise;
While the old man and the maiden,
Speaking naught, with hearts o'erladen,
Pondered on God's wondrous ways.

Fount of love forever flowing
With a burning ardour glowing,
Make me, Mother, feel like thee;
Let my heart, with graces gifted
All on fire, to Christ be lifted,
And by Him accepted be.

Holy Mother, deign to bless me,
With His sacred Wounds impress me,
Let them in my heart abide;
Since He came, thy Son, the Holy,
To a birth-place, ah, so lowly,
All His pain with me divide.

Make me with true joy delighted,
To Child-Jesus be united
While my days of life endure;
While an exile here sojourning,
Make my heart like thine be burning
With a love divine and pure.

Spotless Maid and sinless Woman,
Make us feel a fire in common
Make my heart's long longing sure.
Virgin of all virgins highest,
Prayer to thee thou ne'er denyest
Let me bear thy sweet Child too. . . .

Let me bear Him in my bosom,
Lord of Life and never lose Him,
Since His birth doth death subdue.
Let me show forth how immense is
The effect on all my senses
Of an union so divine.

Make me by His birth be guarded,
By God's holy word be warded
By His grace till all is done;
When my body lies obstructed,
Make my soul to be conducted,
To the vision of thy Son.

All who in the crib revere Him
Like the shepherds watching near Him,
Will attend Him through the night,
By thy powerful prayers protected,
Grant, O Queen, that His elected
May behold heaven's saving light.

MERRY CHRISTMAS, NEARLY EVERYBODY

Christmas time used to be the time when everybody loved
    everybody,
And even in the subway when everybody had their arms
    full of packages nobody shoved everybody.
People went around looking benevolent,
And goodwill was pleasingly prevalent,
And the cockles of people's hearts were all warm and
    cockley
And crisp new bills were scattered on elevator boys like
    broccoli,

And people had grandmothers and were fond of their family,

And the weather acted more New Englandly and less Miamily,

And on Christmas Eve people would assemble their friends and merrily sing carols with them and merrily congeal with them,

And they sent Christmas cards and presents to people because they liked them and not because they hoped to put over a deal with them.

Yes, the good old Yuletide was indeed sublime,

But that was once upon a time,

Because now everybody has somebody they are trying to blow to pieces or dismember,

And people can't concentrate properly on blowing other people to pieces properly if their minds are poisoned by thoughts suitable to the twenty-fifth of December.

Hence my thesis,

Which is that I think it is much nicer to have a nice Christmas than to blow somebody to pesis,

So please excuse me for a moment while I momentarily take my mind off Tokio and Peiping and the Rebels and the Loyalists;

Forgive me if I temporarily ignore the disagreement between Mr. Lewis and the Economic Royalists;

This is not the season for tales of Der Fuehrer and his sportsmanship;

Call again on the twenty-sixth if you want to discuss the Chief Executive and his Supreme Courtsmanship;

Christmas comes but once every Anno Domini,

And I want an old-fashioned one and I invite everybody who is on my side to enjoy it the way it ought to be enjoyed even though everybody on the other side will undoubtedly cover us with ignominy.

OGDEN NASH.

VINTAGE NOTE

IF you would have verjuice at Christmas from your Vine Arbour, when you see the grape opening before it is in flower, cut it off by the stem and the third time let it grow till Christmas. Master Jehan de Stantecourt says that one ought to cut the stock below the grape and the other shoot beneath will put out new grapes.

Le Ménagier de Paris (1393),
tr. Eileen Power.

TO MAKE SACK POSSET

TAKE two quarts of new cream, a quarter of an ounce of whole cinnamon, and two nutmegs quartered, boil it till it taste well of the spice, and keep it always stirring or it will burn too, then take the yolks of fourteen or fifteen eggs beaten well together with a little cold cream, put them to the cream on the fire, and stir it till it begin to boil, then take it off and sweeten it with sugar, and stir on till it be pretty cool; then take a pint and a quarter of sack, sweeten that also and set it on fire till it be ready to boil, then put it in a fine clean scoured bason, or posset pot, and pour the cream into it, elevating your hand to make it froth, which is the grace of your posset; if you put it through a tunnel or a cullender, it is held the more exquisite way.

TO MAKE SACK POSSET OTHERWAYES

TAKE two quarts of good cream, and a quarter of a pound of best almonds stamped with some rose-water or cream, strain them with the cream, and boil with it amber and musk; then take a pint of sack into a bason, and set it on a chafing-dish till it be blood-warm; then take the yolks of twelve eggs with four whites, beat them very well together, and so put the eggs into the sack, make it good and hot, then stir all together in the bason, let the cream cool a little before you put it into the sack, and stir all together over the coals, till it be as thick as you would have it, then take some amber and musk, grinde it small with sugar, and strew it on the top of the posset, it will give it a most delicate and pleasant taste.

TO MAKE A COMPOUND POSSET OF SACK, CLARET, WHITE WINE, ALE, BEER, OR JUYCE OF ORANGES, &C.

TAKE twenty yolks of eggs with a little cream, strain them and set them by; then have a clean scowred skillet, and put into it a pottle of good sweet cream, and a good quantity of whole cinnamon, set it a boiling on a soft charcoal fire, and stir it continually; the cream having a good taste of the cinnamon, put in the strained eggs and cream into your skillet, stir them together, give them a warm; then have some sack in a deep bason or posset pot, good store of fine sugar, and some sliced nutmeg; the sack and sugar being warm, take out the cinnamon and pour your eggs and cream very high into the bason, that it may spatter in it, then strow on loaf sugar.

ROBERT MAY, *The Accomplisht Cook, or The Art and Mystery of Cookery* (1660).

ORGUES

ET maintenant, la messe dite, allez, fidèles,
  Gardant ce souvenir en vos cœurs rajeunis,
Pareils à des oiseaux qui regagnent leurs nids
Avec des cris joyeux et des battements d'ailes;
Et maintenant, la messe dite, allez en paix
Vers la vie attrayante et bonne désormais.
Voyez comme la neige au soleil étincelle,
Voyez la fumée bleue au-dessus des maisons,
Et comme expire, au pâle azur de l'horizon,
Le croissant vaporeux de la lune irréelle.
Et sentez ce bon vent qui mordille le sang
Et qui stimule en nous la bonne ardeur de vivre.
Allez tout chauds du ciel encore et frémissants,
Allez, foulant la neige éclatante et le givre,
Allez vers le bonheur et le charmant Noël
Parmi les pignons blancs et les palmiers de gel;
Allez vers la douceur des fêtes de famille,
Vers le grillon qui chante et la lampe qui brille;
Allez vers les enfants et le bonhomme Hiver
Qui s'assied au foyer avec un sapin vert. . . .

Un Sauveur nous est né! Un Sauveur nous est né!
Un long tressaillement a traversé la Terre,
Et les chérubins bleus chantent dans la lumière:
Noël! Noël! Anges, chantez! Cloches, sonnez!
Noël! Noël! tous les péchés sont pardonnés.

VICTOR KINON.

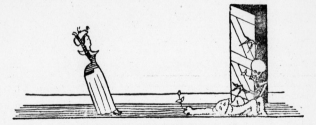

ℭ. *Ceremony upon Candlemas Eve*

DOWN with the rosemary, and so
    Down with the bays and mistletoe;
Down with the holly, ivy, all
Wherewith ye dressed the Christmas Hall:
That so the superstitious find
No one least branch there left behind:
For look, how many leaves there be
Neglected, there (maids, trust to me)
So many Goblins you shall see.

The Ceremonies for Candlemas Day

Kindle the Christmas brand, and then
    Till Sunset let it burn;
Which quench'd, then lay it up again
    Till Christmas next return.
Part must be kept wherewith to teend
    The Christmas log next year,
And where 'tis safely kept, the fiend
    Can do no mischief there.

Upon Candlemas Day

End now the white loaf and the pie,
And let all sports with Christmas die.

ROBERT HERRICK.

[THE END]

322

INDEX OF AUTHORS AND SOURCES

ADDISON, JOSEPH, 86, 288
Ale Recipes, 18
Anglo-Saxon Chronicle, 159, 296
Annales (John Stow), 203, 229
Archives Nationales (Paris), 13
Arnold, Matthew, 90
Arraignment, The (1645), 272
Asbjörnsen, P. C., 117
Augustine, St., 276

Balliol MS., 4, 35, 110, 125, 167
Barbier, Avocat, 153, 303
Barozai, Guy, 220, 224
Belloc, Hilaire, 12, 56, 93, 133, 162, 216
Bentley, Dr. William, 160
Bodleian (Selden) MS., 298
Bonaventure, St., 29
Booke of Cookerie, 89, 110, 111, 239, 260
Bourgogne, Sergeant, 205
Boxiana, 299
de Brébeuf, Jean, S.J., 267
Bridges, Robert, 7
Brillat-Savarin, J. A., 187, 309
Brown, Ivor, 156
Browning, Robert, 237, 281
Burton, Robert, 196

Calverley, C. S., 121
Carey, Hon. Patrick, 70
Catullus, 293
Charles VII., King of France, 190
Chaucer, Geoffrey, 17, 208
Chester Processional, 77
Chesterton, G. K., 165, 202, 255, 273, 277
Claudel, Paul, 35, 246
Clutton-Brock, A., 23
Cookery Recipes, 10, 63, 89, 110, 111, 147, 179, 187, 239, 242, 260
Coventry Nativity Play, 235
Crashaw, Richard, 243

Daudet, Alphonse, 170, 299
Davies, Peter (tr.), 187, 309
Dostoievsky, Fedor, 268
Dryden, John (tr.), 2
Du Cange, 280
Dunbar, William, 6

Egan, Pierce, 299
Emrys, D. (tr.), 278
England's Iliad, 107
Estcourt, Richard, 260
Evelyn, John, 244
Evelyn, Richard, 259

Festiall of John Mirkus, 78
Flying Eagle Gazette (1652), 10
French, Field-Marshal Lord, 23
French Carol, XVIIth Century, 204
French-Canadian Carol, 141
de la Fresnaye, Vauquelin, 150
Froissart, Sir John, 143, 194, 240

Gautier, Théophile, 34
Gay, John, 148
Gentleman's Magazine (1822), 199
German Cradle-Song, 178
Glasse, Mrs., 187
le Goffic, Charles, 258
Golden Legend, The, 234
Grant Kalendrier des Bergiers, 112
Gregory of Tours, St., 161
Grossmith, George and Weedon, 60

Hamilton, Count A., 283
Hardy, Thomas, 107, 199
de Heredia, José-Maria, 234
Herrick, Robert, 11, 140, 282, 306, 311, 322
Hilary of Poitiers, St., 3
History of York, 62
Horace, 121
Howison, John, 215
Hutchinson, Thos., 69
Huysmans, J. K., 267

Inner Temple, Accompts, 264
Irving, Washington, 308

Jackson, John, 242
Jacopone da Todi, 236, 313
James, Henry, 138
John of the Cross, St., 312
Johnson, Dr. Samuel, 295
Jonson, Ben, 47, 154

Kennedy, H. E. (tr.), 68, 189
Kinon, Victor, 321

Labat, Jean-Baptiste, O.P., 97
Lalemant, Jérôme, S.J., 211
Lamb, Charles, 55, 113, 182, 273, 311
Lancaster, Thomas, Earl of, 198
L'Annonce faite à Marie, 35
Lingua, a Tudor Play, 268
Louis, Archbishop of Sens, 164
Lucas, E. V., 132
Ludus Corporis Christi, 70

McElhone, H., and R. M., 18
Machen, Arthur, 152, 292
Malory, Sir Thomas, 63, 134
Marot, Clément, 124
Martial, 59, 169, 190, 228, 245, 257, 292
Mather, Cotton, 43
May, Robert, 319
Memoirs of Grammont, 283
Ménagier de Paris, 319
Meynell, Alice, 52
Milne, A. A., 168
Milton, John, 99
Mirkus, John, 78
Mistral, Frédéric, 66, 279
Monk of Tours, A, 76
Morgan, Siankin, 277
Morton, J. B., 307
Murger, Henry, 44

Nash, Ogden, 98, 317
Navarre, College of, MS., 13
Nobody, Diary of a, 60
Norwegian Fairy Book, 117

Oger, 121
Osborne, Dorothy, 297

Paston, Margery, 106, 123
Peacock, Thomas Love, 144
Pepys, Samuel, 90, 242, 291
Pinkney, Myles, 76
Plum-Porridge, Cissely, 272
Police sous Louis XV., Journal de, 149
Priestley, J. B., 252
Prudentius, 271

Queen's College, Oxford, MS., 166

Rabelais, François, 192
Ramsay, Dean, 283
Registers of the Chancellery of France, 121
Robin Hood's Epitaph, 240
Rolle, Richard, 34
Rowlands, Richard, 137
Russell, Rt. Hon. G. W. E., 74

Shakespeare, William, 71, 98
Sill, Louise Morgan (tr.), 35
Sitwell, Edith, 226
Sloane MS. 2593, British Museum, 20, 27, 28, 42, 53, 85
Southwell, Ven. Robert, S.J., 142
Spectator, 20, 86, 197, 239, 260, 288
Spy, The London, 48, 184
Squire, J. C., 211
Steele, Richard, 20, 197, 239, 261
Stow, John, 203, 229
Strindberg, August, 229
de Sully, Eudes, Bishop of Paris, 196
Surtees, R. S., 262
Suso, B. Henry, O.P., 8
Sussex Archæological Society's Transactions, 197
Swift, Dean, 24, 145, 159, 294
Symonds, John Addington (tr.), 236
Symons, Arthur (tr.), 84

Tennyson, Alfred, Lord, 116
Teonge, Rev. Henry, 43
Teresa of Jesus, St., 84
Thackeray, William Makepeace, 51, 289, 309
Trinity College, Camb., MS., 28
Truisy, 13

Urquhart, Sir Thomas, 192

Vaughan, Henry, 151
Vergil, 2
Verstegan, Richard, 137
Villon, François, 97

Wakefield Nativity Play, 30, 126
Walpole, Horace, 149, 208, 286
Ward, Ned (London Spy), 48, 184
Winslow, Anna Green, 18
Wynkyn de Worde, 225